Anthropology:

BIOLOGY & RACE

Anthropology: BIOLOGY & RACE

A. L. Kroeber

A Harbinger Book
HARCOURT, BRACE & WORLD, INC.
NEW YORK & BURLINGAME

Contents

PROBLEMS OF RACE DIFFERENCE

CULTURAL PSYCHOLOGY

List of Figures

EDITOR'S NOTE

This volume offers a selection of those chapters of Alfred L. Kroeber's classic work ANTHROPOLOGY that deal specifically with matters of *Biology and Race*.

If no selection can ever take the place of the complete work from which it is drawn, this holds doubly true of a work as closely integrated as Kroeber's ANTHROPOLOGY, which covers a vast area of knowledge, illumines each of its parts from a single fundamental point of view, and subjects an entire field of scholarship to the searching inquiry of one mind of uncommon scope.

The present selection (and its companion volumes, which contain other selections) claims no more than that it will serve the convenience of those readers who wish to study the narrower topic only. However, the section numbers, and with them the many cross references, that run throughout the parent volume have been retained unchanged—to point up how much Kroeber's ANTHROPOLOGY is a work that is of one piece, and indivisible.

Anthropology:
BIOLOGY & RACE

What Anthropology Is About

I. ANTHROPOLOGY, BIOLOGY, HISTORY

ANTHROPOLOGY is the science of man. Of course, this literal, etymological meaning is too broad and general. More precise would be: "the science of man and his works and behavior." But even this needs an addition to make it sufficiently specific, since no one means to claim sciences like physiology and psychology as parts of anthropology. Now physiology and psychology focus their attention on particular men, whom they examine as individuals. This gives a clue to the additional limitation we are seeking. Anthropology obviously is concerned not with particular men as such, but with men in groups, with races and peoples and their happenings and doings. So let us take as our provisional basic definition the following: "Anthropology is the science of groups of men and their behavior and productions." This will include any findings on the total human species, since this constitutes an aggregate of races or peoples, a sort of supergroup or total society.

However, man is an animal or organism and he is also a civilized being having a history and social qualities. Thus he is investigated—different aspects of him are investigated—both by the organic or biological or life sciences and by what are sometimes called the historical and more generally the social sciences. True, this latter term, "the social sciences," though commonly used, is not easy to define satisfactorily. But we can leave this difficulty for the philosopher of science. In practice, anthropology is mostly classified as being both a biological science and a social science. Some universities recognize this fact by having certain courses of anthropological study count as the one and certain as the other, or perhaps even the same course counting either way. Such a situation of double participation is unusual among the sciences. If anthropology is not concerned so predominantly with man as an animal, or with man as a social human having a history, that it can be set outright in either the life or the social-historical science category, both aspects are evidently represented significantly in its subject matter. Could it be that the specific subject of anthropology is the interrelation of what is biological in man and what is social and historical in him? The answer is Yes. Or, more broadly, anthropology does at least concern itself with both organic and social factors in man, whereas nearly all other sciences and studies deal with one or the other. Anthropology concerns itself with both sets of factors because these come associated in human beings in nature. Often they are even intertwined in one and the same phenomenon, as when a person is born with hereditary musical capacity and develops this further by study and training. They are not always easy to·disentangle; but they must be separated if the processes at work are to be understood. That job is peculiarly the anthropologist's.

2. ORGANIC AND SOCIOCULTURAL ELEMENTS

To the question why a Louisiana Negro is black and longheaded, the answer is ready. He was born so. As cows produce calves, and lions, cubs, so Negro springs from Negro and Caucasian from Caucasian. We call the force at work heredity. Our same Negro is reputed amiable and easy-going. Is this too an innate quality? Offhand most of us might reply Yes. He sings at his corn-hoeing more frequently than the white man across the fence. Is this also because of his heredity? "Of course—he is made so," might be a common answer, "Probably—why not?" a more cautious one. But now our Negro is singing the "Memphis Blues," which his great-grandfather in Africa assuredly did not sing. As for the specific song, heredity can obviously no longer be the cause. Our Negro may have learned it from an uncle, or perhaps from his schoolmates; quite likely he acquired it from human beings who were not his ancestors, or over the radio, acquired it as part of his customs, like being a member of the Baptist Church and wearing overalls, and the thousand other things that come to him from without instead of from within. At these points heredity is displaced by tradition, nature by nurture, to use a familiar jingle. The efficient forces now are quite different from those which made his skin black and his head long. They are causes of another order.

The particular song of the Negro and his complexion represent the clear-cut extremes of the matter. Between them lie the good nature and the inclination to melody. Obviously these traits may also be the result of human example, of "social environment," of contemporary tradition. There are those who so believe, as well as those who see in them chiefly the effects of inborn biological impulse. Perhaps these intermediate dubious traits are the results of a blending of nature and nurture, the strength of each varying according to the trait or the individual examined. Clearly, at any rate, there is room here for investigation and weighing of evidence. A genuine problem exists. This problem cannot be solved by the historical or social sciences alone, because they do not concern themselves with heredity. Nor can it be solved by biology, which deals with heredity and allied factors but does not go on to operate with the nonbiological principle of tradition or with what is acquired by men when they live in societies.

Here, then, is one distinctive task for anthropology: the interpretation of those phenomena into which both innate organic factors and "social" or acquired factors enter or may enter.

The word "social" is the customary untechnical one for the nonorganic or more-than-organic phenomena referred to. It is, however, an ambiguous word and therefore sometimes a confusing one. As will shortly be pointed out, "social" refers to both social and cultural phenomena. Until the distinction between them has been made, we shall either put "social" into quotation marks or use "sociocultural" instead.

3. ORGANIC OR "PHYSICAL" ANTHROPOLOGY

The organic sciences underlie the sociocultural ones. They are more immediately "natural," less "humanized" in their concern. Anthropology therefore accepts and uses the general principles of biology: the laws of heredity and the doctrines of cell development and evolution, for instance, and all the findings of anatomy, physiology, embryology, zoology, palaeontology, and the rest. Its business has been to ascertain how far these principles apply to man, what forms they take in his particular case. This has meant a concentration of attention, the devising of special methods of inquiry. Many biological problems, including most physiological and hereditary ones, can be most profitably attacked in the laboratory, or at least under experimental conditions. The experimental method, however, is but rarely available for human beings living in groups. Sociocultural phenomena have to be taken as they come and laboriously sifted and resifted afterward, instead of being artificially simplified in advance, as is done in laboratory experimentation.

Then, too, since anthropology is operating biologically within the narrow limits of one species, it has sometimes been driven to concern itself with minute traits, such as the zoologist is rarely troubled with: the proportions of the length and the breadth of the skull—the famous cephalic index—for instance; the number of degrees the arm bones are twisted, and the like. Also, as these data had to be used in the gross, unmodifiable by artificially varied conditions, it has been necessary to secure them from all possible varieties of men, different races, sexes, ages, and their nearest brute analogues. The result is that biological or physical anthropology—"somatology" it is sometimes called in Anglo-Saxon countries, and sometimes simply "anthropology" in continental Europe—has in part constituted a sort of specialization or sharpening of certain aspects of general biology. It has become absorbed to a considerable degree in certain particular phenomena, such as human species or subraces and methods of studying them, about which general biologists, physiologists, and students of medicine are usually but vaguely informed.

4. SOCIOCULTURAL ANTHROPOLOGY

The sociocultural sciences, usually, but somewhat loosely, called the social sciences, overlie the organic sciences. Men's bodies and inborn equipment are back of their deeds and accomplishments as shaped by tradition, and are primary to their culture or civilization as well as to their aggregations in societies. The relation of anthropology to sociocultural science has therefore been in a sense the opposite of its relation to biological science. Instead of specializing, anthropology has been occupied with trying to generalize the findings of history. Historians can never experiment; sociologists, economists, and other social scientists only rarely. Historians deal with the unique; for to a degree every historical or social or cultural event has something unparalleled about it. They do not lay down laws, nor do they verify them by the artificial trials of experiment. But anthropology looks for such general and recurrent processes as may occur in the multifarious events of history and in the diverse societies, institutions, customs, and beliefs of mankind. So far as such processes can be extricated or formulated, they are generalizations.

It has sometimes been said that social and cultural anthropology—that part of the subject which is concerned with the more-than-merely-organic aspects of human behavior—seems preoccupied with ancient and savage and exotic and extinct peoples. The cause is a desire to understand better all civilizations, irrespective of time and place, in the abstract, or as generalized principles if possible. It is not that cave men are more illuminating than Romans, or flint knives more interesting than fine porcelains or the art of printing, which has led anthropology to bear heavily on the former, but the fact that it wanted to know about cave men and flint knives, which no one else was studying, as well as about the Romans and printing presses that history tells us about so fully. It would be arbitrary to prefer the exotic and remote to the familiar, and in principle anthropology has never accepted the adjudication sometimes tacitly rendered that its proper field should be restricted to the primitive as such. As well might zoology confine its interest to eggs or to protozoans. It is probably true that some researches into early and savage history, especially in the initial stages of anthropology, have sprung from an emotional predilection for the forgotten or the neglected, the obscure and the strange, the unwonted and the mysterious. But such occasional personal aesthetic trends cannot delimit the range of a science or determine its aims and methods. Innumerable historians have been inveterate gossips, but one does not therefore insist that the only proper subject of history is backstairs intimacies.

This, then, is the reason for the special development of those subdivisions of anthropology known as *archaeology,* "the science of what is old" in the career of humanity, especially as revealed by excavations of the sites of prehistoric occupation, and *ethnology,* "the science of peoples" and their cultures and life histories as groups, irrespective of their degree of advancement.[1]

5. EVOLUTIONARY PROCESSES AND EVOLUTIONISTIC FANCIES

In their more elementary aspects the two strands of the organic or hereditary and the sociocultural or "environmental" run through all human life. They are distinct as mechanisms, and their products are distinct. Thus a comparison of the acquisition of the power of flight respectively by birds in their organic development out of the ancestral reptile stem millions of years ago, and by men as a result of cultural progress in the field of invention during the past generation, reveals at once the profound differences of *process* that inhere in the ambiguous concept of "evolution." The bird gave up a pair of walking limbs to acquire wings. It added a new faculty by transforming part of an old one. The sum total of its parts or organs was not greater than before. The change was transmitted only to the blood descendants of the altered individuals. The reptile line went on as it had been before, or if it altered, did so for causes unconnected with the evolution of the birds. The airplane, on the contrary, gave men a new faculty without diminishing or even impairing any of those they had previously possessed. It led to no visible bodily changes, no alterations of mental capacity. The invention has been transmitted to individuals and groups not derived by descent from the inventors; in fact, it has already influenced the fortunes of all of us. Theoretically, the invention is transmissible to ancestors if they happen to be still living. In sum, it represents an accretion to the stock of existing civilization rather than a transformation.

Once the broad implications of the distinction which this example illustrates have been grasped, many common errors are guarded against. The program of eugenics, for instance, loses much of its force. There is certainly much to be said in favor of intelligence and discrimination in mating, as in everything else. There is need for the acquisition of more exact knowledge on human heredity. But, in the main, the claims sometimes made that eugenics is necessary to preserve civilization from dissolution, or to maintain the flourishing of this or that nationality, rest on the fallacy of recognizing only organic causes as operative, when sociocultural as well as organic ones are active—when indeed the superhereditary factors may be much the more powerful ones. So, in what are miscalled race problems, the average thought of the day still reasons confusedly between sociocultural and organic causes and effects.[2] Anthropology is not yet

---

[1] Ethnography is sometimes separated, as more descriptive, from ethnology, as more theoretically or more historically inclined.

[2] An example is the still lingering fallacy that individual development of organs by use somehow gets incorporated into the heredity of descendants. This fallacy rests on the misapplication to organic situations of a valid sociocultural mechanism. An example in reverse

in a position always to state just where the boundary lies between the contributing organic causes and the superorganic or "sociocultural" causes of such phenomena. But it does hold to their fundamental distinctness and to the importance of their distinction, if true understanding is the aim. Without sure grasp of this principle, many of the arguments and conclusions in the present volume will lose their significance.

Accordingly, a designation of anthropology as "the child of Darwin" is misleading. Darwin's essential achievement was that he imagined, and substantiated by much indirect evidence, a mechanism through which organic evo lution appeared to be taking place. The whole history of man, however, being much more than an organic matter, a merely or strictly Darwinian anthropology would be largely misapplied biology. One might almost as justly speak of a Copernican or a Newtonian anthropology.

What has greatly influenced some of the earlier anthropology, mainly to its damage, has been not Darwinism, but the vague idea of progress, to the organic aspect of which Darwin happened incidentally to give such support and apparent substance that the whole group of evolutionistic ideas, sound and unsound, has luxuriated rankly ever since. It became common practice in the older anthropology to "explain" any part of human civilization by arranging its several forms in an evolutionary sequence from lowest to highest and allowing each successive stage to flow spontaneously, without specific cause, from the preceding one. At bottom this logical procedure was astonishingly naïve. In these schemes we of our land and day stood at the summit of the ascent. Whatever seemed most different from our customs was therefore reckoned as earliest, and other phenomena were disposed wherever they would best contribute to the straight evenness of the climb upward. The relative occurrence of phenomena in time and space was disregarded in favor of their logical fitting into a plan. It was argued that since we hold to definitely monogamous marriage, the beginnings of human sexual union probably lay in the opposite condition of indiscriminate promiscuity. Since we accord precedence to descent from the father, and generally know him, early society must have reckoned descent from the mother and no one knew his own father. We abhor incest; therefore the most primitive men normally married their sisters. These are fair samples of the conclusions or assumptions of the classic evolutionistic school of anthropology of, say, 1860 to 1890, which still believed that primal origins or ultimate causes could be determined, and that they could be discovered by speculative reasoning. The roster of this evolutionistic-speculative school was graced by some illustrious names. Needless to say, these men tempered the basic crudity of their opinions by wide knowledge, acuity or charm of presentation, and frequent insight and sound sense in concrete particulars. In their day, two generations or three ago, under the spell of the concept of evolution in its first flush, and of the postulate of

is the ascription of environmentally or historically produced cultural backwardness to organic and hereditary inferiority.

progress at its strongest, such methods of reasoning were almost inevitable. Today they are long since threadbare; they have descended to the level of newspaper science or have become matter for idle amateur guessing. They are evidence of a tendency toward the easy smugness of feeling oneself superior to all the past. These ways of thought are mentioned here only as an example of the beclouding that results from bad transference of biologically legitimate concepts into the realm of the history of human society and culture, or viewing these as unfolding according to a simple scheme of progress.

6. SOCIETY AND CULTURE

The relation between what is biological and what is sociocultural has just been said to be a sort of central pivot of anthropology, from which the range of the subject then extends outward on both sides, into the organic and into the more-than-organic. It is now necessary to consider the more precise relation of society and culture within the "organic-plus." In man, social and cultural phenomena normally occur associated much as the joint sociocultural phenomena co-occur with the organic ones. Nevertheless, the social and the cultural aspects within the larger sociocultural field can nearly always be distinguished.

The Latin word *socius* denotes a companion or ally, and in their specific sense the words "society" and "social" refer to associations of individuals, to group relations. When we speak of social structure, or the organization of society, it is clear what is meant: the way a mass of people is constituted into families, clans, tribes, states, classes, sets, clubs, communities, and the like. A society is a group of interrelated individuals.

But in a much wider sense the word "social" is also used, loosely, for whatever transcends the biological individual: for what we have so far designated as more-than-organic or sociocultural. Thus popular usage and university curricula recognize the physical, the biological, and the social sciences. The last-named usually comprise history, government, economics, sociology, anthropology, human geography.[3] All these branches of study deal not only with man but with men. In fact they deal primarily with the interrelations of men, or groups of men.

It so happens that man is an essentially unique animal in that he possesses speech faculty and the faculty of symbolizing, abstracting, or generalizing. Through these two associated faculties he is able to communicate his acquired learning, his knowledge and accomplishments, to his fellows and his descendants —in fact, even to his ancestors, if they happen to be still alive and are willing to listen to him. So he transmits much of his ideas, habits, and achievements to succeeding generations of men. This is something that no other animal can do, at least not to any significant degree. This special faculty is what was meant

[3] Psychology is sometimes also partly included, sometimes reckoned rather with the biological sciences.

when someone called man the "time-binding" animal. He "binds" time by tran-scending it, through influencing other generations by his actions.

Now the mass of learned and transmitted motor reactions, habits, tech-niques, ideas, and values—and the behavior they induce—is what constitutes *culture*. Culture is the special and exclusive product of men, and is their dis-tinctive quality in the cosmos.

Not only is culture a unique phenomenon, but it can be said to have a large degree of influence. Of course culture can appear and go on only in and through men, men in some kind of societies; without these it could not come into being nor maintain itself. But, given a culture, the human beings that come under its influence behave and operate quite differently from the way they would behave under another culture, and still more differently from the way they would act under no culture. In the latter case they would be merely animals in their be-havior. They are human beings precisely because they are animals plus a cul-ture. Somehow human beings began long ago to produce culture and have con-tinued ever since to produce it. In that sense culture derives wholly from men. But the other side of the picture is that every human being is influenced by other men who in turn have been influenced by still others in the direction of maintaining and developing certain ideas, institutions, and standards. And a shorthand way of expressing this is to say that they are all influenced by the culture they grow up in; in fact, in a broad way, they are dependent on it for most of the specific things they do in their lives. Culture is therefore a powerful force in human behavior—in both individual and social behavior. Any given form of culture, whether of the Eskimo or of our contemporary Western civi-lization, has behind it a long history of other forms of culture by which it was conditioned and from which it derives. And in turn each culture is changing and shaping the forms of culture that will succeed it and which therefore more or less depend on it. Culture thus is a factor that produces enormous effects, and as such we study it.

To be concrete, the reason our Louisiana Negro of a few pages back sings the blues, goes to a Baptist church, and cultivates corn is that these things are parts of American culture. If he had been reared in the Africa of some of his forefathers, his dress, labor, food, religion, government, and amusements would have been quite different, as well as his language. Such is what culture does to men. And, as has been pointed out, the process of transmission, a process of acquisition by learning by which culture is perpetuated and operates on new generations, is quite different from the process by which heredity—another in-dubitable force—operates on them. Equally distinct are the results. No religion, no tool, no idea was ever produced by heredity.

Culture, then, is all those things about man that are more than just bio-logical or organic, and are also more than merely psychological. It presupposes bodies and personalities, as it presupposes men associated in groups, and it rests upon them; but culture is something more than a sum of psychosomatic qualities and actions. It is more than these in that its phenomena cannot be wholly understood in terms of biology and psychology. Neither of these sciences claims to be able to explain why there are axes and property laws and etiquettes and prayers in the world, why they function and perpetuate as they do, and least of all why these cultural things take the particular and highly variable forms or expressions under which they appear. Culture thus is at one and the same time the totality of products of social men, and a tremendous force affecting all human beings, socially and individually. And in this special but broad sense, culture is universal for man.[4]

This brings us back to the relation of society and culture. Logically, the two are separate, though they also coexist. Many animals are social. Ants and bees and termites are very highly socialized, so much so that they can survive only in societies. But they have no culture. There is no culture on the subhuman level. Ants get along without culture because they are born with many highly specific instincts; but men have only few and general instincts. Society without culture exists on the subhuman level. But culture, which exists only through man, who is also a social animal, presupposes society. The speech faculty makes possible the transmission and perpetuation of culture; and speech could evidently arise only in a somewhat socially inclined species, though the most socialized animals, the social insects, are held together by instinctive drives and do not need speech. In man, however, language helps bind his societies successfully together. And then culture, with its institutions and morals and values, binds each of them together more and helps them to achieve more successful functioning.

Human society and culture are thus perhaps best viewed as two intimately intertwined aspects of a complex of phenomena that regularly occur only in association; whereas on the subhuman level, societies occur but there is no significant culture.

The occurrence of cultureless true societies among the insects makes it clear that, much as living bodies and "minds" underlie societies and cultures, and precede them in evolution, so also, in turn, society precedes and underlies culture, though in man the two always happen to come associated. At any rate, society is a simpler and more obvious concept to grasp than is culture. That is apparently why sociocultural phenomena—the phenomena of man's total history in the broadest sense, which necessarily contain both social facts and cultural facts—usually have their social aspects recognized first. The result has been that

---

[4] Culture as dealt with by the anthropologist is obviously different from what is signified by speaking of "a man of culture," or "a cultured person," in the popular sense, when high culture, or special refinement of it, is meant. Similarly with the word "civilization." When we ordinarily, as laymen, speak of "civilized" and "uncivilized" peoples, we mean, more precisely, peoples of advanced and backward culture, respectively. By many anthropologists, ever since Tylor, the words "civilization" and "culture" are often used to denote the same thing; and always they denote only degrees of the same thing.

the social-plus-cultural combination came at first to be called merely "social," and in popular and general use still carries that ambiguous name.

For those who like their thinking concrete, it may help if they conceive the sociocultural total in man as similar to a sheet of carbon paper, of which the fabric side represents society and the coated side culture. It is obvious that to use carbon paper effectively, we must distinguish the sides. And yet the sheet is also a unit. Moreover, in certain respects, as when we are not concerned with manifolding but only with some operation like sorting, counting, or packing, a sheet of carbon paper is comparable to and is handled like a sheet of uncoated paper—which in turn would correspond to the cultureless animal societies. But if what we are interested in is the use of carbon paper, the impressions made by it, or if we wish to understand how it makes them, then it is the specific carbon coating that we must examine, even though this comes only as a sort of dry-ink film carried by paper of more or less ordinary cellulose fabric and texture. Like all similes, this one has its limitations. But it may be of help in extricating oneself from the confusing difficulty that the word "social" has acquired a precise and limited meaning—society as distinguishable from culture—in anthropology and sociology, while still having a shifting double meaning—society including or excluding culture—in popular usage and in many general contexts.

There is a real difficulty in the confusion that results from the varying usage of the word "society." The difficulty is unfortunate; but it can be met by keeping it constantly in mind. In the present book, the effort is made to be consistent in saying "culture" or "cultural" whenever anything cultural is referred to. "Social" or "society" are used only with specific reference to the organization of individuals into a group and their resulting relations. Culture, on the contrary, whatever else it may also be—such as a tremendous influence on human behavior—is always first of all the *product* of men in groups: a set of ideas, attitudes, and habits—"rules" if one will—evolved by men to help them in their conduct of life.[5]

---

[5] A further complication arises from the fact that human societies are more than merely innate or instinctual associations like beehives or anthills, but are also culturally shaped and modeled. That is, the forms which human association takes—into nations, tribes, sects, cult groups, classes, castes, clans, and the like—all these forms of social structure are as much the result of varying cultural influences as are the particular forms of economies, technologies, ideologies, arts, manners, and morals at different times and places. In short, specific human societies are more determined by culture than the reverse, even though some kind of social life is a precondition of culture. And therewith social forms become part of culture! This seemingly contradictory situation is intellectually difficult. It touches the heart of the most fundamental social theorizing. A good many anthropologists and sociologists still shrink from facing the problem or admitting the situation to be significant. The beginner is therefore advised not to try to master the difficulty at this stage, but to wait till he has finished the book. He will then presumably understand what the problem is and be in a position either to accept the solution suggested here, or to give his own answer. And if not, he will still be in the company of a lot of professional social scientists of good standing.

7. ANTHROPOLOGY AND THE SOCIAL SCIENCES

All the so-called social sciences deal with cultural as well as social data. Caesar's reform of the calendar was a cultural innovation. His defeat of the senatorial party was a social event, but it led to institutional and therefore cultural changes, just as it affected thousands of individual lives for better or worse. When a historian analyzes Caesar's character and motivation, he has in fact gone beyond both society and culture and is operating in the field of informal, biographical, individual psychology. In economics, a banking system, the gold standard, commerce by credit or barter, are institutions, and hence cultural phenomena.

Of all the social sciences, anthropology is perhaps the most distinctively culture-conscious. It aims to investigate human culture as such: at all times, everywhere, in all its parts and aspects and workings. It looks for generalized findings as to how culture operates—literally, how human beings behave under given cultural conditions—and for the major developments of the history of culture.

To this breadth of aim, one thing contributed. This was the early anthropological preoccupation with the very ancient and primitive and remote, which we have already mentioned as a possible foible or drawback. Unlettered peoples leave no biographies of their great men to distract one with personalities, no written histories of rulers and battles. The one thing we know about them is their customs; and customs are culture. The earliest men in fact have left us evidence of just two things: parts of their organic bodies, as represented by their bones; and, more abundantly, their culture, as represented by those of their tools and implements which happened to be of stone and imperishable, plus such of their customs as may be inferable from these tools.

Now while some of the interest of anthropology in its earlier stages was in the exotic and the out-of-the-way, yet even this antiquarian motivation ultimately contributed to a broader result. Anthropologists became aware of the diversity of culture. They began to see the tremendous range of its variations. From that, they commenced to envisage it as a totality, as no historian of one period or of a single people was ever likely to do, nor any analyst of his own type of civilization alone. They became aware of culture as a "universe," or vast field, in which we of today and our own civilization occupy only one place of many. The result was a widening of a fundamental point of view, a departure from unconscious ethnocentricity toward relativity. This shift from naïve self-centeredness in one's own time and spot to a broader view based on objective comparison is somewhat like the change from the original geocentric assumption of astronomy to the Copernican interpretation of the solar system and the subsequent still greater widening to a universe of galaxies.

A considerable differentiation of anthropology occurred on this point. The other social sciences recognized culture in its specific manifestations as they became aware of this or that fragment or aspect of it—economic or juridical or political or social. Anthropologists became aware of culture as such. From that they went on to try to understand its generic features and processes and their results.

This is one of the few points that sets off from anthropology a science which in the main is almost a twin sister: sociology. Sociologists began mainly with the analysis of our own civilization; they kept the exotic in its place. Therefore as regards culture they tended to remain autocentric somewhat longer. Also, in dealing with ourselves, they dealt mainly with the present, and from that they went on to deal with the future, immediate and ultimate. This inevitably gave to much of early sociology some reformist or ameliorative coloring, and often a program for action. On the contrary, the reproach used to be directed at anthropology that it did not concern itself with practical solutions, or aim at betterment. So far as this was true, it had at least the virtue of helping anthropology to remain a general or fundamental science, undistracted by questions of application from its search for basic findings and meanings. One other distinction is that sociology has been more concerned with strictly social problems: the relations of classes, the organization of family and society, the competitions of individuals within a group. The names are indeed significant here: sociology tends to be concerned with society, anthropology with *anthropos,* man, and his specifically human product, culture.

All in all, however, these are only differences of emphasis. In principle, sociology and anthropology are hard to keep apart. Anthropologists rate Sumner as one of the great names in the history of the study of man; and they feel they stand on common ground with American sociologists like Thomas, Ogburn, Chapin, Sorokin, Wirth, MacIver, Parsons, and Lynd, to name only a few, and with Britons and Frenchmen like Hobhouse, Ginsberg, Durkheim, and Mauss. Sociologists on their side have been if anything even more hospitable. Almost to a man they are culture-conscious, know anthropological literature well, and use it constantly.

The relations of anthropology to psychology are obviously important. The nature of human personality—or let us say simply human nature—must enter vitally into all of man's social and cultural activity. However, the relations of anthropology and psychology are not easy to deal with. Psychologists began by taking their own culture for granted, as if it were uniform and universal, and then studying psychic behavior within it. Reciprocally, anthropologists tend to take human nature for granted, as if it were uniform, and to study the diverse cultures which rest upon it. In technical language, we have two variables, "mind" and culture, and each science assumes that it can go ahead by treating the other variable as if it were constant. All psychologists and anthropologists now know that such constancy is not actual. But to deal with two variables, each highly complex, is difficult; and as for specific findings, only beginnings have as yet been made. This whole set of problems of cultural psychology is taken up in one of the later chapters of this book.

The foregoing will make clear why anthropology is sometimes still regarded as one of the newer subjects of study. As a distinct science, with a program of its own, it is relatively recent, because it could hardly become well organized until the biological and the social sciences had both attained enough development to specialize and become aware of the gap between themselves, and until culture was recognized as a specific and distinctive field of inquiry.

But as an unmethodical body of knowledge, as an interest, anthropology is plainly one of the oldest of the sisterhood of sciences. It could not well be otherwise than that men were at least as much interested in each other as in stars and mountains and plants and animals. Every savage is a bit of an ethnologist about neighboring tribes and knows a legend of the origin of mankind. Herodotus, the "father of history," devoted half of his nine books to pure ethnology. Lucretius, a few centuries later, tried to solve by philosophical deduction and poetical imagination many of the same problems that modern anthropology is more cautiously attacking with concrete methods. Until nearly two thousand years after these ancients, in neither chemistry nor geology nor biology was so serious an interest developed as in anthropology.

Man's Place in Nature

8. ANTECEDENTS TO MAN'S DEVELOPMENT

A NUMBER of major achievements had to be made in the development of life before there could be man. There are more than a dozen such basic innovations, to pause only at the most fundamental ones. These underlie the possibility of human existence and have actually preceded it in evolution.

This is not an insinuation that there was any predetermination of such a sequence of developmental steps leading to ourselves. That the steps happened is all that we can say. But they had to happen, if there was to be man. Conceivably, a quite different series of evolutionary advances might have made possible the coming on the stage of a type as skilled, intelligent, and successful as man, or even superior to him, but different from him. Conceivably, that very thing may have happened on some other planet or in some other galaxy. But on this our own earth, we can read its history in only one way: as it actually happened. What follows, then, is a tally of some of the more dramatic turns of the road which our preancestors traversed through nature before becoming man.

This will not be the usual story of new and higher kinds of animals coming on the scene in successive periods of geology—the age of mailed fishes, the age of reptiles, the age of mammals. We can assume that history as more or less familiar in outline. What concerns us more, with our focus on man as an eventual product, is the specific features of body build and body use that had to be developed before there could even be a prospect of man's developing. It is his *significant antecedents* that count. These are features which we are likely to take for granted: things like heads, legs, senses, nervous system, body heat; like the capacities for play, for sleeping, for living long enough to learn, and for dwelling together in societies. But Nature, if we may momentarily personify her, could not take these features for granted. They were not there when life began on earth. Most of them did not get achieved till long after. They were developed haltingly, partially, one-sidedly, by something like rare and slow steps of trial and error, through aeons and aeons of painfully hesitating evolution.

It is the more outstanding of these structures and faculties that are specially significant for understanding man's place in the totality of nature: for realizing what his humble and unconscious ancestors had to acquire and achieve before he could become man—before he could be even a mammal and a primate, let alone an animal able to develop speech and culture.

This analysis we can make without having to recite the full roster of the conventional periods of geology. But we do have to refer to some of the major groups of animals, the subkingdoms or phyla [1] into which the animal kingdom is classified. Those which follow are the ones we shall have occasion to mention.

Protozoa, [2] the single-celled animals, like the amoeba or the paramecium. The Protozoa underlie all the various kinds of many-celled animals—underlie them in being more basic in structure as well as presumably preceding them in time of origin. But the Protozoa are too tiny in size, too brief in duration of life, too simple in basic plan, to have ever become capable of any commanding place in nature. Their significance is as a start that that had to be made if there was to be anything further in evolution, not as an accomplishment in themselves. So we can pass them over with this mention.

The *Sponges*—perhaps the simplest of the many-celled phyla of animals.

The *Coelenterates:* corals, sea anemones, jellyfish. The name refers to their having a "hollow inside."

Echinoderms, "spiny-skins," include starfish, sea urchins, sea cucumbers, and other such sluggish forms.

Mollusks have fleshy parts—a "foot," a mantle, a siphon—and they often secrete a shell outside their body. They range from immobile forms like oysters through slow-moving snails to swift cephalopods—squids and octopuses.

Of *Worms,* formerly sometimes put all together into the one phylum *Vermes,* two or three phyla are now generally recognized. Of these the segmented annelids, typified by the familiar earthworm, are the only ones we shall need to linger on a bit, on account of their seeming to represent a simpler attempt at the plan of organization of the arthropods.

The *Arthropods*—"jointed-footers," also formerly called *Articulata* because of the elaborate way in which their segments are put together or articulated—include

---

[1] Singular, phylum. [2] Singular, protozoon.

crustaceans, arachnids, insects. Crustaceans comprise crabs, lobsters, shrimps, and many minute forms—all water dwellers, or at least gill-breathing. Arachnids include spiders, ticks, mites, scorpions, and other types regularly unpleasant to ourselves. The arthropods, and among them especially the insects, have been and still are one of the most successful manifestations of life. They show the greatest number of species of any phylum, and probably the greatest diversity of forms.

The *Vertebrates*—fishes, amphibians, reptiles, birds, and mammals—have a vertebral column as the main axis of their internal skeleton, which contrasts so sharply with the arthropod exoskeleton. Technically, the subkingdom is named the *Chordates* after the spinal cord, but the genuine vertebrates constitute 99 per cent of the chordates. The remainder are retrogressive sessile forms, such as tunicates, skull-less forms like amphioxus, or jawless lampreys.

9. MANY-CELLED PROBLEMS: MOUTHS, VENTS, HEADS, TAILS

One of the problems confronting many-celled animals from the beginning was that of their shape, the structure of this shape, and the functional diversification of cells to correspond with the structure. A mere multiplication of like cells into an indefinitely large but uniform aggregate would have only little advantage over the same number of cells each constituting a self-sufficient organism. Some sort of pattern or plan of differentiating direction had to develop before there could be further evolution. The sponges represent such a plan—one of the oldest, and therefore evidently a successful one: it still functions, though humbly. There are four or five kinds of cells in a sponge: those that secrete the horny or silicious skeleton with which we wash; those which contract the openings into it; ciliated ones that whip the water for food and digest it; and so on. But, except for being more or less cavernous, a sponge has little describable shape. One species differs from the next in the pattern according to which it grows rather than by a specific form which it attains. The sponge is at the minimum of individuation. There are no differentiated organs, no nerves, and therefore no sense organs. A generalized continuity still pervades the whole cell aggregate. We can just barely call a particular sponge a particular organism.

The simplest readily definable form of many-celled animal is that of the coelenterates—corals, sea anemones, and jellyfish. They possess a coelum or hollow, a definite body-cavity, in which food is enclosed and absorbed. The opening of this cavity may be construed as a mouth, which a sponge or a protozoan cannot be said yet to possess. Note however that there is no vent: undigestible parts of food, and excretions, are ejected via the mouth; oral-anal differentiation has not yet occurred. More yet than a mouth, the coelenterates have a nervous system. This is a diffuse network of nerves, without any massing of nerve tissue in centers, ganglia, or brains. In fact, there is not enough organ specialization in these animals to make even an incipient brain of any use. No specifically differentiated sense organs, such as eyes or ears, have been discovered, other than tentacles sensitive to touch, to chemicals, and to heat. Movements consist of slow wavings and curlings and closures of the tentacles; of a sudden defensive contraction of the entire organism upon hurtful contact; and in some free-floating forms, of similar contractions expelling the water from the body cavity and thus pushing themselves upward. Many coelenterates are sessile: they spend their lives sitting in one place. And all are radial in plan: they are live cups with fringes and the power of closing.

With a body cavity, a mouth is implicit, but not yet a head. Heads are an achievement that life succeeded in making only after it had run a considerable course. With a forward end to an organism, setting the direction in which it travels, we 'are given also a hind end and a lengthwise axis of the body. With such an axis, we also get—not perhaps by mere logic of space, but certainly de facto in almost all headed animals—an upper and an under side: one habitually hugging the ground or the sea bottom, the other more exposed. With fore and aft and top and bottom established, right and left follow automatically. For things that travel, it is ordinarily advantageous to have their right and left sides equal and alike, as in a ship or a motorcar or a tractor: "bilaterally symmetric" is the technical term. The advantage is mechanically founded. It is obvious what would happen to the motion of a ship whose starboard was bulkier than its port side. On the contrary, however, both vehicles and animals ordinarily travel better if their top and bottom are rather thoroughly different in form and function. Internal lack of right-left symmetry is no disadvantage provided the weight of the two halves is kept equal; and this is as true of our viscera, with the heart on one side and the liver on the other, as of many machines.

Secondarily, cephalization and bilateral symmetry have resulted in other gains, such as the possibility of the organism's centralizing or grouping its organs—plumping them, as it were. The first great advantage of a head and symmetry, however, was undoubtedly in regard to motion. Not all symmetrical animals with a head are swift; but all swift ones have heads and symmetry. Twice at least in the history of life do good-sized groups of animals seem to have given up their bilateral symmetry: most of the echinoderms and most of the mollusks. Perhaps this was because in both cases they developed limy skeletons or shells, and armor protection cuts down mobility, in living things as in fighting ships. Some of the echinoderms, like the starfish, which returned to the radiate plan of the coelenterates, move, but at an incredibly slow crawl. Others, like the crinoids, are sessile, on stalks. Among mollusks, the snails are proverbial for their slow reactions and nearly unique in being twisted screw-fashion in one direction. This twist is a device for coiling most of the animal up compactly, instead of having it drag or bob around awkwardly behind its single, sliding belly-foot, as would happen if the body remained symmetrical. Snails accordingly atrophy their right and have their left side grow into their top, rear, and insides. Other mollusks, comprising most of the bivalves, have given up even slow travel; and an oyster, for instance, is asymmetrical in any dimension. On the contrary, the most mobile and intelligent of the mollusks the squids and the octopuses, have regained or retained their original bilateral symmetry and are very definitely cephalized.

With a head end evolved, it would normally be advantageous to have the mouth within this, and especially so to have set within the head the eyes or other sense organs that help direct motion, also jaws or other parts that take or hold or chew food. Such a gathering of active or sensitive parts needs a corresponding gathering of nerve tissue; and it is in the symmetrical animals that we find knots or ganglia of nerve, and finally brains. At first these are by no means limited to the head; but at any rate they tend to be most strongly developed there. This is already evident in the flatworm *Planaria,* whose head has a pair of eyes of sorts, though its mouth is just a tube out of its belly. It is more evident in the annelid segmented earthworm, which though blind has its mouth near the front tip of the body. Here there is a definite concentration of nerve matter in a ring around the oesophagus, culminating in an almost-brain above the oesophagus. There is a similar ganglion, or a pair of them, in each segment. In some of the free-swimming marine annelid worms, which have sensory antennae and gills at the end of the head, the brain concentration is greater than in the earthworm. Also, worms show synapses or connective intertwinings of the ends of separate nerve cells, something to which coelenterates have not yet attained.

The basic earthworm type of nervous system is retained all through the articulate or arthropod subkingdom—in crustaceans, spiders, insects. The pair of parallel nerve chains runs from segment to segment close to the underside. In the lower forms, each segment contains a pair of ganglia, or a fused ganglion; in the higher, there is always a brain in the head, whereas the centers in thorax and abdomen are variously consolidated, and in some species are united into one great thoracic ganglion. This is of course a plan quite different from that of the vertebrates, which are not repetitively segmented, therefore lack segmental ganglia, and have the main nerve chain in the back instead of the belly, protected by the vertebral column or notochord. Also, the vertebrates from the beginning concentrated nearly all sense organs as well as jaws and teeth in the head, and protected this with a skull, so that a nerve concentration within the head was basic to their structure. The successive developments and encroachings of later parts of the brain, with corresponding growths of "intelligence," are outlined in § 12. The last chapter in this process is constituted by the cerebral cortex which first appears in reptiles and has its fullest development in the primates.

A vent for excreting seems to be a less significant counterpart of the head, and more or less of the same age developmentally. It is found for instance in the echinoderms, some of which, originally symmetrical, have returned externally to the radiate plan of structure characteristic of the headless and ventless coelenterates. There is often a strange economy in life forms that makes a single part serve more than one function. Bowel and kidney waste, for instance, may be ejected by the same or separate orifices—or even the genital products, which are so different in kind. In crustaceans and insects these last leave the body by their own opening, whereas in the vertebrates, up to the mammals, the vent for the three functions mostly is common; and even in the mammals there is a joint "genito-urinary" tract.

Tails—though we men have long since lost our ancient ones, at least externally—were important in their day. The prime function of course is locomotory. Genuinely effective tails come in with the vertebrates, among the fishes. Lower forms, especially in their larval phases, have all kinds of side and hind-end appendages, to flail or flip or jerk with. Lobsters shoot themselves backward by suddenly squeezing their tail against their body, a bit reminiscent of the way an octopus also progresses backward by squeezing water out through its siphon tube—a sort of jet propulsion. The fish is the first organism to have its hind appendage an integral part of its body, streamlined into it, and yet specifically shaped for side-to-side sculling and practically continuous progress. On land, this form of locomotion is not feasible; and though most amphibians and reptiles have kept their tail, many mammals have again lost it, or when they retain it, it serves new functions, of balance, prehensility, or fly-chasing;[3] and in the air, birds have long since replaced structural tails by superstructural ones of feathers.

10. SIZE, BONE, LIMBS

Size has been an important quality to acquire. Not that the bigger the better, but lack of size below a certain threshold is a definite handicap. This is largely because body surface tends to increase as the square of length, but weight as the cube. The very small animal therefore is swayed by every current or wave of water or air. Its medium tends to move it, where the large animal moves through the medium; the tiny one's best control is by clinging or crawling—methods that abrogate or reduce locomotion. All the really gigantic animals, past or present—sharks, whales, dinosaurs, elephants—have been members of the highest subkingdom, the vertebrates. The largest nonvertebrate, the giant squid, belongs to the most active, sensorily keenest, and perhaps most plastically intelligent order in all the invertebrate subkingdoms. Analogously, it is almost surely no accident that man is the second largest living primate, and that in general intelligence the gorilla, the largest, about ties for second place with the chimpanzee, the fourth largest.

Bone is a definite achievement. Or rather, an articulated endoskeleton is such; and bone made the best skeletal substance—strong, light, and discontinuous—once the vertebrates came onto land and had to carry their weight instead of floating it. Limy deposits outside, as in the starfish, the oyster, and the snail, slow up mobility and may abolish it. The active squid secretes itself only a spot

---

[3] When the ancestral whales returned to the sea, they re-evolved a fishlike tail, but in a horizontal instead of a vertical plane. This position is perhaps connected with the need for constant coming up to the surface to breathe.

of shell and then grows its soft tissues around it, with the result that it has, strictly and structurally, no skeleton at all, but a pretty good functional ersatz backbone. Insects have an exoskeleton of chitin that works excellently, but only at their size. A man-size insect would probably be a complete failure, finding it difficult to move, almost impossible to grow by molting, equally so to be warm-blooded; not to mention that minute breathing tubes could not begin to supply so large a bulk with oxygen. It is true that there were caddis-fly and grass-hopper-like insects with 30-inch wing spread in the Carboniferous period, at the very beginning of the known fossil-insect record. We do not know precisely what made them die out; but nature did not repeat the endeavor—they were evidently not a success. The largest living insects are all slow and clumsy; and even crabs have to add so much lime to their chitin that their largest species are sluggish.

True legs—that is, jointed limbs containing an inner or an outer skeleton and primarily serving locomotion, secondarily other functions—have been evolved only twice: by arthropods and vertebrates. Many small organisms move through water by cilia, hairlike fringes that wave or beat,[4] or by flail-like appendages for jerking or kicking. Others just wriggle, like worms; or slowly protrude pseudo-pods, like the starfish; or crawl by contractile waves in their belly muscle, as do snails and slugs. The squids and octopuses have skeletonless tentacles primarily for grasping and holding; their swimming locomotion is by squirting or by waving membrane fins. As to true legs, those of anthropods number many in the lower orders—ten in crabs, eight in spiders, six in insects—as against the basic vertebrate pattern of four. Among water dwellers, legs seem to be a handi-cap rather than aid to speed—compare crabs with fishes and squids. But on land, legs are correlated with speed among runners, and equally so among flyers after conversion of legs into wings in birds and bats.

Adaptation of running legs into holding forelimbs has taken place in several mammalian orders, on a lower partial level perhaps most markedly among beavers, squirrels, and other rodents; then, more thoroughly, in the primates, in connection with arboreal habitat. It was however the grasping of tree branches by primates in escape and travel that led to the handling of food, and was to lead ultimately to the handling and then the making of tools. Our arboreal ancestry thus is an antecedent that proved to be of great importance. A modicum of size also entered this situation: definitely small animals like shrews, mice, lizards, and frogs can climb and live in trees without grasping hands; toenails or pads on the feet mostly suffice to hold them; or if not, their slight weight prevents falls from being fatal, even from great heights. On the other hand, ordinary-sized monkeys, being functionally four-handed and therefore essen-tially without feet properly fitted for ground travel, were pretty well confined

[4] Cilia occur as low in the scale of evolution as one-celled animals, and as high as on the mucous membrane of our human nostrils.

to their tree habitat, which obviously is a quite limited and somewhat narrowing environment. It is difficult to imagine much primitive technology being invented among a race whose extremities were undifferentiated as between climbing and manipulative uses, and which would dare to descend to the ground only fitfully. With increasing size and weight there was a return to the ground among some of the primates. With the baboons this involved also a return to full four-footed locomotion on the level. With the gorilla and the chimpanzee, the return was barely a half-and-half affair: they remain awkward and feeble erect walkers, mostly travel on all fours on the ground, and often swing from arm to arm along tree limbs. This means that their arms and hands still serve locomotion—in fact, locomotion of two quite different kinds. We men have feet serviceable for ground travel and for little else; and we have long straight legs, and therewith have widened the limited arboreal environment of the primates to one that extends as far as land goes. At the same time we fortunately kept, from the former life in the trees, our grasping, manipulating forelimb hands. In other words, men alone among the primates are two-footers and two-handers. As regards structure, this is not strictly so, the anatomists tell us; but as regards use, it is essentially true. We are the only mammal whose two pairs of limbs serve two wholly different sets of functions and do so effectively; and both functions, locomotion and manipulation, are of broad, generalized, fundamental importance. We have in this differentiated combination, accordingly, one of the bases that not only made culture possible but made an effective culture possible. Incidentally, our development of real hands capable of using tools contributed to freeing the human mouth from holding, fighting, catching, and the like, which functions it has among most mammals. With the load of these activities removed, it may well be that the mouth was readier than ever before to serve as a speech organ in addition to an eating organ, as soon as the brain cortex was ready to do its part.

A contributing element to this result again was—size. If ancestral men when they left the trees had been fifteen inches tall and had weighed five pounds, the descent to the ground might easily have been fatal to them before they could evolve much culture. And if they had succeeded, their weapons, no matter how skilled, would at first have had to be thoroughly puny. It was a sound instinct that leds Wells in his *Time Machine* to make his Morlocks not a monkeylike ancestral form, but decadent men, shrunken to diminutiveness, expert mechanics but hiding in deep shafts instead of freely roaming the earth.

11. BODY TEMPERATURE AND VISION

Warm-bloodedness is the faculty of the organism to maintain its own proper constant body temperature, independent of its surroundings. The temperature of most animals is that of their environment, on which they are therefore dependent. Warm-blooders might be said to carry around with them a spot of environment made by themselves, so far as heat is concerned. This autonomous control is of course a tremendous advantage. It is analogous to the advantage that primitive man later had over even the warm-blooded subhumans, once he had learned to carry fire around or to make it. Only the two highest classes of vertebrates are warm-blooded: the birds and the mammals. They are reckoned highest partly because of possessing this attribute.

Acute vision, the ability to see sharp instead of blurred, is uncommon rather than common in the animal kingdom, perhaps because it requires not only a highly developed eye but considerable concentration of organized nerve matter. Even most mammals see motion or gross outline rather than exact details of shape, and many are color-blind. Sharp vision depends upon the presence of a fovea (macula lutea), a little pit of special sensitivity in the retina. Birds have this, and primates have it; and we have it as part of our primate inheritance. Birds need acute vision so as not to smash themselves up when landing from flight, much as a plane wants an illuminated airport, or a fog dispeller, during night landings. Monkeys need clear vision when landing from leaps in the trees. Here again we have a piece of our characteristic human luck: both that our ancestors turned arboreal, and when later they descended again, that they managed to keep their sharp eyesight. Our fine hands would certainly be much less useful if we could see only hazily, as does a dog or a horse. On account of its relation to space control, sight is the most important of the senses for high-powered muscular co-ordination; [5] and it is even more important as a basis for everything mechanical, for all the technological part of culture. Smell and hearing differ from sight in being more diffuse. They can warn of what is around the corner, and therefore help organisms to evade their hunters, or to find their prey or water. They serve the primal business of surviving. As soon as the level of more than survival is entered, sight takes precedence. It is hard to imagine blind animals at play, for instance.

We have left to the last what is possibly the most important consideration of all: organization of nerve matter into a brain of higher faculties.

12. NERVES AND BRAIN

Plants contain no nerve matter and therefore lack nervous irritability. All animals have at least areas of special excitability, though they do not all have nerves, let alone a nervous system. Some of the Protozoa show definite neuromotor masses or strands for perception and feeding. These are grouped in and near hairlike cilia for feeling at the "head" end of the animal, and especially around the inside of what might be called its mouth opening. There are also motor strands for contracting the whole organism. This is really a precocious

[5] Among very small animals, such as insects, sight is not so important for co-ordination, nor for control of alighting from flight or leaps, because these animals are generally too light to break themselves by impact.

organization for a unicellular animal. It is actually more advanced than that found in the most backward many-celled animals, the sponges.

Sponges have the beginnings of muscle tissue, with some power of contraction for a short distance beyond the point of stimulus, if the latter is strong. These cells are undifferentiated receptor-effectors: sensitive muscle tissues, in simple language. There is no nerve tissue for perception as such nor conduction as such, in sponges. They are accordingly less organized, nervously, than the most advanced Protozoa. Presumably this is so because the integration of a number of cells into a diversely functioning unit is a more difficult achievement than the internal differentiation of a single cell.

With the coelenterates, we have seen (§ 9) that there is the beginning of a nervous system. Polyps and sea anemones have certain cells on the surface that are specially sensitive and are directly connected with contractile cells below them. We can accordingly speak of differentiated receptors and effectors, or sets of sense-organ and muscle cells. Sometimes a third set of cells is interposed. In that case we really have conductive nerve tissue also.

In the jellyfishes, there is enough of this sort of nervous matter to form a nerve net extending through the organism. An excitation at a single spot may therefore be diffused and result in the contraction of the whole body. However, the network is pretty uniform and there is no mechanism for central control. In the umbrella-shaped medusa jellyfish, long, movable, sensitive tentacles hang down from the rim of the umbrella. Just inside the rim, these are all interconnected by means of a nerve ring, which represents a definite condensation of conductive tissue as compared with the nerve net. Yet there still is nothing like ganglia or concentrations of nerve matter in masses. In fact, the nerve substance in the ring is continuous, not broken into neurons or cells, and therefore without nerve-cell joints, as synapses might be called. Transmission is more than two hundred times slower than in the fastest human nerves; and it works indifferently either way, according as it gets started. In a famous experiment, a nerve ring was dissected out. On stimulation, the impulse went around and around the ring, contracting the immediately adhering muscle, but unable to discharge itself into the organism. Trapped in the nerve ring, the impulse circulated at a speed of about a foot and a half a second, until in eleven days it had traveled 457 miles! It was tiring then, but less so than the muscles; and it finally stopped because there was enough regenerated tissue to absorb the nervous impulse. It is hard to imagine an apter illustration of the thoroughly mechanical character of neuropsychic activity at this undifferentiated level of evolution.

Above the coelenterates, nerve matter consists mainly of neurons, discontinuous elongated or branching cells connected by synapses. This plan allows both more differentiation and more centralization than the continuous nets or rings of nerve tissue. In the flatworms and segmented worms, the crustaceans and insects, there is an organized "ladder type" of nervous system of two main strands running the full length of the body near its underside, with branches for each segment or limb. The concentration of this nerve tissue into ganglia or miniature brains at the forward end, with a grouping around the swallowing part of the throat in the earthworm, has already been mentioned in § 9 in connection with the evolution of heads. A description of our own brain as an enormous supra-oesophagal ganglion mass would be not too incorrect.

In worms and insects, the head ganglia somewhat dominate the behavior of the animal as a whole, but not altogether so. Earthworms gradually conditioned to take a right-hand turn because a left-hand exit led only to sandpaper and electric shocks, hesitated but took the right turn after their brain end was amputated. This indicates that the acquired habit of making the proper turn was channeled in the whole body, or at any rate in the total nervous system, and not in the brain alone.

The vertebrate nervous system differs from that of the arthropods and worms in being developed from a single main, dorsally situated spinal cord instead of a double-strand ventral nerve "ladder." In the ancestral lowly amphioxus, there is only this cord, without thickening or massing into brain; but it also has no skull. In the fishes, there is a brain, but the cord still outweighs it. The brain lies in line with the cord, with its several bulbous parts, such as cerebellum, midbrain, and endbrain, one behind the other. These parts are well differentiated in function in fishes: the midbrain largely serves sight, the endbrain smell.

In the amphibians, the brain begins to equal the spinal cord in weight; in the reptiles and birds, it is heavier; in mammals, progressively so. Thus a cat's brain outweighs its cord four times, a macaque monkey's eight times, a man's fifty times.

The greatest evolutionary development occurs in the forebrain or in the endbrain or telencephalon. The base or floor of the endbrain is a gray and white striped mass, whence its name corpus striatum; the sides and roof constitute the pallium or "cloak." On the pallium as a foundation the cerebral cortex is gradually built up as higher forms develop. In fishes the main work of co-ordination and integration for the total organism seems to be done in the corpus striatum; almost the whole of the covering pallium serves smelling. Higher up in the scale, the original pallium is distinguished as the archipallium from the later-developed neopallium that overlies it on the sides and behind, and which is in turn overlaid by the cerebral cortex, the "brain rind" or "bark." In mammals the archipallium is largest in keen-smelling forms or in primitive ones like the marsupials; it is altogether lost in the dolphins, who roam the seas without smelling.

The cortex appears first in the higher amphibians, such as the frog. It is larger in reptiles, still larger in mammals. Here it is mostly emancipated from direct relation to any single sensory system, such as the pallium and the archipallium had to the sense of smell. The cortex is rather an intermediary between sensory systems. Its most distinctive function is mnemonic, on which in turn associations and rapid learning can be based. The cortex is like an indexed filing system, from which even single remote experiences can be brought out to be correlated with new ones.

The mammalian cortex is part gray, part white. The white parts, as elsewhere in the brain, consist chiefly of nerve fibers. The gray matter of the cortex consists largely of the cell bodies with their shorter dendrites or ramifications and synapses. The oxygenation, metabolism, and blood supply of the gray matter are higher, compared with the white. The gray, largely outer part of the human cortex has been estimated to aggregate less than a cubic inch in volume, to weigh around 13 grams, but to contain 92 billion separate cells. The total cortex is much larger, enveloping the hindmost cerebellum as well as the cerebrum portion of the endbrain to which it properly belongs. Most of the thickness of the cortex in fact is composed of an endless network of white fibers, the interconnections of which make possible an infinity of combinations and conditionings. It is the number of these that may be assumed as an index of intelligence, much more so than the convolutions or corrugations of the cortex surface.

The foregoing are some of the more significant steps of organic evolution preceding man, as regards structure. It remains to review the more important functional developments that life achieved, or had begun to achieve, before man came on the scene, and of which he was the inheritor from the time of his beginning.

13. SEX

Sex is a device for reshuffling the elements of heredity by first splitting them up, and in the end producing new individuals of greater variety. Sex extends well down into the plant kingdom, though in most species plants are bisexual, bearing flowers that have both stamens and pistils; or if the flowers are separate in sex, as in the tassel and the ear of maize, they nevertheless occur on the same plant. For whole individuals to have flowers of only one sex is much less common in plants, though it occurs, as in willows and yews; but it is evidently a secondarily recurrent character of no great evolutionary depth or significance. Thus the goatsbeard genus, in which some plants carry only male flowers and others only female, crops up secondarily in the rose family, the vast majority of whose genera and species have male and female elements side by side in the same flower. Sex in plants thus tends strongly to be hermaphrodite.

In animals, hermaphroditism also occurs, but is less characteristic, especially of the higher forms. Thus many lower mollusks are bisexual or hermaphroditic, but the free-swimming, active, and intelligent cephalopods are unequivocally unisexual. Vertebrates are bisexual. Arthropods also are basically unisexual; but parthenogenesis—"virgin birth" or sexless propagation from unfertilized eggs—occurs here and there among the insects, including some of their highest forms, such as the bees. Apparently this represents a reversion for coping with special situations.

Since reproductive fertility is cut in half in unisexual species by the inability of males to give birth, sex must have some definite compensation of survival value, else sex-differentiated forms would gradually have been wiped out. The compensation is in the cumulatively double heredity of each individual—already sixteenfold for great-great-grandchildren—which ensures a much greater mixture of genes, and therefore a greater variability of hereditary constitution. And this again makes for greater selective plasticity of the line of descent, and therewith for increased adaptability. With rigorous repetitiveness of the generations, a species theoretically succumbs as soon as it no longer fits its environment. If it constantly varies, some of its members may survive, or even flourish, in a changed environment that eliminates the majority. Sex is thus a form of insurance, of paying a premium to scatter risk and now and then to win a bonus. With its relation to specific adaptability, sex seems almost inescapable for all the highest forms of life.

14. WATER, LAND, AIR

The medium in which nearly all organisms function is either water or the combination of being on land and in the air. The geological record, as well as comparative structure and function, indicates strongly that life in water came first. Thus even in land animals and plants the reproductive cells require liquid surroundings. This priority may be due to the fact that chemical reactions and osmosis are "easier" or more active in liquids. Also, the density of protoplasm being close to that of water, the effect of gravity is very slight in water, and certain mechanical problems of support and motion are much more easily met there than on land.[6] There is very little to hold up: the water itself does nearly all of that. Hence a minimum of stiff framework is needed in marine life. If there are hard parts, they mostly serve as protective armor, as in crabs or clams or corals. The drawback is that the density of the liquid medium offers resistance to rapid motion. Among land animals the medium by which the body is surrounded normally is air, which is over a thousand times "thinner" or less resistive than water; and in all except quite small animals, most of the difficulty of rapid motion on land lies in overcoming the chaining pull of gravity. All terrestrial forms are therefore in a sense crawlers on the bottom of their medium, whereas in water there are in addition to crawlers also free-swimming forms and still more floating ones. The main lines of evolutionary development which have attained to swift, sustained, and controlled power of swimming are surprisingly few: the fishes and the cephalopod mollusks, the two most advanced marine groups. This small number of groups is surpassed by that of the branches of

---

[6] This is not incompatible with the possibility that the density of protoplasm is itself the result of its having originated in a water medium.

insects, reptiles, birds, and mammals which have separately reverted to life and motion in water, although remaining air-breathing. A number of marine phyla or classes include adult or larval forms that essentially float, though they may also kick or flail or jerk or squirt or wriggle or whip themselves occasionally for short distances and without much precision of direction. Mostly they drift passively with whatever currents they find themselves in. There is hardly a counterpart to this in terrestrial life. Sessile forms are wholly confined to water: there are no land equivalents to sponges, corals, crinoids, mussels, barnacles, and tunicates—representing as many different subkingdoms.[7]

All in all, water seems to have been favorable to the origin of life, to the development of mechanisms of protection, to limited or spasmodic mobility, and therewith to restricted intelligence and restricted power of adaptation to situations. All the lowest subkingdoms of animals are exclusively water-inhabiting; so are all forms without power of locomotion. Swimming, the best type of progress in water, has been reattained by terrestrial forms; but flying, its counterpart in air, has not been achieved by any water animals. Within the phyla that on the whole are undoubtedly the highest of all—or let us say the most active and most variedly capable; namely, the arthropods and vertebrates— within these the most advanced classes are mainly terrestrial in habitat and wholly air-breathing: the insects on the one hand, the birds and the mammals on the other.[8]

15. SLEEP AND PLAY

Sleep appears to be a function of higher nervous organization. We men divide our days between periods of conscious activity and periods of withdrawal into unconsciousness. Lower animals give little evidence of letting themselves sink into phases of diminished activity and awareness, other than conditions like the torpor that often is a direct result of cold, or in the sudden but temporary inactivity in the face of danger popularly called "playing possum." Mainly, the withdrawing from external stimuli which we call sleep seems to be recuperation from the responsiveness and activity of the higher vertebrates, and perhaps a function of their warm-bloodedness or autonomous temperature. There is also a subdifference between birds and mammals. With the great majority of birds, waking and sleep are automatic responses to presence or absence of light. Mammals both respond to a greater variety of stimuli, such as temperature or danger, and show more voluntary control of sleeping and waking according as the situation involves boredom, risk, breeding excitement, and the like.

[7] And the tunicates or ascidians are chordates—that is, members, and probably degenerated ones, of the subkingdom of which the vertebrates constitute the main mass.

[8] The one contrary instance of marine forms more advanced than their terrestrial relatives is the rather narrow one of the molluskan cephalopods, which surpass the land snails and slugs.

The two lowest groups of primates, tarsiers and lemurs, are nocturnal, but all other primates are diurnal and seem genuinely to sleep at night.

Play may be defined as wasteful but pleasurable bodily activity performed for its own sake; that is, in response primarily to internal stimuli. On the whole, the lower animals are not sufficiently organized nervously to play, in this meaning of the word. Many are not sufficiently motile. It is doubtful whether play exists even among so highly organized a group as the insects. True, we see the dragonfly darting about, the butterfly fluttering, the midges dancing in the sun; and they are no doubt experiencing a sort of euphoria. But the first two are in the way of finding their food, or their mate; the last is warming up for his courtship; there is always a business involved. And such quasi-play in insects always characterizes only their final, adult, and often brief stage, in contrast with vertebrates, whose playfulness occurs in youth. A butterfly, for instance, spends its youth in the sullenly voracious business of feeding and growing, with its senses, limbs, and mobility much limited. Its adolescence is the stuporlike pupa period of seclusion and immobility. It is only the adult imago ready for mating and death that can properly be said even to act as if it played.

The heavily socialized ants and bees, who are in some ways the most highly developed of insects, lack play altogether. They labor for their fellows, for the hive, its young and its future. Activity is serious, often grim, almost ceaseless. Everything is subordinate to communal welfare; play would distract from this. When an ant relaxes, it is to be fed or cleaned by a self-sacrificing fellow.

Among the arthropods lower than insects, the individualistic spiders, scorpions, crustaceans, life is even grimmer. The male fiddler crab executes a sort of posturing dance, but it is to court females.

Even the vertebrates, when they are cold-blooded, show only traces of playfulness, mostly in connection with mating, and such activities are probably more tense than relaxed. It is only among the warm-blooded vertebrates that well-developed play appears. In the birds, this is still preponderantly attached to mating. It is then that the peacock struts, the pigeon pouts, sparrows chatter and quarrel, songbirds sing; if there is a special plumage, it is assumed now. It is only occasional species such as crows and magpies, to a certain somewhat dour extent also parrots, which are playful apart from courtship, which become mischievous or aggressively tricky, and can serve as human playmates. It is also among these birds that thievishness appears—the picking up and hiding of bright but useless objects. Nesting penguins similarly steal stones from one another. But young birds consistently show no impulse to play. They clamor to be fed, or go about feeding themselves, with a deadly seriousness.

It is among mammals that playfulness is most fully developed, and in youth rather than in connection with reproduction. In fact, mammalian mating tends to be hard, competitive, often vicious. Nor does the mother ordinarily play much with her young; mostly she seems patiently indulgent of their pranks.

In general the carnivorous animals play most and often continue into maturity. All the canines and felines, the bears and raccoons, and the skunk are familiar examples; the seals are among the most addicted. Their protein food is concentrated, so that a meal satisfies for hours, and thus gives them well-fed leisure. Then, food does not occur spread out for them in indefinite amounts like pasture, but has to be found and run down and caught, by means of high sensory activity and motor co-ordination, which are then available for energy play in the periods of leisure. But there are also some carbohydrate-eating animals that are definitely playful, besides lambs and calves with their awkward gambols: the elephant, for instance, and the goat.

Monkeys of course play, but on the whole they are perhaps to be characterized rather as emotional than as playful. They cuddle and hug, embrace and quarrel. They are strongly concerned with their personality interrelations, and establish intricate chains of relationship of dominance. Some of their pursuings may be the stronger chasing the weak in anger rather than sport. Probably a good part of their play is autistic, like gymnastic exercise, instead of mutual. Most monkeys want companionship and affection, but they are full of greed and envy and prone to tyrannize. The baboons, who are large and powerful, seem to play little. They are sturdily selfish and oppressive toward one another, although against the outsider they may resist as a group. Another quality that contributes to keeping some species of monkeys from playfulness is their diffused, nearly continuous sexuality, which is expressed directly, without courtship play. All in all, it is perhaps not unfair to say that emotionality keeps most monkeys from playing as much as their muscles and senses would allow.

But with the anthropoids, the manlike apes, we begin to approach human behavior. They are inquisitive, they get along better with one another than the monkeys, their sexuality is less obtrusive and less diffuse. The playfulness of the young chimpanzee is proverbial and probably equal to that of an energetic child. Even the more melancholy orang and the sluggish gorilla are not far behind. Adults lose playfulness, partly on account of increasing body weight, but no doubt largely because the disposition changes with the maturing of the sexual glands, as in most mammals.

Play impulses in the wide sense are exceedingly significant in man, because in rechanneled form they motivate great areas of human behavior and important achievements of culture. This refers not only to games and sports, but to the influence of curiosity, of desire for variety, of mental restlessness, in the arts and sciences and fashions. If our ancestors had been wholly lacking in playfulness, we should probably have had many fewer aesthetic and intellectual developments in human culture (§ 148). Not that songs or poems or philosophies are mere play or made in play. But they are superutilitarian: pleasurable outlets for excess energy rather than responses to actual needs, and they are thus based on impulses akin to those of play, sublimated as well as matured.

16. AGE AND YOUTH

Two related qualities that are rooted in man's biological heredity, but which have contributed to the success of his unique sociocultural experiment, are a long life span and within this a proportionally long youth. According as we count youth as terminating at sexual maturation or at full growth, youth covers respectively a fifth or a fourth of a long, above-normal life. As it works out, this gives us plenty of time to learn and master our "social heritage." And the fifty or so additional years that in favorable cases are left us beyond youth suffice us to do something satisfactory and full with this heritage once it is learned. This is presumably just a piece of our good fortune. We certainly have no reason to believe that nature anticipatorily evolved a long life for us in order to make us fit vessels for culture when it was only later on that we were to develop the faculty for receiving culture. But if under evolution our youth had happened to eventuate differently, and to be markedly briefer than it actually is, the total culture developed by the human species would probably have been considerably simpler and considerably less. With the one or two years of immaturity of a dog or a cow—to select two familiar animals, one several times smaller and the other larger in mass than we—and a total span of twelve or fifteen years allotted to ourselves, it is obvious how much more meager would be our control of speech, skills, institutions, and ideas. Unquestionably, a short life, and probably still more a short youth, would have put a low ceiling over human possibilities of cultural attainment. There is no direct evidence that as man began to develop culture his longevity increased under the competition of natural selection, those strains which matured more slowly now first having a definite edge of survival advantage in that their members could acquire better skills, speech, and organization. But it is theoretically conceivable that this happened; and in any event, once man had culture, his possession of this culture would prevent his hereditary longevity from shortening in evolution, at least as long as natural selection was operative.

On subhuman precultural levels, longevity is connected with a number of factors, such as size, activity, and fertility. Other things being equal, larger animals live a longer span. A rat outlasts a mouse, a cat a rat, a lion a cat, an elephant the lion. But this holds with reservations, especially when the species are far apart: a bull outweighs five men, but a man may outlive four or five bulls. Also, once a certain life span has become a trait of a species, it is not altered much by giantism or dwarfism, except to a minor extent negatively at both extremes. Big dogs have ten to twenty times the bulk of little ones, but about the same duration of life; that, apparently, became fixed in the genes, the germ plasm, when dogs crystallized into a species; great whales become sexually mature in two years, and seem rarely to live more than two decades. It is inactivity, sluggishness, keeping the candle burning dim, which is evidently connected with the relative longevity of seventeen-year locust larvae, tortoises, and perhaps parrots.

Fertility can be seen as one special negative aspect of activity. In addition, fertility tends to correlate—also antithetically—with longevity. A rabbit, producing large litters in rapid succession, does not have to live long to multiply fiftyfold. After that, the welfare of the species is probably better served by one of her fresh daughters than by having the original mother survive. If rabbits bore only one young at a time at intervals of several years, they would probably die out even if they lived a century, being weak and defenseless. But the elephant, being immune as prey, except to man, and therefore with a low mortality wastage on the way, can get by with his very slow fertility because of his longevity. Yet if he lived no longer than a cow, his species would presumably soon die out, unless it could alter to speed up conceptions and pregnancies.

The foregoing considerations apply chiefly to mammals and birds. It is worth while to glance at conditions among the insects, the class of animals often rated as next to the vertebrates in degree of advancement, and surpassing them in variety and number of species. The most striking difference is that on the whole the immature, prereproductive stages of insects, corresponding to youth in vertebrates, take up most of their life span. It is in the highly specialized insects that the succession of distinct stages—egg, larva, chrysalis, imago—is most accentuated. The first three of these stages are given over to growth and development; the last, essentially to reproduction, and it is often quite brief. In many species a sort of disintegration death follows quickly upon deposition of the eggs. From the vertebrate point of view this is a pretty sorry way of doing, leaving the individual no room for any dignity of personality: not even such as a lion or a bull or a raven or an eagle has. Larval life does not add up much of a stock of experiences and skills for the adult insect to operate with. Nine-tenths of life is used in being a mere eating and growing and passively transforming machine in order to enable the final tenth to function as an egg-fertilizing or egg-laying machine. In the higher vertebrates, growing-up occupies a minority fraction of the whole life span, and its seriousness is relieved by the play impulses we have discussed. And within the longer reproductive phase of vertebrates, sex and reproduction as such actually comprise only a small part of the total activities. To us culture-bearing men, the gearing of the insect organism must inevitably seem particularly inhuman because of its thoroughgoing exclusion of all functions that might contribute even potentially to the development of something like culture.[9]

[9] This highly predetermined disposition is most characteristic of those insect orders, such as butterflies, beetles, and flies, in which the metamorphic stages are highly differentiated. Insects in which the stages are less marked, such as crickets, grasshoppers, and roaches, may be equally or more repugnant to our immediate feelings, but consideration of their life-cycle career arouses less ideological antipathy in us because its general profile is more like that of vertebrates. In line with this is the fact that their behavior is somewhat

It is interesting that the highly socialized ants, bees, and termites have their span of youth and adulthood proportioned inversely from most insects: a short youth, a long age. The ratio may even approximate that of weeks to years. This reversal is undoubtedly a correlate of socialization, and especially of one particular aspect of socialization: the fact that the majority of members in the community are functionally sexless and contribute to its welfare by their labors as "workers." Obviously, the longer they operate, the more benefit does the community get out of them; and mostly they live until they have literally worn themselves out. Ant workers may live up to three or fours years, queens perhaps double to quadruple that; those are remarkable ages for animals at once so small and so active. The brevity of their youth also fits into the total picture of high socialization. Infancy traversed in a matter of weeks instead of months means less absorption of the colony's labor of tending and feeding, and a correspondingly larger building-up of the community's reserves, or its utilization in nourishing additional broods and therewith increasing the populational strength of the society. Also, youth is not a period of learning with the social insects—first because they possess no transmitted culture, and second because their larvae are helpless and undeveloped. It is obvious that in species whose faculties are essentially "instinctive," and relatively little developed by learning and practice, a protracted youth would do next to nothing to make individuals more capable and useful members of society, whereas a brief youth makes them less of a drain and burden.

In short, the lack of capacity for culture and speech (§ 18, 20) among the social insects, as compared with men, is correlated with their relatively much shorter period of immaturity. A culture-bearing and culture-dependent animal like man would no doubt long since have succumbed if human youth had been as brief and as vegetative as that of the ants. But the ants in turn might have lost out in the struggle for survival if they had had to support their young for as long a span, relatively, as human children. On the other hand, apart from culture, it is clear that among the insects socialization is mostly associated with a brief youth, nonsocialization generally with a brief maturity. Man, as the only animal that is both social and cultural, seems consequently to have been pulled both ways. But on the whole, the factors correlated with successful development of culture which make for prolonged youth have been stronger in our species than the factors correlated with successful social development which make for a brief youth.

Among our nearest relatives, the anthropoid apes, the corresponding proportion is not known. Youth is traversed with definitely greater rapidity by the chimpanzee, the orang, and the gorilla. Corresponding stages of development, as marked by dentition, full brain size, sexual maturation, are reached in from half to three-fourths the number of years required by man; perhaps three-fifths

more like that of vertebrates in that it seems to contain less instinctual predetermination and more adaptive responsiveness than the behavior of most metamorphosing insects.

to two-thirds would be not far from a fair average (§ 24-26). Unfortunately, there is no direct evidence on anthropoid longevity. Estimates based on signs of senility suggest a duration of possibly two-thirds of human life. Thus the indications are that anthropoids, while somewhat shorter-lived than we are, distribute their life span in much the same proportion between growing up and being adult. This is only one of a number of close similarities between man and the anthropoids which allow the inference that the development of the faculty for speech and culture was in the nature of a lucky accident of mutation in our heredity. It seems to have been superimposed on a series of basic constitutional traits that the anthropoid ancestors shared with our ancestors, rather than that the decisive mutation was preceded by a long sequence of human specialization away from the anthropoids.

As between the two classes of warm-blooded vertebrates, most birds brood their eggs and literally feed their young as an equivalent to the mammals' suckling theirs; but the period of immaturity and helplessness is relatively shorter in birds. Even large species attain their full growth and faculties in a remarkably short time. This difference is surely correlated with the fact that birds in general possess more instinctive faculties, have to learn less, and apparently do learn less in living, than mammals.

17. SOCIALIZATION

Many lower animals tend to aggregate without being truly social; that is, they cluster, but they do not aid, support, or protect one another. Their eggs or young, for instance, are shed forth and left to take care of themselves. Animals begin to be genuinely social whenever a mother suckles or feeds her young, or when a pair guards them. This makes nearly all birds and mammals social; but the socialization is of a familial or parent-offspring type. From this there must be distinguished the sociability of gregarious animals like sheep. These feel more comfortable in one another's company; but they do not feed or aid each other. Also, the membership of a herd, not being based on kinship, is likely to be transiently shifting; it is reckoned an aggregation, not a true society.

Highly organized animal societies are those which may become large but have a specific structure; which depend on defined interindividual relations; and in which a degree of devotion to the welfare of the community as a whole is evident. Such highly organized societies have developed twice, on a significant scale, in the evolution of life: in man and among the social insects. These two groups are both advanced, but they are also very different. Their societies present striking similarities; yet some of these similarities are analogous rather than homologous. The most fundamental difference is that human societies, beyond the immediate family group, operate with and through culture, but that ants, bees, and termites manage, as was said in § 6, to possess highly developed societies—without which most of them could not survive—without having culture ɔr anything corresponding to it, so far as we can see. In man, society and culture come so intertwined that one never occurs without the other. The presence of cultureless societies among the insects accordingly is an aid in distinguishing the two concepts in the abstract (§ 6). Moreover, man's place in nature, what is common in his status and what is unique, becomes better defined from the comparison, which is also a contrast.

We shall consider first those features which all the social insects have in common as compared with man. After that, the distinction will be given more depth by a comparison of the two chief types of social insects.

18. THE SOCIAL INSECTS

All the many species of ants, honeybees, and termites are thoroughly social. Indeed, it could well be argued that they are more socialized than we. On the whole, the individual in an insect society subordinates his own welfare to that of the group more than most human beings do. Many species live in large communities of thousands to hundreds of thousands or millions of individuals—as populous as human towns or even great cities. Each such community has always a fixed abode, with limits as definite as a city, from which individuals forage but to which they always return, and where the young are reared. But all members of such a hive, hill, or city are normally the descendants of one mother or "queen." [10] A city community among these insects is therefore also a family, in the strict biological sense. The life of the community revolves about the care and feeding of the queen mother, since on her all population increase and replenishment depend, and about the feeding, nursing, and rearing of the young. These young are quite helpless, like small human babies; but unlike babies they remain so until they are fully adult. They cannot feed themselves, or move themselves, or clear themselves of their excrement; in many cases they cannot even come unaided out of their pupa case or cocoon when ready to emerge as adults. All this feeding and rearing, the nest-building and accumulation of surplus food, fall to the lot of the mass of the population, the sterile workers. Between them and the queen mother there is a marked difference of function, and consequently of bodily structure as well as of impulses or drives. This distinction between reproductive queen and sterile worker is fundamental to the plan of ant, bee, and termite society. Human societies may or may not have castes; the perpetuation and existence of the higher insect societies rests upon castes. Conversely, the integration of castes is complete in these insect societies: there is no exploitation. A queenless community and a communityless queen (after the first start of a colony) are alike doomed to extinction. With this interdependence of castes so basic, it is no wonder that some species of ants and most termites have gone further and have added castes or subdivided them—especially a soldier caste for

[10] If she dies, one of her fertile daughters replaces her. Such a new queen is therefore really the sister of the hive members.

offense or defense or both. This professional army again may be differentiated into an aggressive corps with powerful jaws; a sort of flame-throwing or gas-throwing service that squirts a dangerous liquid; a defensive or shield-bearing division that blocks the gate with an enormous impermeable forehead. Workers, in turn, may come in two or even three sizes for indoor and outdoor labor; or they may serve as repositories for honey regurgitated for other members of the hive until they become distended into veritable honeypots or storage bins— a striking example of how the lower cultureless animals may accomplish with their bodies a purpose that man would achieve with a tool or an artifact.[11] Nor are the castes always inflexible. Certain ants use their large-jawed soldiers to crush for them hard-shelled seeds that the workers can bring in but cannot crack. When autumn comes on and the harvest of these seeds is over, when the community goes into winter retreat and ordinarily need fear no further insect enemies, these warrior-millers have become useless and would be a drain on the hoard of the hive. Like the drones among the honeybees, they are therefore killed by the workers—a striking exemplification of the superhuman strength of the overintegrative or totalitarian impulses: not only individuals but even classes are sacrificed for the good of the society.

One other feature of parallelism must be mentioned. Contrary to bees and wasps, all working ants and termites are wingless: they perform their particular labors on or under the ground and therefore travel on their legs. The fertile males and females, however, fly. This is an ancestral inheritance from their common true-insect or hexapod stock and has evidently been retained as an advantage to the perpetuation of the species, which thereby can start new communities over a wide area, instead of each new colony's adjoining the old and perishing with it in any local drought, flood, or other adversity. It is the workers and soldiers, the mass of the community, who among both ants and termites have become specialized away from the original insect condition into wingless-ness and infertility. The fertile females mate with the males after a dispersion flight, of which the nuptial flight or aerial mating of the honeybee is an extreme form. No doubt because of this method of mating abroad, the fertile males and females have also retained the ancestral insect eye—they need to find each other; the workers are poor-sighted or blind.

Immediately after mating, the female shakes off her now useless wings, finds a crevice or makes a burrow, and proceeds to rear a family. Among the ants she does this alone; among the termites, with her partner—a difference the full significance of which we shall see in a moment (§ 19). She begins to lay eggs, to feed the larvae when they hatch, either with what she can forage or with her own saliva, into ingredients of which the henceforth useless parts of her body—wing muscles, optic lobes, and such—are converted. This is a process

[11] Strictly, the honeypots occur among ants, the squirters (nasuti) and shield-bearers among termites; it is the principle of bodily caste-differentiation according to function or service that remains alike.

analogous to that of mammalian milk feeding; not in its physiology or chemistry, which no doubt is quite different in detail, but in its functional mechanism and in the psychic affects and satisfactions by which it must be accompanied. During the whole period of her solitary rearing of this first brood, the prospective queen, although temporarily functioning as a worker, takes no nourishment herself, often for months. Though the initial litter, when hatched into adulthood, is usually undersized or otherwise not quite complete, it immediately begins to operate. It forages, extends the nest, and the like; and above all, begins to feed the queen, who responds by laying more eggs. These, now provisioned by their elder sisters, grow into complete and full-sized worker adults. Only when the community is strong—numerous and well provisioned—do fertile males and females begin to be born, and the cycle of swarming out into new independent colonies can be repeated. This however takes time; and for a community to reach the point where it can bud off communities, to spread and carry on the species, several years are ordinarily required. This means that the queen, on whom everything pivots, must have a long life, and that workers who can survive to help rear innumerable younger sisters and brothers immensely strengthen the hive, especially during its period of upswing. Indeed, queen ants have been known to live fifteen years and workers from three to four—long durations for animals so small; and the indications for termite longevity are similar. It has already been mentioned that the combination of a brief larval and pupal stage and a long working adulthood makes the favorable pattern for prosperity of a highly communized, instinctually endowed type of society, which does not depend on transmission of learned experience; and this pattern has become the universal rule among ants and termites.

There remain some other notable habits of ants and termites: the "agriculture," keeping of "cattle," total wars, and slave-raiding of some species. These habits of course are of special interest because of their resemblance to human institutions. But human agriculture, stock-raising, slavery, and totalitarian war of exploitation are universally accepted as having been invented, and as transmitted by teaching or learning; that is, as being cultural products. It is difficult to accept the corresponding social-insect activities as cultural in nature, because ants and termites neither use nor make tools, nor, as will shortly be shown (§ 19), do they seem to possess that apparently indispensable part and condition of culture which we call language. With these basic elements of culture lacking, it is hard to believe that the social insects really have developed institutional portions of culture. It is more likely that the similarities to man are merely analogous—resemblances of result rather than of mechanism. The actual mechanism of ant slavery and domestication thus would presumably be a directly organic, congenital, instinctual one, in distinction from the suprahereditary, devised, and learning-transmitted human institutions.

When we cast about for such an organic mechanism, it appears that practically everything in the practices in question can be subsumed under the impulses and practices of symbiosis, and that symbiosis is widespread also in the nonsocial realms of the animal kingdom. There is, for instance, the familiar example of the hermit crab who likes a sea anemone on the snail shell he inhabits; and how, if his shell lacks an anemone, he will set one there. This habit may well in the long run have survival value for the hermit-crab species, as is generally supposed. And it evidently satisfies something in the crab's congenital nature—makes him feel more at ease, "relieves a tension." But no one would think of assuming that the crab was taught the practice by his mother, or that he had learned it from his fellows. The symbiosis of ants with their ant slaves, beetle livestock, or fungi is obviously more complex than the crab-anemone relation, but there seems no reason to believe that it is basically different in kind.

Moreover, close analysis shows how really different the workings of social insect and social human practices are: for instance, on "agriculture." Before going out on her marriage flight, a nubile *Atta* queen ant "takes a good meal of fungus." Mated and secure in her little dugout, which is the first cell of her kingdom, she regurgitates this fungus mass, which begins to grow. She manures it and lays her first eggs on it; on hatching, the larvae eat the fungus; when they emerge adult, the queen's realm contains both a society of workers and a bearing vegetable garden; whereupon she retires in state to laying eggs for the further enlargement of the colony. The whole of this "farming" is evidently in its origin a by-product of feeding and reproduction; this by-product, having survival value, came to be part of the congenital behavior mechanism of the species. It is a fairly complex and special symbiosis; it has in it nothing of an invented and learned custom.

So some of the slaveholding ants are shown by the gradation of the habits of different species to have begun with eating the pupae of other nests, then to have progressed to carrying them home to store and devour at leisure, and finally to have arrived at the stage of saving the pupae so long that some of them managed to hatch before they could be eaten, whereupon the irrepressible drive of ants to labor on behalf of their community makes these "slaves" seem to "work for" their "masters." Another line of development is parasitic: the fertilized queen, in certain species, is unable to found her own nest. She therefore invades the colony of another species, kills its queen, or somehow attracts and seduces the workers until they kill her, and then takes her place—with the result that the workers rear her changeling brood instead of their own blood sisters. Where the parasitism is extreme, as when the invading species is so built that it can perhaps fight but not work, the interlopers are dependent for sustenance on their hosts. But as these consist only of nonreproducing workers, they finally die off, whereupon the "masters" also perish.

Perhaps the most significant inference to be derived by the anthropologist from the study of social insects is the light they throw on the nature of society and culture. Human beings all live in societies and they all have culture. This co-occurrence of society and culture is so constant in man that the two appear like two aspects of one set of phenomena. If we had no other knowledge, we might easily assume that societies and cultures could only coexist. The social insects show that society and culture are distinct, not only conceptually but in the phenomena of nature. The communities of ants, bees, and termites allow no escape from this conclusion. Though wholly cultureless, according to all indications, they are as tightly knit, as socially centered, as any human society—if anything more so. The origin of societies now reinforced with culture, somewhere in man's early development, accordingly was a novel and unique event in the history of life on this earth.

19. TWO CONVERGENT SOCIALIZATIONS: ANTS AND TERMITES

So far, the social insects have been viewed as a unit in comparison with man, with whom they certainly contrast as vividly as they agree. However, these insects comprise several thousand species, hundreds of genera, more than a dozen families, and two main stems or orders. Naturally, there is far more variability among these forms than would appear from the foregoing account, where emphasis has been laid on the common or uniform characters. Especially there are significant differences between the most highly socialized groups in one main "order," the ants and the honeybees, and the equally socialized termites of the other order. The insect contrast with human societies thus is double, really; and it acquires depth from consideration of the duality.

Ants are hymenoptera, and relatives of bees, wasps, gallflies, and sawflies, of which some are social, some subsocial, others wholly individualistic. The termites are isoptera, related to the *Blattoidea* or cockroaches, and descended jointly with them from the protoblattoids, who were already distinct from the protohymenoptera in the Palaeozoic Permian period. The two lines of socializing development accordingly have been quite distinct for 200-odd million years, as the geological ages are customarily computed. Evolution, starting from two separate points, has repeated itself to a quite astonishing degree; just as, starting from still another point, it has partially repeated itself again, though less closely, in producing the social animal man.

The difference in structure of ants and termites in parts and organs is a matter of technical features involving more entomology than can be gone into here. But there are also physiological, functional, and life-cycle differences. These can be grouped around diet and reproduction; let us say, to be concrete, around wood and spermatheca.

Ants eat insect and other flesh, seeds, honey, sugary excretions or secretions of aphids and other insects—all concentrated, high-grade foods, most of which must be got in the open world. Most termites eat wood—an exceedingly abundant but low-grade food; they have chosen a quantitative instead of a qualitative course. To nourish themselves on this, they must not only eat a great deal.

but must be infested with an intestinal biota of Protozoa that helps them assimilate it. This fauna they pass on to one another by regurgitating much of their food, also by eating one another's partly-digested excrement. As they eat, they also burrow, and thus excavate their nest. Where they raise hills, these consist largely of their excreta, which harden in air. City-building and feeding are therefore all intertwined by the termites; the ants differentiate the two functions sharply.

Then, like most wood-eaters, the termites literally bore from within, probably in the main for safety. This means that they are adapted to live in the dark, in warmth, and with a minimum of oxygen. So they avoid light, have whitish, soft bodies, no great energies; they depend on numbers, or on defensive fighting. Ants on the contrary are strong, hard, tense, high-strung: many of them prey on termites—as a group they are probably the termites' most destructive enemies. In ant evolution, the workers are evidently the first caste developed; in some species there are potentially or partly fertile workers; the soldiers are a later specialization. On the contrary, some termite species show potentially fertile soldiers, which suggests that among them these preceded the workers.

The female ant, along with the wasp and the bee, possesses a spermatheca, a receptacle in which the male sperm is stored and kept alive for a lifetime, being withdrawn in infinitesimal quantity as needed. One mating therefore suffices. Thereafter the queen has both sexual substances at her disposal and the male can be dispensed with. He is dispensed with. He dies after mating: at any rate he goes off; it is the female who alone starts the burrow and brings up her first young. From then on, until it is time for new colonies to form, males are useless: so the whole society is a female one—workers and soldiers as well as queen.

The termite, remaining structurally more generalized, has no spermatheca. Hence the male is indispensable if a large, long-term, increasing brood is to be raised continuously. The result is that the start of a new termite society is made by male and female conjointly, as already mentioned, as against the solitary ant female. In fact, the first burrow is excavated by the co-operating pair; and fertilization, at least in some species, begins only after they have established this home. Moreover, fertilization goes on for life. The female's belly grows until it may be as large as a finger and she is practically incapable of locomotion; but the male remains with her in the royal chamber, constantly solicitous. There is something appealingly human in this permanent conjugal affection, compared with the utter unconcern of the queen ant for her partner and her divorce from him after she has received from him what she needs for her business in life. But, contrariwise, the diet of the ant is not so different from our own, after allowance is made for size and opportunity, especially in contrast to the disgusting food habits of the termite.

The permanent conjugation of the termite sexes only founds the behavior pattern, as it were. It is continued in the fact that the working and fighting offspring, the great mass of the society, are also of both sexes, instead of female only as with the ant. There are male and female major workers, male and female minor workers, male and female soldiers, and so on. Whatever caste there may be among termites is always bisexual, even though both sexes are in most castes sterile. And the two sexes of one caste are more alike than one caste is to another. In short, the termites follow out the principle of sexual equivalence throughout, in structure as well as function. Their whole social organization is based on this principle, in distinction from the ants who, with their hymenopterous relatives, the wasps and bees, leave the male only one spot in their scheme of things, the momentary and individualistic act of transference of his sperm to the storage sack of the female. The ants and the bees build their whole social life on the one sex, the male reappearing only when new societies are to be formed.

It is clear that we have here closely parallel societies operating on principles distinct at two fundamental points, both in turn resting on anatomical and physiological structure. The distinctions cut deep: ants and termites, springing from different stems of insects, have had a separate history for tens of millions of years, only later approximating each other in their social habits, though to an increasing and striking degree. After the first divergence from the remote common insect ancestry, there was a convergence toward full socialization with all its implications. In the end, the two behaviors have run parallel, with considerable accompanying superficial modification of structure, but without suppression of fundamental pattern of structure.

20. ANIMAL COMMUNICATION

We have seen how a nubile ant flies forth, usually in simultaneous seasonal swarms from all mature colonies in an area, mates, leaves her partner, breaks off her wings, goes underground, and prepares a chamber that is the start of a new colony. There she lays her first eggs, tends and feeds this brood, who become her first workers; after which she confines herself to laying more eggs destined to become additional workers, and then, after a while, eggs that become fertile females and males for founding new colonies. This means that in the continuity between community and community, each of which may run to hundreds of thousands of members, everything funnels down to the life of a single individual—the fertilized queen—and from there builds up again. What the younger community reproduces from its parent community in the way of castes and their varied activities all passes through the one minute physique of the queen's body. It is obvious that this passing-along must be a very different process from the "tradition" or "handing-through" which transmits culture from one generation of a society to another. Human generations overlap: members of a society are of all ages; strictly, one cannot say where within a society one generation ends and the next begins. But among ants absolutely all members of a society except one are literal sisters (and later on a few brothers) because they are all the children of that one pivotal member. Even if a human society counted not eighty thousand but eight hundred, or only eighty, it would be manifestly impossible to pack all the knowledges, skills, and faculties of so many individuals into one body, brain, and memory, for unimpaired transmission to the next generation. The impairment would be heavy, and distortion equally so. Yet the habits and the techniques of an anthill will be unimpairedly identical with those of its parent anthill in the same environment. Evidently cultural transmission is not operative as between anthills, or down the generations of social insects; but congenital, instinctual heredity is operative. Only through this mechanism of heredity could so faithful a copy be reproduced and rereproduced, and transmission by learning be dispensed with.

With this point clear, another follows. The social insects cannot have language—not in the human sense—because language is learned.

Communications of a sort they undoubtedly have; but these, like the noises of all animals other than man, are not language, except metaphorically—something like the language of flowers, or the language of machine guns, which can also be "understood." As here used, the term "language" properly denotes a system of audible symbols able to communicate objective facts. A bird's chirp, a lion's roar, a horse's scream, a man's moan express subjective conditions; they do not convey objective information. By objective information we mean what is communicated in such statements as: "There are trees over the hill," "There is a single tree," "There are only bushes," "There were trees but are no longer," "If there are trees he may be hiding in them," "Trees can be burned," and millions of others. All postinfantile, nondefective human beings can make and constantly do make such statements, though they may make them with quite different sounds according to what speech custom they happen to follow. But no subhuman animal makes *any* such statements. All the indications are that no subhuman animal even has any impulse to utter or convey such information. It is doubtful whether it possesses any concept as generalizing or abstract as "tree," "bush," "burn." This seems to hold as essentially for dogs and apes—or for that matter for parrots—as for insects.

Parrots can reproduce series of speech sounds fairly adequately, but they cannot, except by lucky coincidence, convey intelligible objective information. Dogs can learn to respond to dozens of words and phrases; this might be called passive participation in speech. Chimpanzees, with larynxes, tongues, and lips similar to ours, do not even try to learn to reproduce human words to which they respond in their behavior. There is an old epigram that the reason animals do not speak is that they have nothing to say. Its psychology is somewhat crude, but fundamentally correct. At least, they appear to lack the impulse to say anything, in the sense that "to say" means objective communication.

In some respects the belief that perhaps dies hardest is that the social insects must have something like a language even though we have not yet succeeded in hearing or seeing it. They have societies as we have; they have elaborate and highly adaptive habits which look like institutions until we examine closely their methods of acquisition and functioning; why should they not have communications comparable to our speech? It will be worth analyzing a case that at its anthropocentric face value strongly suggests ability to convey objective fact.

It is known that when a honeybee has first found a new source of honey, an unexploited patch of flowers, other bees from the same hive soon appear there. How is this brought about?

Bees have excellent memories for place. They first orient themselves by recall, then fly to their objective in a "beeline." New masses of flowers attract them from a distance by color. Their color vision is similar to ours, except for probable inability to see the full red end of our spectrum and ability to see some distance beyond the violet. Once among flowers, their preference is to visit only one species at a time. In this they may be guided by smell as well as sight. At any rate, when they return with a load of honey, they reek of the perfume of that species. If the patch is previously unvisited, the haul rich, the nectar unusually sweet and strong, the bee is stimulated by the booty in her crop into a reaction of euphoria or triumph. This is expressed in a peculiar whirling "dance" performed on her return to the hive.[12] The bees there watch her, crowd around, stretch out their antennae at her, smell her. She then returns to her discovery for more; before long her fellows appear there too, in increasing numbers. They have not followed her trail by sight or smell, as we might expect them to do. In actuality, they leave the hive and circle wider and wider around, evidently searching for the impact of a volume of the same smell that the discoverer exuded during her dance. One by one, more and more of them find her patch of flowers, or perhaps other patches equally fresh and strong. Returning, each one now performs the same dance and incites others, until most of the active workers may be visiting the one species of flower. But as they drain off the untapped superabundant supply, or its sugar strength grows dilute, the dances grow laxer with weaker stimulus, and finally cease.

The dance is a reflex to an above-average, highly satisfactory stimulus. It acts as a new stimulus of excitement to other individuals. The cue indicating the particular flower species is merely the reek of the scent of the particular species, physically brought into the hive by the discoverer. The finding of sources of supply is by search and trial and error. Thus there is no purposive communication of factual information anywhere in the chain of events. It looks as if we could rule the bees out from having a communicating language.

---

[12] This is about as close to "play" as the serious-minded social insects come (§ 15).

21. THE PRIMATE ORDER IN WHICH MAN IS RANGED

Man, apes, monkeys, lemurs, and the tarsier were long since grouped to-gether by Linnaeus, at the foundation of modern biology, as constituting the order of *Primates,* one of the dozen or so first subdivisions of the *Mammals* as a class. Their being mammals means that in addition to having a bony skeleton, a spinal cord with vertebral column, skull and jaw, four limbs with a maximum of five digits, and lungs—all of which they share with reptiles and birds—they are also warm-blooded, viviparous, suckling, and furry, and possess diversified teeth. The basic pattern of these mammalian teeth is three incisors, one canine, four premolars, and three molars on each side of each jaw, 3-1-4-3, or 44 in all. This formula may be reduced, and the teeth may vary greatly in shape according to species, but the formula itself is not otherwise altered or expanded.

Both the most backward primates and the geologically oldest ones show definite resemblances to another order of mammals, the generalized one called insect-eaters or insectivores. This order includes moles, shrews, and tree shrews. All the insectivores are small. Their size prevents them from preying on any-thing larger than insects. Consequently they did not evolve specialized tusks, claws, strength, or habitat adaptations. Instead they remained generic in struc-ture and widely open to evolutionary change. As protein-eaters having to catch live food, they needed a degree of co-ordination, quickness, and intelligence in their make-up. Such is the ancestral background of our larger "family," in nontechnical parlance the background of our order, the primates in biological nomenclature. Generalization, littleness, and quickness were the qualities of this root stock that were most important for the future.

One special feature has to be added. The particular subdivision of the insectivores from which the primates are generally believed to derive are the ancestral tree shrews. This fact set our whole primate group off on the tack of arboreal life from the start. Most of them have remained on the trees ever since; and while the baboons, the gorilla, and we have long since come down off them again (the gorilla really not so long ago), the return to the ground, at any rate in the case of man, was with some important acquisitions: especially the fundamental one of complete, clean differentiation of arms and legs, struc-turally and functionally.

The actual fossil record of primates takes us back to the Eocene, at the beginning of the Tertiary, several tens of millions of years ago—perhaps twenty or fifty times as far back as the appearance of anyone who can be properly called a man. Here, at the beginning of the Tertiary, are found an American lemuroid family called *Notharctidae,* and the Old World one of the *Adapidae,* both with 40 of the original 44 teeth, formula 2-1-4-3. There are also a number of fossil genera of tarsioids, again both in the New and the Old World. The modern representatives of these two suborders, lemuroids and tarsioids, are much fewer and more restricted. Both have evidently fought a losing competition.

In fact the tarsioids have shrunk to one species, the spectral tarsier, surviving in spots in the East Indian islands. This is a quarter-pound, rat-tailed, enormous-eyed, nocturnal animal. It frequents the bush, clasps limbs with pads on its fingers, leaps or hops, lives on insects, sees badly in the light, and sleeps during the day. The tarsier's smell sense is poor, its acuity of vision in the dark is high. Correlated with this specialized sense development is a large visual center in the cerebral cortex. The development of the brain and other features put the tarsier nearer to the higher primates than are the lemurs; or to be more exact, ancestral near-tarsiers are thought to have been the direct ancestors of the higher primates.

The side branch of the lemurs has done best in remote and protected Madagascar, where three-fourths of its species survive. The lemurs are nocturnal, furry, snouted; they have their eyes on the sides of the head, with nonstereoscopic vision; and the olfactory lobes in their brains are large. Their faces often look like those of raccoons, civet cats, or foxes. Most of them eat both insects and fruits.

22. MONKEYS

Allied to tarsier and lemurs in having 36 teeth (2-1-3-3), as against the 32 (2-1-2-3) of the higher primates, are the South American or platyrrhine monkeys, also called *Cebidae*. Geologically, they have been found to extend as far back as the Miocene. Living forms include capuchins (*Cebus*), howlers (*Alouatta*), spider monkeys (*Ateles*), and marmosets (*Hapale*). They are short in the face or snout, domed in the skull; the nostrils are on the side of the nose. They are always long-tailed; only these among the primates have prehensile tails that can be used to hang from. They are smallish in size, the maximum weight attained by any species being perhaps 20 pounds, which is far below not only anthropoid apes but baboons. In social behavior all New World monkeys differ markedly from Old World ones. While promiscuous, they are less sexualized and less jealous, and are nearly free from the overmastering impulse of the Old World monkeys to exert dominance and oppress their fellows. They have sometimes been considered less intelligent than other monkeys and apes in tests; but *Cebus* individuals differ markedly one from the other. Klüver's famous female *Cebus* "genius" was rated by him as superior to the manlike apes in solving mechanical problems.

The *Cercopithecidae* or catarrhine monkeys of the Old World agree with the anthropoids and man in having 32 teeth (2-1-2-3). The oldest fossil is Parapithecus, from the Oligocene. This is one period farther back in the Tertiary than the platyrrhine fossils in America. But where so few bones are involved, and those mostly mandibles, mere luck of discovery may play a large part. Specialties of the catarrhines are cheek pouches for stuffing food; sitting pads or ischial callosities, and the sexual swelling and coloring of these. Best known are the macaques (*Macaca*) distributed from India to Borneo and Japan, and including the rhesus; and the baboons and their allies, limited to Africa and Arabia. The baboons have redescended to the ground. They are large and powerful, and walk and run four-legged and plantigrade on their soles and palms. They have also redeveloped a long snout, and great canine teeth; the epithet "dog-faced" (*Cynocephalus*) is appropriate. Best known through the studies of Carpenter, Zuckerman, Maslow, and others, the interpersonal behavior of both macaques and baboons, in the free state as well as in captivity, is aggressive, greedy, jealous, cruel, selfish, shot through with constant sexuality and impulse to dominate.

23. APES

The *Simiidae,* or apes proper in the modern usage of that word, are the anthropoid or manlike apes. They approximate us in structure: they are tailless, for instance. They are also nearer to us in size than other primates; for if the gibbon is much smaller, the gorilla is much heavier than we. The fossil history of the anthropoids has been traced back to the Oligocene Propliopithecus. Later, in Miocene-Pliocene times, there were Pliopithecus and a group of genera associated with Dryopithecus. Once more it is probably only the imperfection of the palaeontological record that makes these anthropoids seem to have evolved earlier than the less-advanced South American platyrrhines. The anthropoid fossils consist mostly of jaws with teeth; they have been found in Egypt, Europe, and India. None has ever been discovered in America.

The anthropoids number four, or technically five. Gibbon (*Hylobates*) and siamang (*Symphalangus*) together constitute the *Hylobatidae*. Then there are the orang-utan (*Simia*), chimpanzee (*Pan*), and gorilla (*Gorilla*). The first three are Asiatic-East Indian; the two latter, African; all are tropical.

The gibbon ranges from Assam in India through Farther India into the larger Dutch East Indies; the allied siamang is restricted to Sumatra. They are both long-limbed but light: 12 to 15 pounds for the gibbon, nearly double for the siamang. Gibbons are wholly arboreal, and progress largely by brachiating or pendulum-swinging from one handhold to the next, interspersed with leaps from the arm. In length of leg compared to trunk the gibbon exceeds all the other anthropoids and stands next to man. But this proportionate leg length is surpassed by an even greater arm length, which is really enormous. And this in turn is part of his arboreal adaptation—hanging and swinging far more than standing or walking. It also keeps him from being a very close relative of man.

24. THE ORANG-UTAN

The orang-utan—"forest person" in the original Malay—is the other Far Eastern anthropoid ape, surviving only in Borneo and part of Sumatra. He is about of a size with man and the chimpanzee. But he definitely diverges more from ourselves than does the chimpanzee, in structure as well as behavior. This differentiation expresses the degree to which the orang is specialized for life in the trees and is tied to such life.

The adult male orang-utan averages at least a foot less in height than a man because of his short legs. But he surpasses him by a couple of feet in reach or span because of his long arms. The trunk is thicker-set than ours and brings his average weight to perhaps a bit above the human male average: 165 pounds or 75 kilograms. Females are markedly smaller: only about half as heavy. The skin is brown, the hair definitely reddish and quite long. The forehead is relatively high, the face and nose unusually flat even for an ape. Very conspicuous in adult males are a pair of hairless cheek pads of tough fibrous tissue framing the face; also, enormous air pouches extending from the throat well down the breast and over the shoulders into the neck. Such air sacs occur also in females, and in other apes, but never of the same size as in the male orang. Their function is not known, nor is that of the cheek pads; but the two together give the male orang a monstrous moon face surmounting a gigantic double chin or crop; such neck as he has is concealed. In this face are set: eyes close together; a pair of nostrils just below them; an incredibly long upper lip; and a mouth that looks like a long, tight, down-curved slit when at rest, because the lip edges have no eversion whatever.

The orang's gnomelike appearance is accentuated by the extreme shortness of his legs compared with the length of his arms, hands, and feet. His arm-leg proportion is 170; man's is only 88; the other large anthropoids are intermediary. Our middle-finger tip, and the gorilla's, reach two-thirds of the way down the thighbone; the chimpanzee's almost to the knee; the orang's just halfway from the knee to the ground. The orang's hand and foot both have the greatest absolute length of any primate. Fingers and toes are tremendously elongated; thumb and big toe, though not malformed, are so short as to look like ridiculous stubs projecting from the wrist and heel. "Big toe" of course fits only man; in all the apes it is not the longest; but in the orang the whole of it, even its tip, lies in the hind half of the foot. The chimpanzee looks like an unflattering but still humorous caricature of ourselves, the gorilla like a somewhat brutal exaggeration, but the orang like a deformity. These are "hominicentric" subjective reactions, of course, but, though affective, they do express the respective degree and kind of differentiations of the big apes from man.

Among the trees the orang is altogether too heavy to leap, and he can brachiate only as far as branches are stout enough to sustain his swinging weight. Beyond that he has to find limbs that cross over from the next tree and are sufficiently big to trust his weight to; if there is doubt, he feels them out first. Anything like tearing through the woods overhead is as out of the question for the orang as it would be for a middle-aged man. That he nevertheless progresses rapidly in spite of his caution is due to his frequenting dense tropical rain forest, climbing skillfully, and no doubt being experienced in perceiving the best way ahead in the tangle. On the ground he is proportionately clumsy. He can stand erect, but does not voluntarily walk upright. Mostly he goes on all fours, with the tips of fingers and toes bent under; or he plants his arms ahead like crutches and swings his trunk and legs forward between. Neither can be a rapid or an effective gait. Compare the simple plantigrade hands and feet of the baboons, who are really readapted for ground-running. The orang is in the dilemma of trying to remain wholly up in the trees while having become too heavy for acrobatics.

This same incongruity, or attempting the nearly impossible, may account for some of the salient habits and attitudes of the orang. He is definitely more solitary than the other apes, being encountered either actually alone or in what seem to be mere biological families. It looks as if he were too heavy to huddle in groups in treetops. Then as to disposition: this is described as melancholy, apathetic, unaggressive—introvert in comparison with the chimpanzee. The orang is equally affectionate, but he is certainly less outgoing about it. While he has been much less intensively studied than the chimpanzee, the indications are that he is little if any behind him in general intelligence. He will learn to ride bicycles, smoke cigars, eat at table, and do other circus tricks about as well as the chimpanzee. Yet in that case, why the unresponsiveness? Again one thinks of the influence of his habitat adaptation that is pushed so near its physical limit and which must constantly enforce safety-first deliberateness and a careful avoidance of impulsiveness.

25. THE CHIMPANZEE

The chimpanzee is probably, all in all, the living ape nearest to man. He is practically never at the opposite end of the scale in his proportions when man and the apes are seriated, and he is often next to man. This last is often true of the gorilla also. But the gorilla's mere bulk must differentiate him widely in his functioning even where his proportions are similar to ours. On the other side, the gibbon is too small and light, and the orang, though his size is about that of a man, is too set-up for a highly specialized life in the trees. In the wild, chimpanzees sleep in trees, but spend about two-thirds of the day on the ground. They also do more of their traveling along the ground than above it between trees. At the same time they climb and brachiate easily. All this suggests a degree of generalization nearer to that of man than that found among other apes.

The chimpanzee weighs less than a man. The average is around 50 kilograms or 110 pounds. Females run about a fifth less, or about the same as the proportional human difference. The chimpanzee is considerably shorter than we, averaging under five feet for males. Most of the difference is in the leg, ours being absolutely about half as long again. The rest is in the neck: the chimpanzee's chin, or bottom of the lower jaw, being about as far below his shoulder level—almost down to his collarbone and sternum—as ours is clear above that level. His trunk, on the contrary, is as long or longer than ours, and considerably broader and thicker in shoulders and chest. The arm is not very different from a human one in absolute length, but more evenly massive; owing to the long body and short leg, the finger tips come lower down the leg. The thigh and calf are about the same in diameter as a man's, but their excessive shortness makes them look actually bigger around; relatively, of course, they are much more thickset. All in all, the chimpanzee's gross bodily proportions are much the nearest to ours of all the apes. He might fairly be described as a considerably undersized human being with powerful neck, chest, and arms, whose underpinning is not weak like the orang's, but sturdy and short; in all, a sort of rugged, well-proportioned dwarf.

With this size and weight, it is hard to understand how Bauman's chimpanzees could have pulled ropes from three to five times as hard as heavier young men pulled them: up to 1260 pounds for a two-hand yank by a female! Later tests do not confirm this really extraordinary strength; but on the other hand, the later tests were unnatural for the animals, in having them pull upward while standing erect.

The chimpanzee's skin is black to brown; his short hair is mostly black but grays with age. The skull is low, with a thick torus or bar of bone shadowing the recessed eyes. The ears are large and round, and stand out from the head like a bat's. Photographs seem to show no white in the chimpanzee's eye, though white does appear in the gorilla's; and there is a less beady effect than in the orang. The chimpanzee's external nose is perhaps the least protuberant of any anthropoid's. But the nostrils are less accentuatedly broad and framed than in the gorilla. As in all apes, the membranous edge of the lips—the part naturally red in man—is narrow and tucked in. The lips in the larger sense—that is, the total fleshy flaps bordering the mouth—are long and very mobile. The lower one is often protruded like a gutter, especially when full of food, and is then inspected. The wide slit of the mouth tends to turn up at the corners, especially in the young, giving them a pleased or humorous expression, in contrast with the orang's glum droop.

While chimpanzees spend much more time on the ground than orangs, they seem to be as good as orangs in climbing, swinging, and brachiating in the trees or along their cages, perhaps because of their one-third less weight.

On the ground they are better than orangs, as might be expected from their relatively longer and sturdier legs. Like all the anthropoids, they walk normally on all fours. In this, the legs are straight, in contrast to a bend at the knee in erect stance. The feet are held about as flat as ours, except that the toes may be kept slightly arched. The first toe—our big toe—spreads out from the others at an angle as if the animal were trying to use it like an opposable thumb to *grasp* the ground or a limb, which in fact is just what it is built for. In the quadrupedal gait the shoulders are higher than the hips, because of the greater length of arm, and this even though some height is lost by the walk's being on the knuckles of the bent-under fingers. Erect progression is rare, and apparently slower and more fatiguing: both back and knees are somewhat bent. The crutchlike gait of swinging the legs between the arms is used chiefly on slopes.

It is not known how long a chimpanzee can live, but there are data on most other aspects of his tempo of living. It is clear that his rates of growth and maturation are definitely faster than ours: perhaps one-half to two-thirds as long, on the average. Here are some comparisons, the chimpanzee always stated first, man second.

Intrauterine life, 8 months; man, 9. Appearance of first milk teeth: month 3; [13] 4-8. Last milk tooth: month 15-16; 20-36. First permanent teeth: year 3; 4-7. Last teeth: year 11; 20 ±. Cranial capacity at birth, proportion of final: 46%; 26%. Age of attainment of full cranial capacity: year 6; 18. Fusion of epiphyses, first: year 7; 15; last: year 11-15; 25. Menarche: year 8-11; 16. Termination of body growth, males: year 12; 20-21. Appearance of controls, in weeks after birth: [14] On back, raising head, 5; 15; rolling over, 8-10; 29; sitting unsupported, 13; 31; pulling self erect, 15; 47; standing free: 20; 62; walking unassisted, 25-29 (on all fours); 64 (on feet only).

Temperamentally, chimpanzees are outstanding in their responsiveness. Especially in youth they like people and their own kind. Their feelings are lively; the expression of them is often vehement. They grimace, cuddle, beat with their arms, or throw tantrums on slight provocation. They are generally cheerful, and, like sea lions, they are natural show-offs. Nor are they as greedy, selfish, and sexualized as many of the smaller monkeys; and as they much more nearly approximate us in size and general functioning, it is no wonder that they are favorites equally with showmen, the public, and psychologists.

There is one matter of ability in which chimpanzees partly resemble and partly differ from us in a manner of which the significance is not altogether clear. This concerns memory and the related function of what the psychologists call the "delayed-response faculty." As regards recognition memory, chimpanzees show about the degree of this we might expect from what we know of

[13] Figures following year, month, or week are *ordinals*. Thus "month 3" means "in the third month."

[14] One chimpanzee ("Alpha") as against average of 25 babies.

children, dogs, and other mammals. They recognize companions and human friends after months or years, and react with pleasure. They also recognize situations to which they have learned the answer and established a successful habit response: they fall back almost without hesitation into the familiar groove of action. This sort of reaction can be directly observed. On the other hand, delayed-response behavior is studied in formal tests. A stimulus is given, such as letting a chimpanzee see some food. Then the food is buried, or set in a receptacle of particular color or shape, which is promptly taken away. After a stated time has elapsed, the chimpanzee is let into the yard where the burial was made, or in front of several different receptacles, to see whether he can still pick out the right spot or the right box. The results are extremely interesting: Chimpanzees react far better and longer to positional stimuli than to those of form, color, or quality. For instance, chimpanzees even after two days of delay will go directly to where they have seen food buried and will dig it up. What is in a way even more convincing is that after four days they have forgotten the precise spot but search the correct vicinity. But if it is a matter of "holding" the proper color or shape of a box in which they have seen a banana or an orange put, they can do this for only about half an hour. Human beings react about equally well to the two kinds of tests after the same interval.

It has consequently been inferred that the chimpanzee is able to form some sort of representation or internal image response to a positional situation, and can carry this over the interval during which he is prevented from acting; but that his ability to form an idea or a symbol of a shape or a color is much more weakly developed. Since we human beings can do this last equally well, and since we have language, it has been thought that we employ covert or suppressed language movements—"thoughts" or ideas—in such cases. Put simply, we remember that something has been put in a red box by saying or "thinking" the *word* "red."

This is important if true. But then, how is it that chimpanzees recognize their friends, and even fall back into the channel of operating with familiar objects, after much longer periods than they can recall where food was buried? First, *recognizing* a situation is evidently a simpler and easier process than *remembering* it enough to re-create it. Next, the artificiality of the delayed-response experiment perhaps cuts in to produce an artificial result. In nature, responses tend to be immediate. If they are blocked, new stimuli ordinarily impinge, and the delayed responses just do not get acted out. The whole type of experiment which first stimulates, then blocks or frustrates, and then releases has something unnatural about it. Men, living in a sense "unnaturally" under culture, as they do whenever they accept duties and responsibilities, get trained in modifying or postponing many of their responses. Cultureless subhumans generally either act the response out or inhibit it completely. It is therefore questionable what the difference in blocked reaction to positional and non-positional stimuli really means. But it is clear why the two Yerkes operating with such tests find so great a difference, and Koehler, observing unblocked recognition, is unaware of a difference between the two kinds of stimuli. Koehler's chimpanzees were in the position we are in when we meet a long-separated brother, or when we resume swimming, paddling, skating, or driving after ten years away from water, ice, or cars. There may be a moment's hesitation, or conscious fear, but then we slide back into the slot of preserved memory or habit functioning.

In short, what is not wholly clear is whether it is primarily the chimpanzee's memory-functioning or his response to artificial testing that is different from ours.

26. THE GORILLA

The gorilla comes in two geographically separated races, sometimes counted as distinct species. There is a lowland form in the heavy forest of French Equatorial Africa, which covers a fraction of the territorial range of the chimpanzee. Hundreds of miles to the east, along the edge of the Belgian Congo, the mountain gorilla inhabits a bamboo forest whose altitude is from seven thousand feet up.

The gorilla is much the largest and heaviest surviving primate, and he must certainly rank among the very largest primates ever evolved. He is not a giant in height, but he is almost incredibly massive. With body length in human range—from over 5 to about 6 feet—his weight is at least three times ours. Males ten to fifteen years old, corresponding in adulthood to humans of eighteen to twenty-five, weigh at the lowest in the three hundreds, more often in the four, five, or six hundreds of pounds; females weigh from 300 to 400 pounds. This means that trunk, neck, and limbs, as well as the bones in them, are enormously thick and powerful. Everything seems exaggerated: the beetling brow ridges of the skull, its high ridges or crests for attachment of muscles the powerful, jutting jaw. The neck buries the occiput of the skull; above, the rear of the cranium rises to an extraordinary peak, not of brain but of bony ridge, neck muscle, and callosity. Chest girths measured range from 50 to 69 inches; there is no waist constriction, the paunch is large, and the trunk tapers somewhat only as it approaches the hips. What with wide shoulders, long arms, and large hands, the span is enormous: from one and a quarter to one and a half times the body height.

Both skin and hair are black or nearly so; the hair grays with age.

The nose is like a diagonal beveling-off of the great upper jaw, chiefly revealing two wide nostril cavities. The eyes are sunk deep below the brow shelf, from which a long scooplike concavity rises in profile to the occipital peak. It is a face that easily expresses ferocity, because its obvious power only too readily suggests to us weaker human beings what the animal might do if angered. However, observation, or even prolonged study of photographs, tones down the impression of savage brutality. One comes to feel that the gorilla's features—and this is corroborated by his postures and movements—express above all self-sufficiency, dignity, reserve, consciousness of strength, and relative indifference to surroundings. The effect tends to become one of aloofness and of a heavy, slow thoughtfulness; almost of a certain nobility. Such an impression is fairly in accord with what observers report on gorilla behavior and temperament. If as quiet and faithful an animal as a St. Bernard dog were magnified to weigh from 500 to 600 pounds, most of us would stand in a degree of awe of him and would presumably be ready to construe signs of his irritation as symptoms of incipient ferocity.

The gorilla sits or occasionally squats much like a heavy-set man. He is much inclined to lean against something while seated; in captivity a corner is preferred to a straight wall. A doorway is favored because it provides both back rest and foot brace. A favorite stance is on one foot, the other leg bent up with the foot against a tree or a wall on which the back also leans, and one hand taking hold above and behind the head. All this leaning has a very human effect; most animals do not practice it at all: it is a sort of tool-using. A gorilla stands free, with spread and bent legs, to do particular things, such as reaching, beating his chest or slapping his belly, fighting or getting ready to fight, or play wrestling. In this last, a pair clinch, jaws over shoulders, and each tries to bite the back of the other's neck. All this is about what a bear stands up for.

Ordinary locomotion of the gorilla is as definitely quadrupedal as a bear's, though a man can presumably outrun a gorilla about as much as a bear can outrun a man. The gorilla's feet, which are the most human of anthropoid feet, are flat-soled on the ground, with the first toe well spread away from the others. It is not the longest but it is considerably the biggest toe. In quadrupedal stance, the hind legs tend to be spread apart, but not flexed. The front legs, as we might appropriately call the arms in this position, are longer, often bowed forward, and rest on the knuckles; that is, the middle finger-joints. These knuckles showing at the edge of a roundish fist at the end of a massive arm made bigger and more shapeless by longish hair give a suggestion of an elephant leg planted on the ground. In walking, the "hind" feet are not in line with the front. One foot is set squarely between the two hands, the other definitely outside. The gait therefore sidles markedly—that is, the axis of the trunk is carried not in the line of motion, but diagonal to it.

On account of the length of the arms, in all-fours position the gorilla's shoulders are considerably higher than his rump, with a bit of swayback between, due no doubt to the animal's great weight. Between the shoulders, the great head hangs out, the profile of the back line rising to its highest point with the peak over the rear of the head. Apparently in this position the eyes look down somewhat. To look out level from under the brows, the head has to be thrown back, still farther elevating its peak. The whole quadrupedal stance of the gorilla has something almost sad about it, as if it were ill-adapted and not coming off very well.

Young gorillas climb, but cautiously; and they brachiate, but not often. As they get their full weight, serious tree-climbing and branch-swinging are obviously over. Even sleeping nests for adults are presumably most often on the ground or on bedded masses of vegetation. It would take a pretty sizable tree crotch to support a quarter-ton body.

His giantism colors everything about the gorilla, from his motions to his disposition. Five times as heavy as a chimpanzee, he could not maintain the latter's volatility and restless responsiveness without being a complete physiological misfit. Although the gorilla has been much less studied, available observations suggest a degree of intelligence very similar to the chimpanzee's but expressed through a quite different temperament and rapport, with most of the difference between them being apparently a function of size.

The following are epithets applied to gorillas by psychologists and other observers: cautious; conservative; not skillful mechanically or manually; watchful; incurious; unimitative and countersuggestible; introverted and aloof; demure or dignified; stoical; constructive rather than destructive; not quarrelsome, but good-natured, at least while young; fearless, deliberate, and determined. There are no doubt more personality traits in this list than can be explained as due merely to size. But as compared with a chimpanzee, it is evident that the gorilla's qualities are something like those of a Newfoundland dog compared to a fox terrier. In tests of memory, box-stacking, and the like, and in observations of smear-painting, nest-building, responding to a mirror, and play, gorilla and chimpanzee come out much alike when allowance is made for the gorilla difference of slower physique and disposition.

While authentic data are pretty scrappy, growth and development seem to be somewhat slower than in the chimpanzee, but definitely more rapid than in us. The first milk teeth erupt perhaps within two months, sitting up comes at five, walking at eight months. Born smaller and lighter than a human baby, a female gorilla is likely to approach 100 pounds by the age of five, a male to surpass it. Three females living just off Fifth Avenue in New York, and estimated to be seven, eight, and ten years old in late 1946, were believed to weigh 180, 200, and 210 pounds respectively. The authenticated weighings in the 400-, 500-, and 600-pound range have all been of animals estimated to be not over fifteen years old. The daily intake of food supporting this rapid growth is about 6 per cent of the body weight, or, with water, close to 10 per cent. Nearly all the food is carbohydrate. The bulk that has to be consumed is bound to affect disposition and behavior.

27. MAN AMONG THE ANTHROPOIDEA

Man and his ancestors are usually made into a separate family in the order of the primates: the *Hominidae*. So are what we have been calling the anthropoid or manlike apes or simply apes, technically named the family *Simiidae*.

Do these names reflect a positive opinion that gorilla, chimpanzee, orang, sia-mang, and gibbon form one group of common origin that can be contrasted with all men as another though related group? Or are the names perhaps merely hangovers from a pre-evolutionary descriptive classification that set man apart because he had speech and "reason," and put the great apes together because they were similar in constituting a sort of hairy mockery of ourselves? There remains a certain hesitation in the technical answers to this question. There are no easy answers, as is shown by the term *"Anthropoidea"* being used some-times for the *Simiidae* or great apes proper; sometimes for them plus man—that is, for all man-size and untailed primates; sometimes more broadly still to in-clude the monkeys, or all primates except lemurs and the tarsier.

Let us first look at some family trees (Fig. 1). The meaning of these lies in which limbs split into what branches, and where on the ladder of time. A split near the trunk, or far down the ladder, denotes ancientness of connection and therefore remoteness of relationship. It is like going down five generations to a great-great-grandmother and climbing back up five to reach a third cousin: he is indubitably somewhat related, but he is not a near relation.

Every authority seems agreed that the gibbon is such a third cousin. He branched off in the early Oligocene, 25 to 30 million years ago according to one of the radiation-based estimates of the age of the earth's strata.[15] The gibbon branches off somewhere in the vicinity of the fossil Propliopithecus and shortly after the Eocene fossil Parapithecus. The gorilla and the chimpanzee, as well as we, and even the orang, have to go back as far as that remote crotch to trace blood connection with the gibbon. Obviously he was the first to leave the com-pany and go off on his own development.

From the Miocene, 10 to 15 million years ago, we have two fossils, Dryo-pithecus and Sivapithecus, which may have lasted into the Pliocene. Somewhere about the time that those two forms appeared, there was another branching. Possibly this split was single, and consisted of the remaining apes (orang, chim-panzee, gorilla) going one way and man the other. Such is the view of Keith and Broom and the present view of Hooton. Or perhaps the split was double, first the orang branching off from the chimpanzee-gorilla-man group and then this latter group promptly subdividing. That is how Gregory sees it and Hooton formerly considered it. All these authorities are high-grade: it just is well to realize that in matters like this the best experts will differ, because evidence on ancient days is always incomplete and gaps in knowledge have to be bridged over by opinion. Actually in this case the differences are largely formal and

[15] Computed from degree of loss of radioactive constituents in rocks of different rela-tive ages. This is only one of several ways of computing the lapse of geological time. These methods lead to different results; none of them are certain; but the radiation method has been in most favor in the last decade or so. Even the radiation-based figures vary, according to the authority, as to the beginning of the Oligocene and the Miocene respectively; 40 and 25 million years are also estimated, besides the 25 to 30 and 10 to 15 cited in the text.

really quite slight, because in two of the four genealogies the two branchings come one right after the other,[16] really differing only as to whether it was the orang who first separated off (Gregory) or man (Broom). Actually the dissenters are Keith and Hooton, who have the orang stay with the gorilla and the chimpanzee until the early Pliocene.

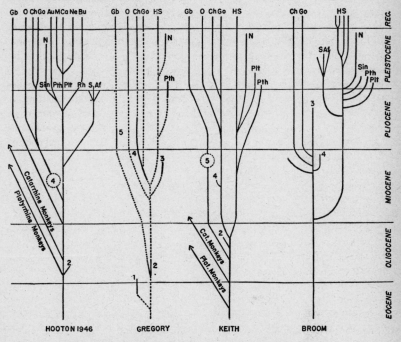

FIG. I. MEN AND APES: FOUR FAMILY TREES

Relationships of fossil and living forms, according to four authorities: redrawn to facilitate comparison. HS, *Homo sapiens,* living man: Au, Ng, Ca, Mo, Bu, Australian, Negro, Caucasian, Mongoloid, Bushmen races. Living apes: Gb, O, Ch, Go: gibbon, orang, chimpanzee, gorilla. Extinct men (Chapter Three): N, Neandertal; Sin, Sinanthropus; Pth, Pithecanthropus; Plt, Piltdown; Rh, Rhodesian. Extinct apes: 1, Parapithecus; 2, Propliopithecus; 3, Sivapithecus; 4, Dryopithecus; 5, Pliopithecus.—S Af, South African forms Australopithecus, Paranthropus, Plesianthropus (§ 42).

This leaves only the gorilla-chimpanzee differentiation to be placed in time. Broom sets this in the very end of the Miocene, Gregory on the Miocene-Pliocene boundary, Hooton formerly put it early in the Pliocene. Obviously the authorities are once more close together. Hooton in 1946 and Keith postpone this

[16] Which may be a polite technical way of saying that they are unsure whether man or orang was the first to branch off from the rest, but that the two events were not far apart.

gorilla-chimpanzee split until the Pliocene-Pleistocene transition; that is, 1 to 2 million years ago, more or less, as against 5 to 10 million years of the other opinions.

Taking these genealogies at face value, we should have to conclude that man belonged *among* the *Simiidae* or apes, since in his genetic ancestry he is as close to gorilla and chimpanzee as is the orang, and closer than the gibbon. With this view the current static classification of the *Hominidae* as *outside of* and co-ordinate with the *Simiidae* is in flat contradiction. Of course such a clash does not make us lose faith in the authenticity of "science," as soon as we realize that in this case both genealogy and taxonomy rest partly on admitted facts but partly also on construal of fact—in other words, on opinion.

Huxley long ago compared man and the manlike apes. He determined the following percentages of measured lengths:

MAN AND MANLIKE APES

(Percentages) *

	Spinal Column	Arm	Leg	Hand	Foot
European man	100	*80*	**117**	26	35
· Gorilla	100	115	96 †	36 †	41
Chimpanzee	100	96 †	90	43	39 †
Orang	100	**122**	*88*	**48**	**52**

* Heavy type, **maximum**; italics, *minimum*. † Nearest to man.

Huxley wrote when Darwinian evolution was new doctrine that was still resisted in many quarters as shocking. He was trying to prove relationship of man and the apes. He therefore used the above figures chiefly to argue that the apes often differed more from one another than some one of them differed from man. Thus man and chimpanzee differ 16 per cent in arm length, but orang and chimpanzee 26 per cent. If such a relation held for all or most traits, it would tend to suggest that man should be classified in the group of the apes rather than alongside it, much as the reconstructed family trees have already suggested.

However, what Huxley in the ardor of his argument did not note is that, in the proportions cited, man is regularly at one end of the ape scale, at either the maximum or the minimum of the joint range. This gives us pause, because it seems to suggest that man does after all stand off on one side by himself. At any rate such would be the compelling inference if it held true for enough other traits beyond the four just cited from Huxley. One thinks at once of the obvious human specializations for which it does hold: erect posture, big brain, little jaw, no projecting canines, hairless body, long head hair, and so on. But these features obtrude just because they differentiate us; and a fair judgment ought to be based on all traits, or at least on a reasonably random sample of all. Such a comparison has never been made systematically, and would prove to be pretty elaborate. An incomplete survey quickly shows that there are some traits in which man does stand within the ape range. Accordingly he is not always on this or that side of it. But it shows also that such traits are not particularly numerous, that some have little visible significance, and that in others man's middle position is due to some secondary or special factor which causes this or that ape now and then to deviate beyond man without basic relationships seeming to be involved.

Huxley himself cited one such instance. For the gibbon, he found the arm, leg, hand, and foot lengths to be respectively 173, 133, 50, and 46 per cent of the spinal column. That gives a relative arm and hand length greater even than in the long-armed orang, and farther away from man. But the gibbon leg proportion of 133 surpasses the human one of 117 almost as much as that surpasses the gorilla's of 96. In other words, here is a case where man seems to be caught squarely intermediate between two apes! But it is a spurious instance, as a little analysis quickly reveals. The gibbon is ultra-arboreal, slim, and light. He has a tiny body but spidery limbs. His legs are long not in themselves but only when they are measured against his reduced, miniature torso. The significant point at issue is whether the leg is long because the animal is built for ground walking, or whether the arm is long because it is built for limb-swinging. A direct interlimb comparison is therefore really the most pertinent. In the case of the bigger apes, who are more or less our size, it does not seriously matter if the trunk or the spine length is used as a scale of reference. But with the feathery, light gibbon, trunk length is misleading on this interlimb proportion. With the comparison made directly between the limbs, Huxley's figures for arm/leg length reconvert to: man, 68 per cent; chimpanzee, 107; gorilla, 120; gibbon, 130; orang, 139.[17] This is certainly convincing. The gibbon is back among the apes, and not only does man now stand again at one end of the series, all by himself; but his limb proportions are decisively reversed from those of all the apes—well under 100 as against above 100.

Most traits or proportions that have definite meaning for the characteristic functioning and behavior of the several species come out this way, with man off to one side of all the apes. Where such is not the case, and man finds himself caught in the middle of the group of his anthropoid cousins, it seems to be usually because the feature in question has been chosen not for its significance in life, but for convenience of measurement. Such proportion traits are the cephalic index or ratio of head breadth to head length; proportion of chest breadth to chest depth; proportion of foot length to trunk length. Not one of these has any known meaning that can be told in words; they seem quite indifferent from the angle of abilities or that of behavior.

[17] Hooton, using Schultz's measures of the body in place of the mounted skeletons of Huxley, gets results that are consistently 20 per cent to 30 per cent higher but follow the same *order*: man, 88; chimpanzee and gorilla, 136-140; gibbon, 162; orang, 170; siamang, 170.

All this leaves us then with man pretty closely related to the anthropoid apes. In fact, possibly man is a nearer cousin to the chimpanzee and the gorilla than either of these is to the orang—certainly nearer than to the gibbon. Nevertheless, at every significant point man long since began to edge off to one side of this group of his closest kin and has consistently kept edging away from them. Meanwhile, to be sure, the apes have also differentiated from one another: the chimpanzee from the orang, the gorilla even more markedly from the gibbon. But however far the anthropoid species have spread apart from what they were originally, it is clear that man has spread away even farther. There is then a basis of justification for the descriptive classification of him as a hominid, of them as simiids. While maintaining our kinship with the apes, we have also pretty regularly managed to transcend it.

28. ANTICIPATIONS OF CULTURE AMONG APES: INVENTION

It is evident that the great apes are close to ourselves anatomically. It is also clear that they are close to us physiologically and psychologically, in their mental make-up and most of their faculties. At the same time, their total behavior, and the capacities inferable from their behavior, differ conspicuously from our total behavior and capacities. It is also pretty plain that, basically and in the large, most of the behavior practiced by men but not by apes is the result of man's possessing genuine language and genuine culture. There is no doubt that the acquisition by ancestral man of these two related activities—"gifts" they would have been called formerly—was an event of unusual novelty on this planet, if an evolutionary development may be verbally telescoped into an event. Now it is just possible that this development came as a sudden leap; that it came as a sort of supermutation—in the genes—of inherited faculty which suddenly added to the existing process of hereditary transmission the beginning of a powerful new process of nonhereditary transmission. But the run of scientific experience is that vehement changes and sudden decisive overturns are rare in nature. Just on probability, the betting would be strong that the faculty for culture did not spring fully formed out of the blue, but developed through transitions. Or at least, if the final act of achievement was a relatively swift and drastic one, it was preceded by minor anticipations, by significant premonitory symptoms. That is why an inquiry into how near the apes have come to manifesting culture and speech is important. It might even be said in a sense that the less actual culture we find them to have, the more precious will be the slight evidences of their rudiments or foreshadowings of it.

The case for a sort of protoculture among apes is probably strongest as regards tools. The anthropoids now and then use ready-made tools, and occasionally they will make them. Captive chimpanzees take up sticks to draw to themselves food that is outside the bars beyond reach of their arms. They beat with sticks for the same purpose, or cast ropes or ropelike objects. If the desired food is out of reach overhead, if jumping to reach it has led to failure, and if there is no other chimpanzee about that can be climbed onto and used as a take-off for a higher leap, many of them finally have recourse to moving a box or other convenient object under the prize. If, after they have learned to use a box, the food is hung still higher, chimpanzees may learn to pile a second box on the first; and the more versatile ones will pile three or four. Gorillas and monkeys will also do this. It has justly been pointed out that the piling of the second box on the first is psychologically a quite different thing from moving the first box; there is in it the element of combination, or construction. In a small way, the difference is somewhat like that between rolling a stone and building with stones.

When the convenient reaching tool happened to be a bundle of straws, one chimpanzee, finding the straw too soft to engage and move a banana, without hesitation stiffened the bundle by doubling it. Even then the tool was ineffective, so she redoubled it. That it was now too short to reach the banana rendered the result ineffectual, but this does not detract from her credit as an inventor: she grasped the problem and knew in principle what to do about it. Incidentally, the proclivity of chimpanzees to try to use pliable, ropelike objects for tools is an unexplained foible of the species.

Especially interesting is the rather rare but repeated observation of two canes being joined one into the other to draw in food that lies beyond the reach of a single cane. This is indubitable tool-making; especially so when the end of a stick is chewed down to fit into the hollow of a cane.

How far apes under proper stimuli might progress in devising tools for themselves is difficult to say; just as the observations leave it somewhat obscure how far slower-witted individuals tend to profit by imitating or making the discoveries of a more inventive one. There are however some interesting observations as to the circumstances of the process of invention.

First, the chimpanzee strongly dislikes the strain of situations that call upon his rudimentary inventive faculties. The process of invention is visibly and disagreeably arduous for him. His first impulse is to give up, or to become angry, if he cannot arrive at a solution by purely physiological means such as leaping or biting. Characteristic is the fact that if an implement for reaching is in line of vision with the desired object, it is usually promptly utilized. If on the other hand a previously handled and well-known stick lies behind the ape's back as he faces the food, it may not be "thought of" or noticed and taken up for a long time. This is true especially if the experiment is a novelty to the animal: with repetition, he finds the stick more quickly; but the first time he usually does not remember or observe it at all until after repeated renunciations and recurrences of desire. Emotions clearly are important, constituting a strong resistive factor. The individuals who meet difficult problems most readily, and carry their little inventions farthest, are evidently those best able to control or inhibit the desire or other emotion which the prospective goal arouses in them.

But emotions of another kind can be an impelling influence toward invention. These are the social emotions. His desire for affection, and for approbation from human beings, certainly helps a chimpanzee to invent tools. In a state of nature it is probable that competitive emotion—jealousy—is even more stimulating. Significant is Koehler's observation of the behavior of an adult female chimpanzee when a loaded box or heavy obstacle was placed to interfere with her reaching food beyond the bars. She was perfectly capable of moving the obstacle; but the problem weighed on her for two hours. When however a young unconfined chimpanzee began to stray in the general direction of the food, she suddenly seized the heavy box, shoved it out of the way without hesitation, and grasped the prize out of reach of the competitor. Next day she found the same solution in one minute without first letting herself go into a fit of depression.

The same chimpanzee objected to using sticks for reaching unless they were, so to speak, thrust into her hands by their placement. For half an hour she neglected a stick that was close behind her and which, as a retinal image, she saw whenever in aimless irritation she turned around; but she would not see it with her mind. After a while she stood on the stick. She must have felt it with her soles; but again, as a personality, she refused to receive the sense impression. After half an hour a free chimpanzee came near the food. The jealousy which his approach excited was now utilized to repress the sulking emotion hitherto displayed; suddenly the ignored stick was perceived, seized, and used to draw in the food.

These observations may not throw much light on the question of how far apes possess culture. They do however suggest something as to the psychology that underlies human culture, and which is a factor in what we are accustomed to term its progress. They indicate that the total elimination of competitive factors among men would lessen effort in individuals and might deprive civilization of one of its principal prerequisite impulses. The data suggest further why the institutions, codes, and ethics of all peoples have so strongly emphasized inhibition; why, for instance, courage—the repression of fear—has always been esteemed a high if not the highest virtue; and why, similarly, all social groups condemn incest. Not that the anthropoid apes set up moral standards. But all human groups do; they have evidently learned, on the basis of individual life experiences, the social importance of restraints. The historical inference is that from soon after the time when men began to possess institutions at all, and were able to formulate these in speech, they have never seriously swerved from an insistence on some sort of a social limitation on the natural sex impulse.

Play is evidently an important element in chimpanzee invention. Situations are often first met, or devices prepared, not from a desire to achieve a useful end, but as a matter of sport or amusement, as a means of satisfying pure manipulative interest; utilization comes later. There are plenty of cultural parallels: the use of gunpowder first for fireworks, of the pneumatic tire for sport bicycling, of animal domestication probably for the satisfaction of having pets (§ 148, 165). There is in many men an element that makes them strive for mastery or excellence or perfection of achievement for its own sake, apart from the satisfaction of any definable utilitarian need. It is the driving of such impulses to the point of physiological discomfort, even of bodily strain or damage, that can give organized sport and science and art a certain quality of "unnaturalness." At their fullest, they are exaggerations if not perversions of the play impulse.

No chimpanzee seems capable of being so extreme; he is too unintelligent, from our point of view, but also too sensible, too direct, too concordant physiologically. For better or for worse, however, we men are prone to this exaggeration of the play impulse; and, again for better or for worse, the exaggeration has perceptibly aided the gradual accretion of the stock of culture, as well as the betterment of athletic records; as is discussed in more detail in § 127-128.

The chimpanzee in his youth is as playful, restless, curious, and explorative as any human being. He does not go very far in tool invention, because his central nervous system seems to become quickly and healthily fatigued by situations that put on the nervous system any strain that cannot be promptly discharged into striped-muscle activity. He is physiologically a clear extravert. The gorilla is generally described as imbued with more sense of personal dignity, reticence, and caution even to the point of countersuggestibility. Evidence as to whether in the field of pure intellect the gorilla is the equal of the chimpanzee will have to wait until we have learned to establish satisfactory relations with him in terms of his withdrawing temperament.

The demonstrated ape trait is lack of patience in the solution of a problem, of irritation, sulking, or ignoring as soon as difficulties are encountered which cannot be solved by direct use of hands, feet, or mouth.

This is of interest because it finds a parallel in the history of culture. There was required actually less skill to fashion many of the ground or polished stone implements of the New Stone Age than some of the specialized chipped ones of the Old Stone Age, tens of thousands of years earlier (§ 259). The reason seems to be that while chipping requires definite manual control, it is a rapid process. A dozen failures occupy little time; each may suggest the possibility of an improvement; and the thirteenth attempt may be reasonably satisfactory. Grinding, however, although one of the simplest of operations, is of necessity slow. Very early man was apparently better able to mobilize a fair degree of manipulative skill than a great amount of patience. This resemblance to the ape—and to children—may be only a coincidence, but looks as if it were more than that.

That the chimpanzee possesses the beginning of an ability to reverse his primary impulses is shown by a series of experiments. After a group of the animals had learned to use a stick to gather in food from beyond their reach, the fruit was placed behind a barrier, in a low, open, three-sided box with the farther side broken out. To get his banana, the ape had therefore either to lift it with his stick out over the front or side edge of the box, which was almost impossibly difficult for him; or he had to reverse his first impulse of scraping the fruit toward himself, and instead push it farther away, until it was clear of the box; after which of course the familiar raking-in process could successfully commence. Without exception the apes found this problem difficult. Some never solved it except when the box was partly turned to help them; others only by the aid of accident, such as the banana's rolling favorably; and even those who had learned the necessary reversal tended occasionally to relapse into their earlier, direct, impossible efforts. Still, some of them did learn, and with practice came to perform quickly and efficiently.

This experiment developed a type of success that has its parallel in culture: invention partly by accident (§ 147). The banana, prodded by the stick, rolls or bounces near an open corner of the box, or entirely clear of it, and the animal immediately sees a solution that has been beyond his grasp while the problem remained unmitigated. After this partial aid by chance, the whole problem may soon be mastered.

The chimpanzee depends much more than we do on muscular strength and gymnastic skill. Even the most intelligent anthropoids manifest little sense of statics. They pile three or four boxes randomly and precariously and then climb on top and balance their own bodies to counteract the imbalance of the mechanical pile. Boxes are set on a narrow end or an edge and the animal tries to mount them—in some cases even succeeds because of his natural acrobatic capacity. Gorillas proceed more like human beings in adjusting and trying out the boxes; but they are much heavier animals, and with much less climbing and jumping impulse. Of course a solution that depends for its effectiveness primarily on muscular skill is in that degree farther from an invention in the cultural sense. An imperfect tool suffices; the congenital body makes up the deficiency. If men had the strength of arm and jaw of the great apes and their enormous canine teeth, they would no doubt have continued for a long time to meet many situations with muscle rather than with tools.

The impulse to perform with his body is strong in the cleverest chimpanzee; by comparison, performance with a tool is usually clumsy and always an arduous act at first. Given a suspended banana and an available pole, his first impulse is to climb the pole before it can fall and make a quick grab at the fruit—a sort of pole-vault reaching. Sticks are brandished threateningly in play combat. But let a chimpanzee lose his temper, and he drops his stick and plunges into attack with hands and teeth.

Nevertheless some use of tools is spontaneous. Stones are hurled. Sticks are used to dig in play or for roots; to tease fowls or other animals behind wire netting; to touch fire, lizards, live wires, or other things that provoke both curiosity and fear. In removing filth from his body, the chimpanzee prefers a stick, a chip, a leaf, or a rag to his fingers. He will lick up ants, or hold out a straw for the ants to crawl on and then lick them off. He has not been observed, outside of posed problems, to manufacture tools or to lay them aside for the future; he does certainly, without human stimulation, use simple tools that come to hand, and use them in a way that in a human being we should call intelligent.

Sometimes an ape sits down in front of a problem that has baffled him, detaches himself from his previous efforts, and looks the situation over, seemingly thinking. How far he may actually "study" the situation is difficult to say; but he certainly appears reflective. Suddenly then, sometimes, the solution comes and is applied without hesitation or awkwardness. Again, it may come overnight and with seeming irrelevance. When a human being acts in this manner we say that he has thought the problem out. At any rate the ape's solution may come as a whole, as an abrupt synthesis; it looks suspiciously like what in ourselves we would call an insight.

Left to themselves, chimpanzees are destructive. They love to demolish. Like small children who have grown up uncontrolled, they derive immediate satisfaction from prying, ripping, biting, and deliberately smashing. Once they begin, they rarely desist until an object has been reduced to its components. They learn with difficulty to lace shoes; they find spontaneous pleasure in unlacing them. They love to pick knots, as a special form of taking things apart; they have no inclination to tie or fasten things. The impulse to construct is infinitely weaker than that to destroy; it is called into activity only by special problems, and the solution of these is trying.

One of the few exceptions is nest-building. This the chimpanzee does from an early age, and apparently without being taught. So do gorillas and orangs. Here we seem to have a genuine case of what in the older terminology was called "specific instinct." Nest-building is psychologically interesting because it is directed toward an inanimate objective outside the body. But, according to both Koehler and Yerkes, as well as Nissen, the building is partly a drawing and tucking of branches under the body. Some of the twigs snap off and help to hold in place the branches that remain half-attached to the tree. In this way a tolerable mat or platform is built up. This however remains, during the act of building, in contact with the ape's body; it is built against his skin, he feels it during the process of construction, and the autistic sensations aroused may be an important element in the carrying out of the process. The orang even seems to cover himself with nest. Some captive chimpanzees, if trees are not available or loose material does not suffice, lay down a ring of hay or the like which outlines their body and merely suggests the nest—a nest gesture, as it were. This is an indubitable though simple construction.

The powerful impulses of chimpanzees toward destructiveness may help to explain further one phenomenon in the history of early human culture already touched upon: the long precedence in time of the chipping over the grinding technique in stone. After all, the earlier and grosser process of production by fracture is one of breaking apart. Grinding, being so slow as to be almost imperceptible in its results, must be quite inadequate as a means of satisfying the demolition impulse. As an object is slowly rubbed into form, there is probably rather a sense of shaping and constructing. Of course, the Abbevillean and Acheulian hand axes (§ 263, 273) are not by-products of a mere interest in cracking boulders; they are too definitely adaptive, too patternized, too utilizable as tools. But preceding them are ruder flake tools and putative tools (§ 260). In the light of ape behavior we may venture the tentative inference that our ancestors were like chimpanzees and children—and many modern human adults—in taking pleasure in demolition.[18] Learning among other things to smash boulders, and especially nodules of flint, which would be resistive but then shatter cleanly, they may have found themselves provided with attractively sharp and shining flakes, affording a novel toy. Manipulation of these may have led to the discovery that the flakes furnished the possibility of a new satisfaction in hacking or scraping other objects. From such play in turn might have grown increasing habits of tool use, leading, when the mechanism of culture fixation and transmission became sufficiently developed, to the manufacture of tools as tools.

29. OTHER POSSIBLE FORESHADOWINGS OF CULTURE

The occasional use of tools in place of limbs, or as extensions of organs, is the most fully authenticated case of precultural or protocultural manifestations by the apes. This is not too surprising, since a few species much lower than primates are authentically reported to make regular use of inanimate objects in certain particular situations. Thus the solitary wasp *Sphex urnarius* carefully selects a pebble that fits her jaws and then uses it to tamp down the dirt filling that closes the burrow in which she has deposited an egg and a paralyzed caterpillar. This is particularly interesting because it is tool use not through intelligence but as part of a specific instinct, that is, through heredity. In the Galápagos Islands there is a tree finch, *Camarhyncus* or *Cactospiza pallida,* which feeds by using a spine or a thorn or a small stick to impale or rout out insects that are too far down in crevices of bark for it to reach with its bill. More relevant to the problem of the origin of culture is noninstinctual toolmaking or invention, as just discussed; this seems to be confined to the primates and has been most often reported of chimpanzees. Possible anticipations of culture other than technological or inventive activities are hazier than the foregoing, but the following are some suggestive situations.

Chimpanzees are indifferent about being clothed; perhaps it might be said that they tend to dislike, but accept, clothes, although they appreciate a blanket in which to wrap themselves at night. On the contrary, they voluntarily drape themselves with strings and rags, wearing these for hours or days. The satisfac-

---

[18] The gorilla, and the small *Cebus* monkey, are described as exploratory rather than destructive.

tion is clearly in the wearing as distinct from the act of putting on. The heightening of kinaesthetic bodily consciousness appears to be what gives the pleasure. Chains or strings or pendants that swish and sway with the motion of the body are favored. These observations confirm what has long since been concluded from observation of men; namely, that human dress for protection and for human adornment spring from separate sources or motives.

A group of Koehler's chimpanzees, in digging, discovered some white earth. Tasting it and finding it inedible, they spat it out. Wiping their lips on the wall, they saw it whitened. This soon became a game. First with their lips and then with their hands—this order is perhaps significant—they painted with white earth whatever walls and surfaces were available, but rarely their own bodies. There was no attempt at design or figure. The stuff was smeared on, and the more the appearance of a surface changed, the greater the satisfaction. The pleasure apparently lay in using the muscles to produce a visible external effect. Similar painting or drawing has been reported for gorillas and *Cebus* monkeys.

These observations accord with the behavior of very small children, whose first spontaneous attempts at what we are wont to call drawing or painting normally result in nothing more than smearing or drawing arcs. It is evident that the small child, left to himself, does not attempt to draw a house or a dog or a man. He converts a white paper into a red or black one, a monotonous into a variegated surface. Like the chimpanzee, he gets a kinaesthetic pleasure from his motor discharge, accompanied by the pleasure he gets from seeing the defacement or alteration achieved. This is not yet art; it is subaesthetic motor functioning out of which art accomplishments can develop.

A pair of young chimpanzees in playing began to stamp and circle about a post. Others then ranged themselves alongside until they formed a ring, presenting much the appearance of a savage tribe in a dance. But while the stamping of each ape was definitely heavier with one foot, there was no unison—only a tendency to keep time together. And there was nothing to show that the dancing followed any pattern—that there was imitation in the cultural sense, with social acceptance of a form. The dancing of one individual stimulated other individuals into analogous behavior; but the performance of each apparently remained an unconditioned physiological response. When the gamboling of one lamb sets others to gamboling, or when one startled sheep runs and the flock follows, the lambs or the sheep do not possess culture because they follow one another's example. If one ape had devised or learned a new dance step or a particular posture or an attitude toward the post about which the dance revolved; and if these new acts were taken up by other chimpanzees and became more or less standardized; especially if these survived beyond the influence of the inventor, were taken up by other communities, or passed on to generations after him—in such a case we could legitimately feel that we were on solid ground of an ape culture. But of this there is no indication.

It is the same with chimpanzee fads in smearing· chalk, or the game of teasing chickens by unexpectedly jabbing them with a stick through the wire mesh. These actions are comparable to the vogue that a game has among ourselves, to the fact that the first boy who brings out his kite or his marbles in spring is likely to set other boys of his school to bringing out their kite and marbles. What is cultural in such phenomena is not the fact that one individual leads and others follow, but the game or fashion as such. The kite, the manner of manipulating the marbles, the cut of a garment, the tipping of one's hat— these remain as cultural facts after every physiological and psychological consideration of the individuals involved has been exhausted. Of any such institutional residuum of unmitigatedly cultural material there is as yet no clear demonstration among the apes.

Religion is difficult to conceive without formulated ideas, and thus without speech. Even its rudiments could therefore hardly be looked for among the apes. Yet there may be some subcultural anticipations. Koehler made a rude rag animal with shoe-button eyes which vaguely suggested a miniature donkey. It was altogether too crude to be mistaken for a live animal, yet had sufficient resemblance to one to set it off from ordinary inanimate natural objects, or from artifacts such as boxes and chairs. The apes responded instantly with manifestations of fear. It was not terror as great as an ox or a camel inspired; it can perhaps best be characterized as similar in its expression to what human beings would call awe. There was not a trace of either the frank curiosity or the later unresponsiveness that a new lifeless object provoked; interest there was, but also respectful staying at a distance for a long time. Even food placed in proximity to the image was shunned, and was snatched only at last and cautiously, with a precipitate retreat. A dog manifested a similar interest in the figure, except that, being carnivorous and therefore a basically aggressive organism, his interest took the form of hostility. He convinced himself, however, as soon as he dared, of the inanimateness of the image, and from then on was completely indifferent to it. The chimpanzee, like ourselves, is less "practical," perhaps as the result of possessing more imagination.

The relation to religion of this reaction of the chimpanzees lies in their manifesting something like the awe that is regarded as an important or essential ingredient of what we call the religious feeling: the religious thrill. It is generally recognized that religion could not well originate without the presence of emotions of which awe may be taken as the prototype, and that these emotions tend to persist or to be reawakened in religion, no matter how crystallized this becomes with time. Also, the kind of object that arouses the awelike feeling in chimpanzees has a certain quality of resemblance to the basic concepts of religion. Souls, ghosts, spirits, deities, like stuffed rag donkeys, do not occur in ordinary experience; like them, also, they are thought to be at once similar to living bodies and different from them. A dummy donkey with button eyes evidently is literally supernatural to a chimpanzee, or at any rate is close to being supernatural. We can say pretty positively that the ape does not have a religion; we can also say pretty positively that he acts at times somewhat as if he were religious. Another way of putting it is that there are certain situations in which apes manifest reactions which strongly suggest feelings similar to those experienced by human beings in religious connections, but that there is no indication whatever that apes have any religion itself or that they are capable of the systematic conceptualization that a religion involves.

On the side of speech it is remarkable that the apes are completely deficient in imitativeness of human beings. Observations, experiments, and training attempts like those of Furness and Boutan are uniformly negative. At this point the successful manual adaptations are significant that are shown by circus-trained chimpanzees and orangs and by those brought up in close human associations. Such apes do learn easily to ride bicycles, to smoke cigars, to brush their teeth, to eat with a spoon, to go to bed, and to do a hundred other things the family is doing. They cannot be taught to speak at all. They do not seem even to have the least impulse to imitate the speech of their human associates, or, if willing to try, they are wholly at a loss how to do so. This is the more striking because of the general similarity of their mouth parts to our own—a similarity that is certainly far greater than that of a parrot's or a magpie's mouth.

All in all, it is clear that we have in the anthropoid apes beings remarkably close to ourselves. They are animals behaving in many respects like men and differently from other animals. Impulses that we are accustomed to regard as specifically human, such as "painting" and hanging things on our bodies, prove to be present in them in rudimentary form. What they do lack totally, so far as we can judge, is speech and culture. In this regard they are as subhuman as the other mammals and the birds. This is really remarkable in view of their possessing one of the ingredients going into the make-up of culture: inventiveness. That the tools an ape now and then devises are simple and crude is to be expected; that he can and does originate them makes us wonder why he did not pass on to develop an elementary culture. The absence of speech undoubtedly is an important factor in this deficiency.

With the ape inventive but cultureless, the question arises whether we have not perhaps hitherto exaggerated the importance of invention in human culture. We are wont to think of it as the creative or productive element in civilization. The idea of progress, which has so powerful a hold on the unconscious as well as the conscious thought of our day, may have led us to overemphasize the role of invention. Perhaps the thing that essentially makes culture is precisely the transmissive and preservative elements, the relational or binding factors. It may be that invention, for all its dynamic potential for change, will prove to be what in the long pull is incidental in culture, despite the fact that it has become the tendency of the day to look upon it as primary. What may ultimately be recognized as counting for more is the way the patternings of culture shape themselves to permit or prevent or induce invention, or, for that matter, other changes of civilization. This shaping of patterns is a matter of interrelations of culture content; and what appears to be indispensable for the existence of such inter-relations is a certain social relation, an organization, or form, almost a stand-ardization. The fundamental thing about culture then would be the way in which men relate themselves to one another by relating themselves to their culture material. If however the relational forces in culture phenomena are the intrinsic ones, then the indispensability of speech to the very existence of culture becomes understandable. It is the fact of communicating, perhaps, more than the thing communicated, that counts. At any rate the fact that speech, to the best of our knowledge, is as thoroughly wanting among the anthropoids as is culture tends to confirm this conception.

These problems will be gone into at greater length in the chapters on cul-ture, especially Chapters Seven to Eleven.

30. HUMAN SPECIALIZATIONS AND THEIR INTERRELATIONS

Many of the described anatomical human specializations away from the general primate stock, and then from the narrower protoanthropoid stock, are interrelated, structurally and functionally. Particularly interrelated are brain, jaw, posture, hands, feet, and vision. A failure of any one of these to develop as it actually did would have interfered with the evolutionary development of the others—in some cases considerably, in others vitally. Most fundamental, of course, was the brain development, and specifically that of the brain cortex, where the culture-and-speech faculty must be thought to be localized, so far as it is localized. A chimpanzee brain in an otherwise human body would cer-tainly not have led to those accomplishments of man which it is the business of history and anthropology to tell about. But contrariwise a human brain originating in chimpanzee bodies might conceivably have led to a world not so very different from our human one, though a more unlovely one. The critical phases of the species would in that case presumably have come early in its history, in connection with difficulties of travel and spread, of self-defense in the open, of dietary limitations, and possibly some technological restrictions due to lack of a fully opposable thumb. But once our hypothetical ape with culture-geared human brain had survived these initial handicaps and had piled up a measurable stock of cultural contrivances, his culture would presumably have been as successfully adapted to his physique, and to survival, as ours is to our physique. Tool grips would in that case have been shaped for nearly thumbless hands instead of thumbed ones. Travel on foot would presumably have had added to it at an earlier time transport by riding or on wheels or on stilts or the like. And with such minor modifications there might have been a general mode and subvarieties of cultural living fairly parallel to our own.

Of least specific importance in the matter of human specialization is vision, because our eye faculties seem to differ little from those of the apes and monkeys.

It need only be reaffirmed that without the kinds of eyes we have our hands would be much limited in their manipulations, and with these restricted a fine brain would often be ineffectual in coping with tangible situations. But the qualities we chiefly needed in our eyes to make the rest of our bodies fully effective—namely, their being set to look forward together instead of apart at the sides, their muscular co-ordination and stereoscopic faculty, and their sharpness of vision in the fovea—were acquired early in primate evolution.

Color vision, by the way, seems to have been of consequence chiefly for the aesthetic potentialities it added. Its survival value was and is relatively low; many large groups of animals never see colors. Nor are the 5 per cent or so of color-blind male human beings (§ 72) seriously handicapped in living in the culture evolved by the 95 per cent of color-seeing men and nearly 100 per cent of women. Only a few professions using color signals are closed to them, even in our mechanized contemporary civilization. And until rather recently, nearly all the color-blind got through life without their or their associates' suspecting the condition. The first reference in history seems to have been less than three hundred years ago, in 1684, and the first scientific description was that of the chemist Dalton in 1794. Of course color-blindness, being hereditary, was presumably just as frequent before these dates as afterward. The point is that if it could go unnoticed in history until then, it cannot be a very material defect.

31. THE UNKNOWN ORGANIC BASIS OF THE FACULTY FOR CULTURE

The foregoing discussions have established culture and speech as essential possessions limited strictly to human beings. Some faint approaches toward culture are discernible here and there in the animal kingdom, especially among the great apes, as just discussed in § 28-29. Also, it seems to be established that certain birds possess a mimetic faculty and inclination which bring it about that some of them can modify their specific hereditary and instinctual song. They modify it in conformity toward phonographed bird song to which they are exposed for a sufficiently long period in youth, whether such song be merely that of a slightly different strain or race, or of a different species. Further, once trained in such a modification of their congenital song, the older birds will similarly influence the younger birds reared within earshot of their voices, so that a sort of tradition is carried on. This is externally very like human tradition. But it differs fundamentally from the transmission of culture and speech in that it is wholly lacking in the conveyance of any facts or any ideas; it does not contain an element of abstraction. It is obviously allied to the mechanically reproductive faculty of parrots, magpies, and mynahs, which learn to repeat fragments of speech but do not learn to convey objective meanings.

These slight and ineffectual approaches to language or culture possess a very real interest in that they show that the human faculty for these behaviors is not something entirely outside of nature, is not a sort of foreign body or miracle mysteriously injected into the otherwise continuous course of natural events. There are just enough subhuman anticipations of speech and culture, just enough stirrings and foreshadowings toward them, to make clear that their development has its roots in animal structure and evolution as completely as has the development of our bodies and physiology. But the fact of such· rooting should not cause us to overlook the other fact that the great vine of culture and speech which has grown in man out of this rooting is a thousandfold as large and strong as the poor, rare, struggling, seedling counterpart among nonhuman animals. Destroy our culture and speech capacity, and it is clear that well over 99 per cent of what fills our human lives specifically, of our total actions and behavior, would be obliterated.

Now the remarkable thing is that while the results or outgrowths of the faculty for culture are so great—and for the rest of this argument let us consider speech included in culture—by contrast man's visible equipment, his whole structure as it is analyzed, is so closely similar to that of the apes. That we are nearly hairless, that our teeth are smaller and our thumbs more opposable, that we are better built for prolonged standing and walking—these are anatomical and physiological differences of detail and degree, and mostly of no very great degree. But the difference as regards culture is one of so enormous a degree, when we consider its effects—complete absence of religion, law, art, and science among even the most manlike apes or the most socialized insects—as to become virtually equivalent to a difference in kind.

It seems that this situation drives us to one conclusion: From the angle of what is organic and hereditary in nature, the evolutionary acquisition of capacity for culture was an organically small thing, a by-product, which at first was so insignificant that a nonterrestrial observer would perhaps have overlooked it. Even now the most advanced biological science cannot level a finger and say: This is when and how culture faculty developed, out of such and such an antecedent, and here is where it still resides and basically operates. The "here," the anatomical seat of the faculty, is presumably in the cortex of the brain. But this cortex differs from that of the cultureless apes only in being somewhat larger, somewhat thicker, presumably somewhat more complex with a somewhat greater number of nerve cells and interconnections of them. There is no new organ, no new layer, no new chemical substance that we know of, peculiar to the human cortex. The "somewhat" heightening, the elaborating of degree, of the structure of the apelike cortex, seems to have sufficed to turn the trick. It seems to have started our ancestors on the path of a culture which then grew cumulatively. That is, the culture accumulated, or could accumulate, independently of further evolution of anatomical structure or heredity, so far as we know.[19]

[19] This is an anticipation of what will be more fully set forth below, but the point must be made here if man's peculiar place in nature is to be defined thoroughly. See particularly § 49, 99, 112-115.

This situation, in turn, suggests that from the angle of organic evolution, which means change in heredity, the increment or mutation that first introduced the capacity for culture was a very small increment. It may have been no more than a change in one chromosome, perhaps no more than in a few genes. The individual organism in which this new constitutional factor [20] first cropped out may well have been still overwhelmingly like its parents and ancestors in total appearance and behavior, in bodily shape, motivations, and abilities. But on top of this likeness, the innovating or mutant individual manifested a new inclination to communicate, to learn and to teach, to generalize from the endless chain of his discrete feelings, actions, and experiences. And therewith he began to be able to act as a receiver and a transmitter, and to begin the accumulation that is culture. We cannot in the least prove by evidence that this is what happened; but it is very difficult, in the light of what we know of heredity and of culture, to conceive that it did not happen.

With the appearance, in the stream of anthropoid-hominid heredity, of the first gene bearing the faculty of cultural acquisition, a critical point may be said to have been reached in evolution. There had been critical points passed before: the first head, the first eye, the first brain, the first warm blood. But this one was different in that the genetic change set something going outside of heredity also: a process that could be operative only through organisms and by their agency, but which would have a growth and development of a separate kind, apart from germ-plasm development: cumulatively instead of recapitulatively, and with each idea or invention making others possible.

Critical points—tipover limits, we might call them—occur scattered all through nature. Thus, when a book on a table is shoved an eighth of an inch farther until its center of gravity is just over the table edge, it topples. Or water is chilled degree after degree without notable change of its properties until it reaches 0° C and turns to solid ice. Or two gases will explode only when their mixture reaches a certain proportion and the necessary flash point is reached. These are recurrent critical points. The critical point in evolution that resulted in the birth of the faculty for culture is infinitely more dramatic because quite probably it was reached only once in the earth's history. And it was dramatic too in that at the time of the event its effects probably were only infinitesimally perceptible, whereas the ultimate effects were to become indefinitely great for the species concerned, and were often to react back on the physical and organic streams of nature, as when men change the face of the earth by their labors, or exterminate or propagate animals and plants.

[20] Or possibly the first one of a series of related factors successively reinforcing one another.

32. SPECIALIZATIONS ASSOCIATED WITH POSTURE

If now, leaving these somewhat wide-range reflections, we return to concrete specializations and review the human particularities, those peculiarities which characterize man as against his nearest ape relatives, it appears that much the greatest number of such differentiating features fall into three groups, each consisting of a set of traits correlated with one another around a nucleus. These nuclei may for convenience be designated as posture, brain size, and domestication.

Hands, feet, and posture are intimately interconnected. We are built to walk and stand erect indefinitely long, with a "double" curvature of our backbone— really a triple one: convex at rump and at shoulders and neck, concave at small of the back. The apes have a single convex curve forward. They do not stand well, nor walk erect freely. Usually they progress on the ground on all fours, planting their weight on their soles and knuckles. If not too heavy, they perhaps most often climb or swing, and progress by brachiating—"arming" it from an overhead support instead of "legging" it over the ground underfoot. This, as we have seen (§ 21-26), is connected with the arboreal habitat of the primates generally, which the anthropoids retain, with only incipient abandonment by the chimpanzee and somewhat more by the ponderous gorilla. The result is that both apes and monkeys are functionally quadrumanous, four-handed, as compared with ourselves—as already told in § 10. The clean differentiation into feet for walking on the ground and hands for taking and holding is unique to man. So is full opposability of the thumb, which is obviously useful in tool-handling but may be as much of a detriment as an advantage in swinging from and to branches. Yet if our ancestors had not once lived for a long time in the trees, along with the rest of the primates, we should probably never have had any kind of hand. The clever or lucky thing we "did" was to come down out of the trees after we had hands, and early enough to re-evolve a pretty fair true foot—that is, a limb extremity built for general terrestrial locomotion.

Erect posture in one sense is essentially an expression of this full differentiation in the function of our two pairs of limbs. If the hands were really to be emancipated to serve as manipulators, they had better come wholly off the ground; and the mechanical end, and in a sense the perfection, of this new type of design was complete erectness, with whatever correlated changes in backbone, pelvis, leg, and foot were involved, if they could be attained. And they were reasonably attainable, as the evolutionary outcome showed.

Man is the only vertebrate, perhaps the only animal, that stands and moves fully erect: with his head directly over his feet, his legs vertical, his trunk and neck on a vertical axis, even his arms essentially vertical when at rest. Our forefathers of some centuries ago saw in this posture a symbol of his aspiring toward

God, or of an inherent "upwardness," "rectitude," or worthiness. We of today rule such subjective and moral judgments out of our biology; but the thorough uniqueness undoubtedly has certain significances that are also objective, and not moral: significances of cause and effect, or let us say of history and correlation. There are evidently certain mechanical and organic problems to be solved, or requirements that have to be met, before erect posture becomes feasible; and these problems are presumably by no means simple, else erect forms would have been evolved repeatedly in nature. There are only incomplete approximations. Birds are bipedal but not erect; their trunk is at most slanting, often nearly horizontal, when they are on the ground; in flight it is fully horizontal. The kangaroo's legs are flexed, the thighs being horizontal at rest; and they are both braced and balanced at the hip by a long, massive tail. The plane of the kangaroo's pelvis is vertical, not horizontal, and the trunk slopes definitely forward. And so in every subhuman case; the erectness is only partial, or false, or can be maintained only momentarily. Evidently a series of conditions had to be fulfilled before the cluster of traits co-ordinated with fully erect posture could be successfully achieved and preserved in evolution. Presumably adaptation to arboreal life was one such antecedent. Subsequent full return to the ground almost certainly was another. A minimum of size may also have been necessary for the innovation to be successful.

33. BRAIN SIZE

The size of the human brain is another uniqueness. This holds especially for absolute size. It holds less for relative size, since in animals of the same structure and development, the smaller will always have the proportionally larger brain. The reason for this is that a house cat, weighing perhaps one-fiftieth of a tiger or a lion, will nevertheless have just about as many sensations to receive and as many and complex motions to execute, and apparently cannot do this work with a brain fully shrunk to one-fiftieth of the lion's. So its brain actually weighs one-tenth that of a lion, or relatively five times as much. In the same way, a mouse's brain is of course smaller than a rat's, but a greater fraction of a mouse than of a rat consists of brain: 2 per cent as against .05 per cent. Similarly, as between a hummingbird and an eagle, a sparrow (one-twentieth of its body) and an ostrich (one three-thousandth), a 2-ounce lizard (one four-hundredth of its body) and a 400-pound alligator (one fifteen-thousandth). A similar difference holds as between infant and adult in the same species. Thus a male white baby's brain makes up a full tenth of his body weight at birth (320-340 grams of 3000-3500), as against only about 2 per cent when it has become adult.[21] In a rough sort of way, brain size perhaps tends to be larger by about

---

[21] This is on the basis of brain weight in grams holding constant at seven-eighths the cranial capacity (§ 57, 60) in cubic centimeters in man. A child is born with a fourth of its ultimate brain volume or slightly better, has doubled this probably by its ninth month, and

the square while body size is larger by the cube; or inversely as regards shrink-age—square root versus cube root.

Man's brain weight is about one-fiftieth his body weight; around 3 pounds out of 150. The absolute mass of this fiftieth is surpassed by only a very few giants among living animals. These are the whales, the bodies of whose larger species range up to 100 tons; elephants that weigh 5 tons; possibly but probably not the rhinoceros and the hippopotamus, though there appear to be few authentic figures available as to these. This means that among land animals we must proceed to bodies at least twenty times heavier than man's before the human brain is surpassed in mass. Cattle and horses, the bulk of which will balance five to ten men on the scales, have brains much smaller than each of the ten.

The table shows the elephant as the only land animal with a brain larger than a man's. The great whales, with a total weight up to a thousand times that of a man, manage to get on with only four or five times our brain mass: they are a sort of warm-blooded mushrooms. The small whales on the contrary make a surprisingly good showing: a 300-pound porpoise not only has a bigger brain than we but approaches us in its ratio of brain to body. That this is no error of observation is shown by the stupid-looking walrus, which is half again as heavy as a cow but has a brain three times as heavy; and by the seals, whose brains equal those of land carnivores five to ten times as heavy. The cause, or need, of this sea-mammal brain size is not clear; but it may explain the popularity of the seal in circuses. Tame animals generally have smaller brains, or at least larger bodies without increased brains, than their wild ancestors. Compare the Cape buffalo with cattle, the quagga with our horses.

The lightness of the gibbon's brain shown by the table is surprising; it is barely bigger than the brains of subanthropoid monkeys weighing only half as much. And the supposedly primitive platyrrhine American monkeys like the *Cebus,* spiders, and howlers match evolutionistically higher Old World catarrhines like the rhesus rather closely in mass and in ratio. This accords with the judgment of some observers as to their intelligence (§ 22).

Even as compared with our closest relatives, chimpanzee and gorilla, the human disproportion is glaring. The full-grown chimpanzee weighs about seven-tenths as much as a man, his brain around three-tenths as much. An adult male gorilla weighs a good 200 per cent *more* than a man, his brain at its maximum record is well over 50 per cent *less,* to judge by volume of the skull case (§ 26). Then too, we have already seen (§ 31) that the human brain differs from the ape brain rather little in its structure—at any rate in its gross structure, which is basically quite homologous. But as soon as we turn to mass, the difference of three to one is more than perceptible: it is striking.

has attained three-fourths of the total around the age of two and a half or three years. Thus the development of most of the brain mass, and its most rapid rate of growth, occur in the period of least intellectual functioning.

BRAIN AND BODY WEIGHTS OF MAMMALS

	Brain (Kilograms)	Body (Kilograms)	Body-brain Ratio, approx
Mammals			
Blue whale	6.8	58,000.	8,500
Humpback whale	5.78	35,000.	6,000
Finback whale	5.36	38,000.	7,000
Elephant, African	5.7	6,650.	1,170
Elephant	4.7	3,000.	640
Elephant	4.	2,000. *	500 *
White whale (6, ♂, ♀)	2.35	400.	170
Porpoise	1.73	140.	80
Man—see also below	1.32	62.	47
Walrus	1.13	670.	600
Dromedary, domestic	.76	400. *	530 *
Hippopotamus	.72	1,350.	1,900
Hippopotamus	.58	1,750.	3,000
Giraffe	.70	1,220.	1,750
Giraffe	.68	530. *	750 *
Horse, maximum (5♂)	.71	480.	700
Cape buffalo (2♂)	.67	650.	1,000
Quagga zebra (3♂)	.58	275.	480
Horse, domestic	.53	370.	700
Polar bear (2)	.50	260.	520
Cattle (200 Holstein cows)	.42	570.	1,400
Cattle (213 Jersey bulls)	.41	410.	1,000
Grizzly bear	.39	150.	375
Harbor seal	.27	12.6 *	50 *
Ringed seal	.25	40.	160
Tiger (2)	.26	185.	700
Lion (2)	.26	190.	700
Wild pig	.18	55.	300
Uintatherium (extinct, Eocene), estim.	.15	2,000.	13,000
Coyote	.085	8.5	100
Dog, domestic (9)	.08	13.5	170
Cat, domestic (10)	.025	3.3	130
Opossum (4, ♂, ♀; marsupial)	.0048	1.15	240
Norway rat	.0024	.45	200
Mole (insectivore)	.0012	.04	35
Mouse	.0004	.02	50
Shrew (68, ♂, ♀; insectivore)	.00035	.017	50
Primates			
Man (41, ♂, ♀)	1.32	62.	47
Chimpanzee (♂)	.44	57.	130
Chimpanzee (♀)	.33	44.	135
Orang (10♂)	.37	73.	200
Orang (11♀)	.30	36.	120
Black spider monkey (17♂, ♀; platyrrhine)	.115	9.1	80
Red spider monkey (63♂, ♀; platyrrhine)	.11	7.6	70
Gibbon (9♂; anthropoid)	.09	6.	70
Rhesus macaque (11♂, ♀; catarrhine)	.09	3.5	40
Cebus capuchin (14♂, ♀; platyrrhine)	.07	3.1	45
Black howler (28♂, ♀; platyrrhine)	.05	6.2	125
Brown howler (6♂, ♀; platyrrhine)	.04	3.2	75
Marmoset (16♂, ♀; platyrrhine)	.022	.85	40

* Probably not fully grown. This would presumably not affect very much the absolute brain weight, but it would certainly lower the body-brain weight ratio.

What we have, then, by and large, that is outstandingly unique about the ..uman brain is two things. One is its exceptional weight—exceptional among both our near kin and our more remote size mates. The other is its functional ability to symbolize and abstract and transmit. It would be hard to believe that these two unique features are not somehow related. Not that one can infer in the absolute from quantity to quality: the case of the cat and the tiger show that. Nor is it at all sure that the human bearer of a brain of 1700 cc is necessarily more intelligent than one with 1300 cc. Yet the brain mass of man compared with that of our nearest and same-sized relatives, and the symbolizing or thinking faculty of man, are both so extraordinarily singular that their co-ocurrence must indicate some sort of connection, however indirect and unexplained as to mechanism. What may chiefly be involved is an increase in the number of possible interconnections of neuron cells, greater even than the increase in number of cells which follows the increase in mass. This would be on the principle of a bigger switchboard meaning a more complex one also; or of a series of numbers going up, but the frequency of their possible combinations going up faster still. This comparison must not be taken as a proven explanation, but it suggests in contour what may have happened in early human evolution. Whatever the detail of brain structure that underlies the kind of psychosomatic functioning that makes human culture possible, it is almost certain to be associated with that unique multiplication of brain mass which characterizes *Homo sapiens*. Even in our remote fossil precursors Sinanthropus and Pithecanthropus (§ 37-38), who were only rudimentarily culturalized, the brain bulk is already fully double that of the ape average.

34. SPECIALIZATIONS ASSOCIATED WITH SELF-DOMESTICATION

Man has been said to be a domesticated animal, which is of course in one sense an absurdity, because there is no domesticator. But man may without objection be called self-domesticated in that, while he is not kept or bred or used by another species, he does live under conditions of shelter, of normally stable food supply, and of absence of rigorous natural selection, much like the domesticated animals. The mechanism is different, but some of the results are the same. This point is discussed further in a subsequent chapter (§ 73); but it will be of interest to list here those anatomical peculiarities associated with our "self-domestication." They comprise: probably, the long hair on our heads, which has no exact parallel among mammals; the near-hairlessness of most of our bodies, which is atypical except for very thick-hided, or armored, or wholly aquatic mammals such as elephants, armadillos, and whales; curly and woolly hair; the partial albinism that in man we call fair skin, blond hair, and blue eyes; and perhaps jaw reduction, brachycephalization (§ 60), steatopygia (§ 64), and lip eversion.

It is evident that most of these specializations associated with self-domestication are related to appearance rather than to the viability or the success of the species. They have no positive survival value in themselves. In fact they seem to be either indifferent or sometimes even on the negative side as regards survival. But they might be described as having aesthetic significance, so far as such a term is applicable in biology—as in connection perhaps with the effects of sexual selection, or with the "elegance" of form mentioned by palaeontologists as sometimes attained by mature lines of evolution.

35. GENERALIZED HUMAN TRAITS

In summary, then, apart from the rather superficial features connected with self-domestication, the specializations of man are essentially those connected with his brain and his erectness. He lacks all the various specializations that come to mind when we think of elephant, seal, whale, bat, anteater, sloth, armadillo, cat, beaver, porcupine, deer, giraffe, or kangaroo. He has kept all four of his original limbs, and each of them retains its full five digits, just as these are tipped with nails and neither hoofs nor claws. He has kept the basic mammalian dentition well preserved in differentiation of kind and only slightly reduced in number. He is quite extraordinarily able to thrive on any one of a variety of different diets. In fact he may well be classed with the bears and the pigs as omnivorous. He is only moderately swift in any one mode of locomotion, but can make tolerable shift at a greater number of modes than most mammals or submammalian forms: running, jumping, climbing, burrowing, swimming. And his distribution is one of the widest of all mammals, partly, it is true, because he can to some extent control his environment through fire and housing, but evidently in some measure preculturally also, especially as compared with the other primates.

In short, where man is significantly specialized, he tends also to be uniquely specialized. The rest of him appears to be rather unusually well generalized, in function as well as in structure. And generalization is normally a precondition for further development in organic evolution.

Living Races

A RACE is a valid biological concept. It is a group united by heredity: a breed or genetic strain or subspecies. It is not a valid sociocultural concept; the term "race" is usually ambiguous and is best not used in sociocultural situations, as we shall see more fully in § 80. But physical anthropology (§ 3), being concerned with man's organic features, is properly and necessarily concerned with the human races.

58. RACE ORIGINS

Almost everyone sooner or later becomes interested in the problem of the origin of the human races and the history of their development. We see mankind divided into a number of varieties that differ strikingly in appearance. If these varieties are modifications of a single ancestral form, what caused them to alter, and what has been the history of the change?

In the present state of science, we cannot wholly answer these important questions. We know very little about the causes that change human types, and we possess only incomplete information as to the history of races. Stray bits of evidence here and there are too scattered to afford many helpful clues. The very earliest men, as we know them from fossils, are too far removed from any of the living varieties, are too primitive, to link very definitely with the existing races, which can all be regarded as intergrading varieties of a single species,

Homo sapiens. In the latter part of the Old Stone Age, in the Aurignacian period, at a time perhaps twenty-five to eighteen thousand years ago, we commence to encounter remains of Cro-Magnon man (§ 49) which foreshadow the modern races and are believed to have entered into the composition of several European populations of today.[1] We can conclude that the races of man as they are spread over the earth today must have been at least some tens'of thousands of years in forming. What caused them to differentiate, on which part of the earth's surface each took on its peculiarities, how they further subdivided, what were the connecting links between them, how the differentiating races may have reblended—on all these points the answer is as yet incomplete.

It is no different in other fields of biology. As long as the zoologist or the botanist reviews his grand classifications or the wide sweep of organic evolution for 50 million or 500 million years back, he seems to obtain striking and simple results. When he turns his attention to a small group, attempting to trace in detail its subvarieties, and the precise relations and history of these, the task is seen to be intricate and the accumulated knowledge is usually insufficient to solve more than a fraction of the problems that arise.

There is, then, nothing unusual in the situation of partial bafflement in which anthropology still finds itself about the human races.

59. RACE CLASSIFICATION

What remains is the possibility of making an accurate survey of the living races in the hope that the relationships a classification brings out may indicate something as to the former development of the races. If for instance it could be established that the Ainu or aborigines of Japan are closely similar in their bodies to the peoples of Europe, we would then infer that they are a branch of the Caucasian stock, that their origin presumably took place to the west of their present habitat, and that they have no connection with the Mongolian Japanese among whom they now live. This is working by indirect evidence, it is true; but sooner or later that is the method to which science always finds itself reduced.

---

[1] Decades ago it began to be asserted that the Cro-Magnon strain still persisted in south-central France, as by Ripley, following French authorities; then also for the modern population of Dalarne in Sweden, for Westphalia in Germany, and so on. Among the European racial types, Coon in 1939 recognized four as partially Palaeolithic in origin: (1), the Brünn type, or Tronder, "in solution" among Scandinavian and British populations; (2), Borreby, "the unreduced brachycephalic strain in Cro-Magnon," a major population element in northern and central Germany; (3), Alpine, a "reduced foetalized" and brachycephalized survivor of the Upper Palaeolithic population of France; (4), Ladogan, containing an east-European Upper Palaeolithic element. These particular derivations, and even some of the types themselves, rest on somewhat speculative opinion; but they illustrate how freely, and without challenge in principle, anthropologists have come to connect modern with late-Palaeolithic Europeans, and thus by implication to admit these as already Caucasian.

The desirability of a trustworthy classification of the human races will therefore be generally accepted without further argument. But the making of such a classification proves to be more difficult than might be imagined. To begin with, a race is only a sort of average of a large number of individuals; and averages differ from one another much less than individuals. Popular impression exaggerates the differences, accurate measurements reduce them. It is true that a Negro and a northern European cannot possibly be confused: they happen to represent extreme types. Yet as soon as we operate with less divergent races we find that variations between individuals of the same race are often greater than differences between the races. The tallest individuals of a short race are taller than the shortest individuals of a tall race. This is called *overlapping;* and it occurs to such an extent as to make it frequently difficult for the physical anthropologist to establish clear-cut types.

In addition, the lines of demarcation between races have time and again been obliterated by interbreeding. Adjacent peoples, even hostile ones, intermarry. The number of such marriages in one generation may be small; but the cumulative effect of a thousand years is often quite disconcerting. Also, the half-breeds or hybrids are as fertile as each of the original types. There is no question but that some populations are nothing but the product of such race crossing. Thus there is a belt extending across most of Africa, and quite wide in East Africa, of which it is difficult to say whether the inhabitants belong more to the Negro or to the Caucasian type. If we construct a racial map and represent the demarcation between Negro and Caucasian by a line, we are really misrepresenting the situation. The truth could be expressed only by inserting a transition zone of mixed color. Yet as soon as we allow such transitions, the definiteness of our classification begins to crumble.

In spite of these difficulties, some general truths can be discovered from a careful race classification and certain constant principles of importance emerge from all the diversity.

60. TRAITS ON WHICH CLASSIFICATION RESTS

Since every human being obviously possesses a large number of physical features or traits, the first thing that the prospective classifier of race must do is to determine how much weight he will attach to each of these features.

The most striking of all traits probably is *stature* or bodily height. Yet this is a trait which experience has shown to be of relatively limited value for classificatory purposes. The imagination is easily impressed by a few inches when they show at the top of a man and make him half a head taller or shorter than oneself. Except for a few groups which numerically are insignificant, there is no human race that averages less than 4 feet 11 inches (150 cm) in height for men. There is none that averages taller than 5 feet 10 inches (178 cm). This means that practically the whole range of human variability in height, from the race standpoint, falls within less than a foot. The majority of averages of populations do not differ more than 2 inches (5 cm) from the general human average of 5 feet 5 inches (165 cm).

Then too, stature has been proved to be rather readily influenced by environment. Each of us is a fraction of an inch taller when he gets up in the morning than when he goes to bed at night. Two races might differ by as much as a couple of inches in their heredity, and yet if all the individuals of the shorter race had been well nourished in a favorable environment, and all those of the taller group were underfed and overworked, the naturally shorter race might well be actually the taller one. All European and American populations for which there are measurements going back from one to three generations, and the Japanese also, have gained from about 2 to 5 cm (1 to 2 inches) or more in height. This is undoubtedly due to the acceleratory rise in the standard of living in Western civilization during the past century. For the same reason the economically better-off classes at any one moment regularly average taller than the poorer classes. Of course there is no reason to believe that this gain will continue indefinitely.

The *cephalic index* expresses in percentage form the ratio of the length and the breadth of the head—both measured with hinged calipers, basically as the diameters of logs are measured. This is perhaps the most commonly used anthropological measure.[2] It has certain definite practical advantages. The head measurements are easily made with accuracy. The index is nearly the same on the living head and on the dead skull, or one is easily converted into the other. This makes it possible to compare present and past generations. The index is also nearly the same for men and for women, for children and for adults. Finally, it seems to be little affected by environment—at least, not in one consistent direction.[3] The consequence is that head form has been widely investigated. There are few groups of people of consequence whose average cephalic index we do not know fairly accurately. The difficulty about the cephalic index

[2] The usual nomenclature for cephalic index is on the basis of rounded numbers: broadheaded or roundheaded, or brachycephalic, above 80; medium-headed, or mesocephalic, between 75 and 80; narrow-headed or longheaded, or dolichocephalic, below 75. Yet, as the average for mankind is in the neighborhood of 79, this terminology makes far more brachycephalic than dolichocephalic peoples. Groups frequently spoken of as longheaded are often really mesocephalic by the accepted definition: a large proportion of Europeans, for instance. It would result in both more accuracy and a better balancing of the limits if the three types of head form were set, as has been suggested, at 81 and 77 in place of 80 and 75. The index of the skull (strictly, the *cranial index*) is two units less than that taken on the living head. In this book, terms like "dolichocephalic" are used *relatively* throughout; that is, as meaning long as compared with others or with the average; not as indicating a specific and technical percentage range.

[3] See § 75. However, the head is easily deformed in infancy by bandages, pads, and cradle pressures, and some peoples have practiced such deformation deliberately. The change of shape does not reduce the size of the brain or harm the child or seem to diminish intelligence, but it may distort the hereditary head form completely.

from the point of view of race classification is that it does not yield broad enough results. It is often useful in distinguishing subtypes, nation from nation, or tribe from tribe; but it is not uniform for the primary races. There is, for instance, no typical head form for the Caucasian race. There are narrow-headed, medium-headed, and broad-headed Caucasians. The same is true of the American Indians, who are on the whole a rather uniform major race, yet vary much in head form.

A tendency toward progressive brachycephalization has often been observed, both in geologic and in historical time, but is unexplained. Virtually all Pleistocene skulls, except at the very end of the period, are narrow. In America, wherever there is an older and a more recent aboriginal type in the same area, the older is regularly the narrower. For Europe the fact has been established repeatedly. Thus, the percentage of the population that is brachycranial—index of 80 and up in the skull, 82 and up in the living—is:

MODERN INCREASE OF FREQUENCY OF ROUNDHEADS

Sweden: modern, 13%; Iron and Middle ages, 3% to 7%
Denmark: modern, 33%; Iron Age, 2%
Bavaria: modern, 83%; Late Mediaeval, 50%; Early Mediaeval, 32%; period of Migrations, 14%
Slavs: modern, 85%; 6th to 12th century, 9%
Greeks: modern, 54%; Classic, 10%
Crete: modern, 38%; Minoan, 9%

The *nasal index,* which expresses the percentage relation of breadth and length of nose, runs much more constant in the great races. Practically all Negroids are broad-nosed, practically all Caucasians narrow-nosed, and the majority of peoples of Mongolian affinities medium-nosed. But the nasal index varies according to the age of the person; it is utterly different in a living individual and a skull; [4] it seems to reflect heredity with more variability than the cephalic index; and finally it tells us nothing about the elevation or profile or general formation of the nose, which is generally observed descriptively.

Prognathism, or the degree of the protrusion of the jaws, is a conspicuous feature of the profile, and would seem to be of some historical importance as a sign of primitiveness, because all other mammals are more prognathous than man. The trait also has a general correlation with the fundamental racial types. Negroes are almost all prognathous, people of Mongolian type moderately so, most Caucasians very slightly. Prognathism is however difficult to measure or to denote in figures. Various apparatuses have been devised without wholly satisfactory results.

[4] On the living, broad or platyrrhine noses have an index of breadth compared with length above 85; medium or mesorrhine, between 70 and 85; narrow or leptorrhine, below 70. Skeletally, the same three terms denote proportions above 53, between 48 and 53, and below 48.

The *capacity of the skull* was measured formerly by filling it with shot; now generally with millet or mustard seed, or with water in a highly elastic rubber bag. Shot measurements run about 80 cc the higher. By seed measure, the average for European males is about 1450 cc; for females about 10 per cent lower, or 1300. East Asiatic Mongoloids are about the same, as are the large-bodied Polynesians. Negroes seem to have somewhat less capacity, though the few series available run somewhat variably. Australoids are definitely small, around 1300. Bushmen, Negritos, Veddas, all small-bodied, are also small-brained. It appears that cranial capacity is considerably dependent on bodily size. Slender as well as short races run to small capacities. The heavy Bantu surpass the slighter-framed Sudanese, and Hindus stand well below European Caucasians, just as the shorter Japanese seem to average less than the Chinese. Broad-headed populations show greater cranial capacity than narrow-headed ones: Alpine Europeans (§ 62) generally surpass Nordics in spite of their shorter stature.[5] Individual variability is also unusually great in this measurement. The largest-skulled and the smallest-skulled healthy individuals of the same sex in one population differ sometimes by 500, 600, or 700 cc, or more than one-third of the racial average. Overlapping between races is accordingly particularly marked in cranial capacity. Furthermore, the measurement obviously cannot be taken on the living, except by computation estimates based on diameters, such as have been used also for fragmentary fossil skulls. In spite of its interest as an evolutionary development in the past, especially the more remote ancestry of man (§ 57), cranial capacity is thus of restricted value in distinguishing races.

The *texture of the hair* is now universally regarded as one of the most valuable criteria for classifying races, possibly the most significant of all. Hair is distinguished as woolly in the Negro, straight in the Mongolian, and wavy or intermediate in the Caucasian. This texture depends principally on the diameters of each individual hair as they are revealed in cross section under the microscope; in part also on the degree of straightness or curvature of the root sacs of the hair in the skin. Hair texture seems to run rather rigidly along hereditary racial lines, and to be uninfluenced by factors of age, sex, climate, or nourishment.

Hairiness of the body as a whole is another trait to which more and more attention is coming to be paid. The fullness or scantiness of the beard, and the degree of development of the down which covers the body, are its most conspicuous manifestations. Caucasians are definitely a hairy race, Mongoloids and most Negroids glabrous or smooth-skinned. It is largely on the basis of their hairiness and hair texture that races like the Australoids have been separated from the Negroids, and the Ainus from the Japanese. Strangely enough, baldness occurs most frequently in association with heavy beards and body hair—in line with which fact women are rarely bald.

[5] There is a physicomathematical reason: With a given surface, the contained volume is greater for a sphere than for an elongated shape.

Except possibly for stature, *color* is probably the most conspicuous trait of any race. Under color must be included the complexion of the skin, the color of the hair, and the color of the eyes. All of these are due to varying amounts of the same pigment: melanin.[6] All of them present difficulties to the anthropometrist. There is a complete series of transition shades, and it is difficult to express these differences of shade quantitatively. They readily impress the eye, but it is far from easy to denote them accurately in numbers. Environment also affects skin color markedly. A day's exposure to the sun may darken an individual's complexion by several shades. In spite of these drawbacks, however, complexion remains sufficiently important to warrant consideration in every classification.

Hair color and eye color are practically immune against direct change by environment. They unquestionably are excellent hereditary criteria, although they offer much the same resistance to measurement as does complexion. The utility of these two traits is moreover limited by another factor: their narrow distribution. Blue eyes and blond hair are racially characteristic of only a single major subrace, that of northern Europe. In central Europe they are already much toned down: the prevailing type here is brunet. In southern Europe, blue eyes and blondness rarely occur except where admixture with northern peoples can be traced. Outside of the Caucasian stock, virtually black hair and black eyes are the universal rule for the human family.

Special race traits occur, besides blue eyes and blondness. The Mongolian "slant," "slit," or "oblique" eye is due to an overdeveloped *epicanthic fold* of the eyelid, especially at the inner corner of the eye, partially covering the lash-bearing edge of the lid. It is associated with prominent cheekbones, a flat nose, a smooth forehead. It is found occasionally outside of East Asia, but becomes sporadic as soon as Oceania and America are entered, whereas it is fairly marked among the Bushmen of South Africa. The *Mongolian spot* of bluish pigment in the skin of the lumbar region, gradually fading after birth, was first observed in East Asia, and is probably most frequent there, but occurs also in other races. *Steatopygia,* a heavy deposit of fat in the buttocks, is characteristic of Bushmen and Hottentot women. It serves to accentuate the hollow back and projecting rump which characterize their men as well as themselves. *Supraorbital ridges,* a development of the lower part of the frontal bone of the skull, are marked in all Protoanthropic and almost all Palaeoanthropic fossil types, and are therefore usually regarded as a primitive trait. Among living races, supraorbital ridges are probably most marked among Australoids. They occur also among Veddoids, northern Europeans, and most North American Indians. They are little developed in most African Negroes, and perhaps least of all in East Asiatic Mongoloids. These ridges are perhaps even more a masculine than a "primitive"

[6] Except for red-hairedness, which seems due to a separate hereditary factor and pigment. Red hair is most conspicuous with marked blondness, and perhaps is often present otherwise but "smothered" by abundance of melanin.

characteristic; in races in which they occur, their ruggedness and that of the mastoids are used to determine the sex of unidentified skulls. *Baldness,* and its association with hairiness of face and body, have already been mentioned. How far its highest frequency among Caucasians is wholly a congenital race trait or may be added to by environmental factors in their mode of life is not clear. *Shovel-shaped incisor teeth,* concave on the side facing the tongue, are characteristic of Mongoloids, both American and Asiatic.

61. THE GRAND DIVISIONS OR PRIMARY STOCKS

Obviously it would be easiest to arrive at a clear-cut classification by grouping all the peoples of the earth according to a single trait, such as the shape of the nose, or color. But any such classification must be artificial and largely unsound, just because it disregards the majority of traits. The only classification that can claim to rest upon a true or natural basis is one that takes into consideration as many traits as possible, and which weights the important more heavily than the unimportant features. If the outcome of such a grouping leaves some peoples intermediate or of doubtful place in the classification, this result is unfortunate but must be accepted. If we follow this plan and review the peoples of the earth, each with reference to all its traits, we obtain an arrangement something like that given in the table on the following page, and whose geography is roughly mapped in Figures 6 and 7.

This classification is summary in that it operates with the smallest number of classes possible, while attempting at the same time to account for every human group and leave no blanks on the map of the globe. Technically, it is impossible to do this and still remain wholly authentic and accurate; the classification is admittedly simpler than the complex and sometimes conflicting facts warrant. But it is in the interest of clarity to begin with this slightly oversimplified scheme, which is believed to be pretty close to the consensus of almost all anthropological opinion, and to follow this, in § 67-71, with qualifications, refinements, and contrary views.

On the basic view, there are three grand divisions, of which the European, the Negro, and the Chinese type may be taken as representative. These three primary classes are generally called Caucasian, Caucasoid, or Europoid; Negroid; and Mongoloid.[7] The color terms "White," "Black," and "Yellow" are also often used, but it is necessary to remember that they are employed merely as brief convenient labels, and that they have no real descriptive value. There are millions of essential Caucasians—Hindus—who are darker in complexion than millions of Mongoloids—Chinese.

These three main groups account for more than nine-tenths of all the nations and tribes of the world. As to the number of individuals, they comprise

[7] The suffix *-oid* or *-id* means "like."

OUTLINE RACIAL CLASSIFICATION OF MANKIND

Primary Stocks and Races	Texture of Hair of Head	Hair of Body and Face	Head	Nose	Prognathism	Skin Color	Stature	Remarks
CAUCASIAN OR "WHITE"								
Nordic	Wavy	Abundant	Narrow	Narrow	Slight	Very fair	Tall	Often blond, eyes light
Alpine	"	"	Broad	"	"	Fair	Above aver.	Hair brown, eyes brown
Mediterranean	"	"	Narrow	"	"	Dark white	Medium	"Regular features," graceful
Hindu	"	"	"	Variable	Moderate	Brown	Above aver.	Dark admixture espec. in S.
MONGOLOID OR "YELLOW"								
Mongolian	Straight	Slight	Broad	Medium	Medium	Light brown	Below aver.	Broad face, Mongolian eye
Malaysian	"	"	"	"	"	Brown	"	
American Indian	"	"	Variable	"	"	"	Tall to medium	Broad face
NEGROID OR "BLACK"								
Negro	Woolly	Slight	Narrow	Broad	Strong	Dark brown	Tall	Everted lips
Melanesian	"	"	Broadish	"	"	"	Medium	Some aquiline noses
Pygmy Black	"	"	Narrow	"	"	"	Very short	
Bushman	Peppercorn	"	"	"	Slight	Yellowish	"	Wrinkles, steatopygy, thin lips, Mongolian eye
OF DOUBTFUL CLASSIFICATION								
Australoid	Wavy	Abundant	Narrow	Broad	Strong	Dark brown	Medium	Negroid traits preponderate, some Caucasian resembl.
Veddoid (Indo-Austral.)	"	Moderate	"	"	Medium	Brown	Short	Generalized proto-Caucasian, some Australoid resembl.
Polynesian	"	"	Variable	Medium	"	"	Tall	Mongoloid and Caucas. traits, with local Negroid admixture
Ainu	"	Abundant	Narrow	"	"	Light brown	Medium	Prob. generalized Caucasian

Hair and eyes are "black" unless otherwise stated.

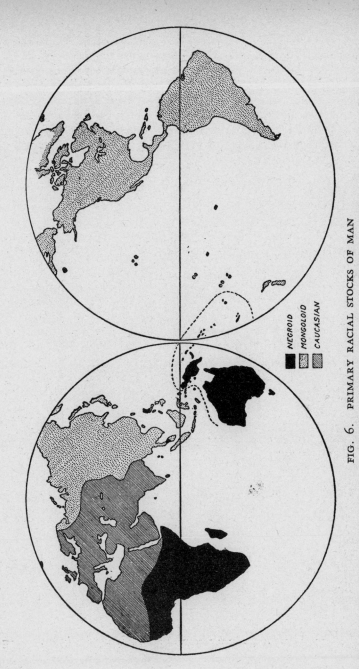

FIG. 6. PRIMARY RACIAL STOCKS OF MAN

Outline distribution of the primary racial stocks of mankind according to the threefold classification. Australians, Ainu, Veddoids, Polynesians, etc., are included in the stock with which they appear to affiliate most closely. A larger map with more shadings would be required to do even approximate justice to the intricacies of a complete race classification.

probably 99 per cent of all human beings. The remaining minor, aberrant forms are best kept separate, provisionally. Some of them, like the before-mentioned Ainu and Australoids, appear to affiliate preponderantly with one of the three great classes, but still differ sufficiently in one or more particulars to prevent their being included with them outright. Other groups, such as the Polynesians, seem to be, at least in part, the result of a mixture of races. Their constituent elements are so blended, and perhaps so far modified after the blending, as to be difficult to disentangle.

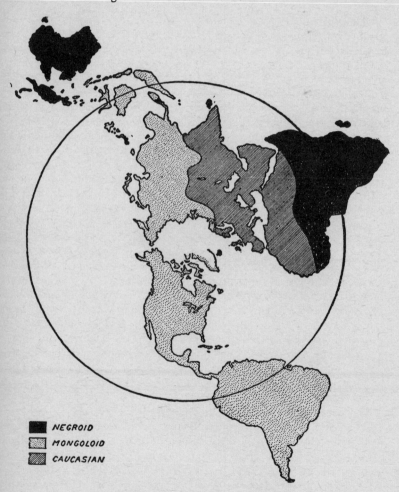

FIG. 7.   CIRCUMPOLAR DISTRIBUTION: PRIMARY RACES

Each of the three great primary stocks falls into several natural subdivisions. The distribution of these will now be described as it existed before the era of exploration and colonization that began toward the end of the fifteenth century. Although for practical purposes they have been submerged by Caucasians in large parts of the Americas, Australia, and South Africa, it is the native races whose distribution is referred to here.

62. CAUCASIAN RACES

Three of the four major Caucasian races originally lived, in whole or in part, in Europe; the fourth consists of the Hindus. The three European races are the Nordic, the Alpine, and the Mediterranean. More can be recognized, and most authorities insist on a greater number, some of which will be discussed in § 68 to 71, but all admit at least these three. They occupy horizontal belts on the map. Beginning with the Nordic and ending with the Mediterranean, they may be described as successively darker-skinned, darker-eyed, darker-haired, and shorter in stature. The Alpine race, which lies between the two others, is however more than a mere transition; for it is broad-headed, whereas the Nordic and Mediterranean are both relatively narrow-headed.[8] The Nordic type is essentially distributed around the Baltic and North seas. The Mediterranean race occupies the shores of the Mediterranean Sea, in Asia and Africa as well as in Europe. In ancient times it seems to have prevailed everywhere along these coasts. At present the Balkan Peninsula and Asia Minor are mostly occupied by broad-headed peoples of more or less close affinity to the Alpines. This Alpine race is perhaps less homogeneous than the two others. A central Frenchman, a Serb, a southern Russian, and an Armenian are clearly far from identical. In some respects, however, they have enough in common to warrant their being put into the one larger group.

It must be clearly understood that these races have nothing to do with the modern political nationalities of Europe. Northern Germany is prevailingly Nordic, southern Germany, Alpine. Northern Italy is Alpine, the rest of the peninsula Mediterranean. All three races are definitely represented in France. The average northern Frenchman stands racially nearer to the northern German than to his countryman from central France, whereas the latter links up in physical type with the southern German. Nationality is determined by speech, customs, religion, and political affiliations. Its boundary lines and those of race cut right across one another.

The British Isles did not escape the process of race-blending that has gone on in Europe for thousands of years. The bulk of the blood of their inhabitants

---

[8] The narrowness or length of head of the Nordics has been greatly exaggerated in popular repute. They are not nearly as dolichocephalic as Melanesians, most Hindus, many African Negroes, the Eskimo, and so on. In fact, the average of no Nordic European nationality succeeds in falling within the technical limits of dolichocephaly—below 75.

during the past thousand years or longer has been Nordic, but there is a definite "Iberian"—that is, Mediterranean—strain. The first settlers in America carried this mixture across the Atlantic, and through the years immigration has increased its compositeness. Scandinavians and northern Germans have added to the Nordic component in the population of the United States; southern Germans, former Austro-Hungarians, and Russians have added to the Alpine component; and the Italians have injected a definite Mediterranean element. The Negro alone has not been fully admitted into the make-up of our white society; but the reverse holds: a considerable percentage of the "colored" people in the United States are from one-sixteenth to fifteen-sixteenths Caucasian.

The foregoing tripartite classification was chiefly codified in Ripley's famous *Races of Europe* in 1899, a work that has been superseded by elaboration rather than rejection, as is set forth in § 68.

The Hindu is in the main a narrow-headed, dark-skinned Caucasian, not very different from the Mediterranean. He constitutes the easternmost block of Caucasians and may therefore be presumed at one time to have entered India from the northwest. There he seems to have encountered an aboriginal population that may have been Negroid but is more often thought to have been Australoid or perhaps to have constituted a dark proto-Caucasian or "Indo-Australoid" race. A fairly thorough intermixture has taken place in India during the last several thousand years, with the result that the original Caucasian type of the Hindu has been somewhat modified, while most of the less numerous or less vigorous aboriginal population has been submerged or assimilated. On the whole, the definite Caucasian type, with somewhat narrower noses and lighter complexions, is best preserved in the northwest; traces of the dark-skinned aboriginal race are strongest in southern and eastern India.

Attempts have been made, by citing measurements, to prove the Brahmans and other high castes of India as being Caucasian in their physical type, and the low castes as dark-skinned and aboriginal in race. There is some indubitable correlation to this effect. But it is even more remarkable how small the correlation is; with a limited amount of biased selection or weighting of data, one could make it disappear. The theory is therefore at least partly of the wish-fulfillment order. Hindu castes have not kept themselves as pure as they like to believe; and the racial differentiation within India seems on the whole to be geographical, national, or tribal rather than along the lines of social status.

63. MONGOLOID RACES

The Mongoloid stock divides into the Mongolian proper of East Asia, the Malaysian of the East Indies, and the American Indian. The differences among these three types are not very great. The Mongolian proper is the most extreme or pronounced form. It was probably the latest to develop its present characteristics. For instance, the oblique or "Mongolian" eye is a peculiarity restricted chiefly to the people of East Asia. The original Mongoloid stock must be looked upon as having been more like present-day Malaysians or American Indians, or intermediate between them. From this generalized type peoples like the Chinese gradually diverged, adding the epicanthic fold of the oblique eye and a certain generic refinement of physique, while the less civilized peoples of America and Oceania kept more nearly to the ancient type.

Within the East Indies, and especially in the Philippines, a less specifically Mongoloid and a more specifically Mongoloid strain can at times be distinguished, which have been called Proto-Malaysian and Deutero-Malaysian. In certain respects, such as relatively short stature and broad nose, the former somewhat approaches the Indo-Australoid type described below. Among the American Mongoloids, the Eskimo appear to be the most particularized subvariety, according to almost all anthropometrists.

64. NEGROID RACES

The Negroid stock falls into two large divisions, the African Negro proper and the Oceanic Papuo-Melanesian. There is in addition a third division, the Dwarf Blacks or Negritos, who are very few in numbers but possess a wide and irregular distribution. The Negroes and the Melanesians, in spite of their being separated by the breadth of the Indian Ocean, are clearly close relatives. A trained observer can distinguish them at sight, but a novice would take a Papuan from New Guinea or a Melanesian from the Solomon or Bismarck islands to be an African. Perhaps the most conspicuous difference is that the broad nose of the African Negro is flat, the broad nose of the Melanesian often aquiline. The latter also has thinner lips, on the whole, and is shorter. The Melanesians probably contain some absorption of alien blood. Their Malayo-Polynesian speech also points to this. How these two Negroid branches came to be located on the opposite sides of a great ocean is a fact that remains unexplained.

The Negrito or Pygmy Negroid race has highly localized representatives in the Philippines, the Malay Peninsula, the Andaman Islands, probably in New Guinea, and in equatorial Africa. These peoples are the true pygmies of the human species. Wherever they are racially pure the adult males are less than 5 feet in stature; in fact, 150 cm, or 4 feet 11 inches, for adult males is usually set as the upper average limit of true Negrito populations; some say 148 cm. Negritos also differ from other Negroids in being relatively broad-headed. Their skin color, hair texture, nose form, and most other traits are, however, the same as those of the other Negroids. They are in no sense malformed, but a well-proportioned small people. Their scattered distribution on two sides of the Indian Ocean is difficult to account for. It is possible that they are an ancient and primitive type which once inhabited much wider stretches of territory in Africa, Asia, and Oceania than it inhabits now. On account of their unaggressiveness and backwardness, the Negritos, according to this theory, were gradually crowded to the wall by the larger, more energetic populations with which they came in contact, until only a few scattered fragments of them now remain.

Another view is that they represent a stunting of stature, or series of genetic aberrations of unknown cause, from full-size Negroids. They are all forest-dwelling hunters without settled habitations. Whether this environment and mode of life might repeatedly produce a selection toward shortness is somewhat speculative. Their broadish short heads might well be a function of their short stature—head length decreasing as part of body length.

The Bushmen and in some degree the Hottentots of South Africa may also be provisionally included with the Negritos, or related to them, although distinctive in a number of respects. They are yellowish-brown in complexion, wrinkled, longheaded, short and flat eared, very broad and flat nosed, short armed and legged, hollow-backed, and steatopygous. On the whole, Negroid characteristics prevail among them. They are, for instance, frizzy, with the head hair coiling in tight "peppercorn" tufts. In spite of this, some observers have recognized Caucasoid or Mongoloid features in them. Thus they are non-prognathous and thin-lipped, and a fair proportion of them show some degree of epicanthic eye fold. They are a very specialized race, but the extremely short stature of the Bushmen may justify their tentative grouping with the Negritos.

65. POPULATIONS OF DOUBTFUL POSITION

One thing is common to the peoples who are here reckoned as of doubtful position in the classification: They all present certain Caucasian affinities without being similar enough to the recognized Caucasians to be included with them. This is true of the black, wavy-haired, prognathous, beetle-browed Australians, whose first appearance suggests that they are Negroids, as it is of the brown Polynesians, who appear to have primary Mongoloid connections through the Malaysians.

The native *Australians* are black-skinned, very broad-nosed, long-legged, narrow-headed, prognathous, but their hirsuteness, full beards, and wavy head hair take them out of the pure Negroid sphere. Their heavy eyebrow ridges—in the bone—are only one of a series of features that lead most observers to reckon them as, on the whole, the most primitive living race. This was a numerically limited race. In spite of having a continent to themselves until recently, they seem never to have comprised more than a couple of hundred thousand souls, and are now diminished far below that.

In India, Farther India, and the East Indies live a scattered series of uncivilized *Veddoid* peoples more or less alike in being dark, short, slender, wavy-haired, longish-headed, broad-nosed. The brows are knit, the eyes deep-set, the mouth large, the jaws peaked, the beard development medium. Resemblances are on the one hand toward the Caucasian type, on the other toward the Australian, just as the geographical position is intermediate. The alternative name "Indo-Australoid" is thus appropriate for this group; although "Veddoid" has come into most general use. Typical representatives are the Vedda of interior Ceylon, whence the usual name of the race; some of the backward Dravidian and Munda tribes of India; the Nicobar Islanders; certain of the Moi of Indo-China; the Senoi or Sakai of the Malay Peninsula; the Toala of Celebes. Some also find a Veddoid strain prominent in southeastern Arabia. The Veddoids are almost invariably culturally retarded hill or jungle people who evidently represent an old stratum of population pushed back by Caucasians or Mongoloids, or almost absorbed by them. The dark strain in India seems more probably due to these people than to a true Negroid infusion. Possibly the Indo-Australoids branched off from the Caucasian stem at a very early time before the Caucasian stock was as "white" as it is now. In the lapse of ages the greater number of the Caucasians in and near Europe took on more and more their present characteristics, whereas this backward branch in the region of the Indian Ocean kept its primitive and undifferentiated traits. This is a tempting theory to pursue, but it extends so far into the realm of the hypothetical that its just appraisal must be left to the specialist.

The *Ainu* survive in northern Japan in much the same relation to the Japanese as the Indians occupy to the whites in the United States, except that the contact has been longer and the Ainu are fewer. They are not slant-eyed, their hair is wavy, and they favor bushy beards which give them a superficial resemblance to Russian muzhiks of the old school. Many anthropologists have accordingly reckoned them as an early Caucasoid offshoot or outpost. However, to the north of them, in easternmost Siberia, there lives a series of uncivilized peoples, sometimes grouped together as Palae-Asiatics—"Ancient Asiatics"—who, though generically Mongoloid in type, are less markedly so than the Mongols, Chinese, Japanese, and so on. For instance, their eye fold is less pronounced, and they incline to longish instead of round heads. Take this Mongoloid subtype and let it genetically develop hirsuteness and hair waviness through a mutation in the former relative isolation of the northern Japanese islands, and we have the Ainu pretty well accounted for, without bringing in the Caucasian relationship, which raises other geographic and historical problems. However, neither of the alternative views can as yet be claimed as fully demonstrable.

The *Polynesians,* living within the great island triangle Hawaii-New Zealand-Easter Island, are one of the tall, large-boned, and large-featured races of mankind. There has been much diversity of opinion as to their origin and relationship. There is almost certainly a definite Caucasoid strain in them. The Mongoloid element appears perhaps to be larger, but it is not very specialized Mongoloid. Locally, there may be minor Negroid absorptions—to reach the central Pacific the ancestral Polynesians had to pass by or through archipelagoes which now are Papuo-Melanesian Negroid. The Polynesian race problem is made more difficult by the fact that any population derived from a small number of ancestors, such as a few canoeloads of migrants, is quite likely to manifest now special features that originally were individual peculiarities. In a population sprung from many ancestors, such personal traits may also persist, but ordinarily will reappear only in a few individuals in each generation, and will not come to characterize the average or racial type. Thus the accidents of isolation selection, as well as previous mixture, have contributed to make the classification of Polynesian racial type difficult, though culturally and in speech the Polynesians are not only a well-defined but a closely knit group. Most of the more recent world-wide race classifications tend to emphasize the Caucasoid resemblances of the Polynesians.

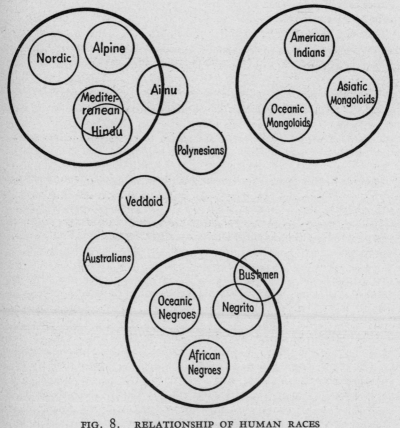

FIG. 8.   RELATIONSHIP OF HUMAN RACES

Distances between the centers of circles are representative of the degree of relationship.

Figure 8 attempts to represent graphically the degree of resemblance and of difference between the principal physical types as they have been summarized in the table and in preceding discussion.

66. CONTINENTS AND OCEANS

One fact about the classification stands out clearly; namely, that the three grand races are not limited to particular continents. It is true that the center of gravity of the Caucasians is in or near Europe, that the biggest block of Negroids is situated in Africa, and that the largest mass of Mongoloids is in Asia. It is even possible that these three types evolved on these three continents. But each of them is *intercontinental* in its recent distribution. Western Asia and northern Africa as well as Europe are Caucasian. There are Negroids in Oceania as well as in Africa, and the Mongoloids are found in Oceania, Asia, and both Americas.

In fact the distribution of the three primary races can better be described as oceanically marginal than as continental. The Caucasian parts of Europe, Asia, and Africa surround the Mediterranean Sea. The African and the Oceanic branches of the Negroid race are situated on the left and right sides of the Indian Ocean. The Mongoloid habitat in Oceania, in East Asia, and in North and South America almost encloses the Pacific Ocean (Figs. 6 and 7).

67. HISTORY OF THE CONTINENTAL AND THE THREEFOLD CLASSIFICATIONS

Most of the early classifications of mankind tried to identify races and continents too closely. The first attempt was that of Linnaeus in the middle of the eighteenth century. He distinguished and described four varieties of mankind, which he called *Europaeus albus, Asiaticus luridus, Americanus rufus,* and *Afer niger;* that is, European White, Asiatic Yellow, American Red, and African Black.

The next classification, that of Blumenbach in 1775, is essentially the same except for adding a fifth or Oceanic variety. Blumenbach's five continental races—Caucasian, Mongolian, Ethiopian, American, and Malayan—long survived in many elementary geographies, usually under the designations of White, Yellow, Black, Red, and Brown.

As time went on, the continental principle of race classification came to be recognized as inadequate, and there was a tendency among anthropologists to accept the distinctness of certain specialized groups, such as Australians, Bushmen, Eskimo, and Ainu, which were often elevated into races substantially equal in rank with the great races like the Mongoloid. Thus the early American writers Nott and Gliddon recognized seven races: European, Asiatic, Negro, American, Malay, Australian, and Arctic. This is the fivefold scheme of Blumenbach with the Australoid and the Eskimo added.

On the other hand, the feeling gained ground, especially among the French physical anthropologists of the mid-nineteenth century, that mankind could be satisfactorily, or at least essentially, accounted for by a division into Caucasian, Negroid, and Mongoloid. Those who adopted this principle tried to fit divergent types like the Australians and the Polynesians into one or the other of these three great groups. Some little doctoring had to be done in this process, and some salient facts estimated rather lightly. It is for this reason that it has seemed best here not to make our tripartite classification too exhaustive. This threefold classification clearly absorbs the great mass of mankind without straining, but it is soundest to recognize that this same basic classification requires a certain margin of extensions along the lines indicated in our table.

68. FINER SUBDIVISIONS OF THE WHITE RACE

While the basic grouping of white Europeans into Mediterraneans, Alpines, and Nordics as first fully developed by Ripley [9] is still accepted, there is also general agreement that more refined distinctions are necessary: that there are several subvarieties of Alpines, of Mediterraneans, and of Nordics. Moreover, there is reasonably close agreement as to most of these subvarieties or local races, as to what distinguishes them, and in what regions they are best characterized. Unfortunately there is much less agreement when it comes to names; here each author is likely to play his preference, as is also true in the field of accounting for origins, where subjective opinions as to mixtures, mutations, Palaeolithic survivals, genetic behavior, environmental influence, and the like have had free run. Fortunately, this last diversity is not a very serious matter, because as yet almost nothing can be proved on *how* any race *came to be* as it is, and any opinion remains just an opinion. On the other hand, *what* races there *are* is much more a matter of fact, once enough measurements and observations are available, and on this the authorities agree much better.

For instance, within the generic Alpine or broad-headed Caucasian subrace, a Dinaric and an Armenoid type are quite generally set off, and a Lapp type is added by some.

The Dinaric type is tall, with a long and large nose, often convex; the face is long, though the head is broad. This type is most prominent northeast of the Adriatic Sea.

By contrast, the specific Alpine type is medium-statured, thick-necked, of pyknic bodily habitus (§ 79), with high forehead, and a nose tending to a concave or snub profile. It can be described as a somewhat infantilized or foetalized type, whereas the rugged-featured Dinaric inclines to the senescent. Alpine distribution proper is more westerly than Dinaric. The center of characterization would perhaps be central France or the Alps, as against Yugoslavia.

[9] Ripley himself still used the language term "Teutonic," but Deniker's "Nordic" quickly replaced it in general usage.

The Armenoid type is brunet, short-headed, and especially high-headed; the nose is both long and prominently convex. The area of characterization is eastern Turkey and adjacent districts.

The Lapps of northerly Scandinavia were formerly classed outright as Mongoloids, but they show perhaps as many Alpine as East Asiatic traits. They are a very short people—under 160 cm—light-framed and small-bodied, with delicate hands and feet. They are brachycephalic, extraordinarily small-jawed, and snub-nosed; and the majority are brunet, though there are some blonds. The Mongoloid eye fold and stiff, jet-black hair are rare. They have without question absorbed some Nordic or East Baltic blood; but their total features do not at all fit the expectable picture of a Nordic-Mongoloid cross. The Lapps live in a hard environment and have never been numerous. They may therefore well represent either a sub-Alpine or a sub-Mongoloid type that has become not only mixed but stunted, infantilized, and otherwise specialized.

The most pronounced or extreme Nordics are those of northwestern Europe, plus of course their descendants by immigration in other continents. A sub-Nordic type is generally accepted as prevalent in northeastern Europe. This East Baltic type is somewhat less tall than the Nordic, heavier-set, broader-headed, and thicker-nosed; the hair tends to be ash-blond instead of golden, the eyes gray or greenish rather than blue. Field Marshal Hindenburg is cited as a classic example. The East Baltic distribution is in northeastern Germany, the former Baltic states, and Finland, Poland, and Russia, especially in the north.[10] Various names have been used for the type: Sub-Nordic, East Baltic, East European, Neo-Danubian; some of these suggest further subdivision or grouping. The term "East Baltic" has the advantage of being geographically descriptive without too many other implications.

The basic Mediterranean race also shows subtypes. If we weight stature, North Africa and the Mediterranoid element in Britain are set off by relative tallness. This strain has been called Atlanto-Mediterranean. As regards features as a whole, the aquiline-nosed, slender Arabians and Egyptians are in some ways Mediterraneans par excellence. Some have made them into an "Oriental" subrace. Persians and Afghans resemble them rather closely, but also approximate the Hindu type. All in all, Mediterraneans tend to considerable uniformity.

In East Africa, in Ethiopia, Somaliland, Kenya, and parts of the Anglo-Egyptian Sudan, whites and blacks abut, and there has been hybridization. The white element is clearly Mediterranoid, and appears stronger than the Negroid, in the areas mentioned. Complexion often gets pretty dark, and the hair crisp, but the nose remains salient, the jaws are straight instead of protruding, the lips do not evert. Most of the peoples are tall and slender, some to an extraordi-

[10] Whereas the full-Nordic habitat covers north-central and northwestern Germany, Denmark, Sweden and Norway, Holland, northern France, the British Isles, and Iceland.

nary degree. This hybrid or transitional Mediterranean type has generally been called Hamitic, but as that is the name of a family of languages, it is inadmissible for a biological race, and we shall substitute East African. Some influence of the type extends westward in Africa on the Caucasian-Negro border, and the Nilotic Negro tribes—Dinka, Nuer, Shilluk, and so on—may have derived the ultraelongation of their physique from an absorption of blood of the type under discussion. But the most marked characterization of the type is in the east, in and toward the "Horn" of Africa.

Summarizing, we have:

RACES IN AND AROUND EUROPE

Nordic:	Nordic proper
	East Baltic or Sub-Nordic
Alpine:	Alpine proper
	Dinaric
	Armenoid
	(Lapp—part Mongoloid?)
Mediterranean:	Mediterranean proper *
	Atlanto-Mediterranean *
	Oriental and Irano-Afghan *
	East African (Negroid admixture)

* Not very sharply differentiated.

The Jews everywhere considerably approximate the local Gentile type. In Algiers they tend to resemble Mediterraneans, in Turkey Armenoids, in northern Germany Nordics. There has evidently been more mixture across the religious caste line through the generations than either side likes to admit. To put it differently, normally a part of any Jewish population is physically indistinguishable, by measures or by observation, from the Christians or the Mohammedans of the same area. The part that is differentiable appears to be so through hereditary persistence of either Armenoid or Oriental-Mediterranean traits. In large measure, popular recognition of Jews as such is based on nonracial externals such as name and association, or on expressions in manners, gestures, bodily habits, dress, and the like which conceivably might be racially hereditary but much more probably are socially conditioned and can therefore be learned and unlearned. There is certainly no single crude physical trait that is a safe index of Jewishness. Convex noses are not only Armenoid and Oriental but Mediterranean, Dinaric, East African, Hindu, Papuo-Melanesian, and Plains Indian! What is most characteristic of the so-called Jewish nose is not its total profile—which can be abundantly matched in many Gentile populations—but its "nostrility," a little accentuation of the curl of the nostril where it joins the face. This is a trait that was first noted by a Jewish observer, and which is on the border line between an organic "feature" and a functional "expression."

69. TRAIT DISTRIBUTIONS

Trait maps, such as Figures 9, 10, and 11, are both more accurate and more reliably representative than race maps. If the stature of adult males in a given district averages 168 cm, that is a perfectly definite fact, whose utility is not done away with by the circumstance that any average is an abstraction or generalization, and that the separate individuals of the group may range all the way from

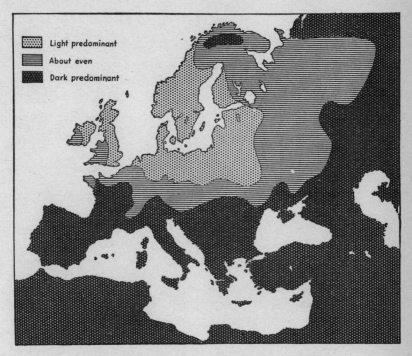

Light predominant
About even
Dark predominant

FIG. 9.   HAIR AND EYE COLOR: EUROPE

The regular, graded distribution, here centering around the Baltic, often characterizes single traits. (Modified from Coon and Struck)

145 to 200 cm. But most physical traits pass along through heredity independently of one another.[11] The result is that where there has been shuffling or mixing of populations of different type, an individual can have, say, typical

[11] There are linked traits, such as hair, eye, and skin pigmentation, which all depend on abundance of melanin. But even here the linkage is only partial, else we should not have so many blue-eyed dark heads in Ireland and Wales, and so many brown-eyed blonds in Russia.

Nordic body height, Alpine head form, and Mediterranean color, or any other combination of these or other traits. Now most of Europe has been well shuffled populationally in its long racial history. And from this it develops that individuals conforming in every trait to one racial type, and to that only, are fairly rare. One person is a good Nordic except that his hair is too dark, the next has too broad a face. By the time we have run through a fair sample of a population we may have found 10 per cent of definite Nordics, 5 per cent of indubitable Alpines, 40 per cent who are prevalently Nordic, 30 per cent prevalently Alpine, 10 per cent about evenly Nordic-Alpine, and perhaps 5 per cent more nearly Mediterranean, Dinaric, and scattering. In unit mapping, such a population might have to be entered as Nordic, but it is evident with how much qualification. Actually such a group would differ more from the purest Nordic groups than from some near-by group in which the Alpine element just nosed out the Nordic, and which would accordingly be represented as Alpine on a map whose

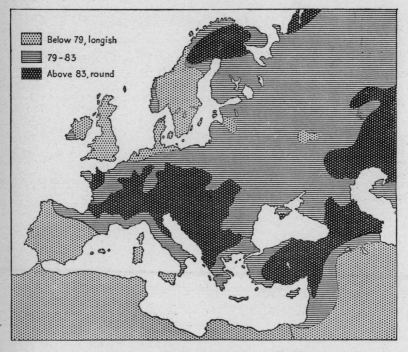

Below 79, longish
79 – 83
Above 83, round

FIG. 10.   CEPHALIC INDEX: EUROPE

An Alpine-Dinaric-Armenoid-Mongoloid wedge of broadheads separates two medium-headed groups: the Nordics and East Baltics on the north, from the several Mediterranean subgroups on the south. (Simplified from Coon and Struck)

units were determined by pluralities. An accurate racial map is therefore normally complicated by having to show "degrees of Nordicness" and the like by means of variations of color and shading; or by interdigitating bars of "Nordic" and "Alpine" color, or colors representative of three or four races, and by varying the width of the bars proportionally to the strength of the several racial elements; all of which makes for loss of that incisive comprehension which is the purpose of a map or diagram.

A partial solution is to color or shade only the areas of most decisive characterization, as in Figure 12 (page 152), leaving the transitional ones blank. If this plan could be extended to contours of intensification for each racial type, it would be almost ideal; but in practice this is scarcely feasible except for traits or features considered one at a time. Trait maps can be made objective, and a series of them builds up into a substitute for a race map. Thus Figures 9, 10,

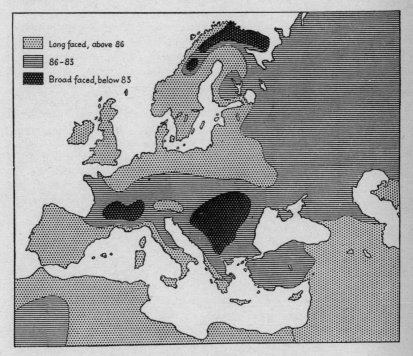

FIG. II. FACIAL INDEX: EUROPE

Again a wedge, now of broad-faced peoples, separates narrow-faced blonds from narrow-faced Mediterraneans. Within the wedge, the Alpine, Dinaric, and Lapp centers of characterization are evident as areas of specially broad or short faces. Only the short-headed Armenoids are long-faced. (Reduced from Struck)

and 11, used cumulatively, outline not only the basic Nordic-Alpine-Mediter-ranean classification, but the subdivision of the "Alpine" into Alpines proper, Dinarics, Armenoids, Lapps, and Mongolians, the separation of blonds into longish-headed Nordics and roundheaded East Balts, and so on.

70. THE DENIKER, HUXLEY, AND BOAS SCHEMES

It cannot be too much emphasized that all race classifications yet made rest somewhat on subjective judgments, no matter how much these judgments may be validated by objective measures and statistics. Similar subjective factors are present in most of that part of science which cannot be dragged into a labora-tory or tested by experiment: evolutionary biology, for instance, or the question of the age of geological periods in millions of years. This is nothing to be dis-concerted over. Opinions may remain personal, but they vary from sensible through flighty and fantastic to insane ones; and they may be supported by overwhelming masses of coherent evidence, or again merely by highly selected and fragmentary data. In short, there are such things as sound judgment and unsound judgment—or let us say, sounder and less sound—in those realms of science in which absolute proof is impossible. Much of the intellectual training of anthropology is precisely in learning to discriminate between better and worse judgments and better and worse evidence.

For this reason, some additional race classifications will be outlined here. This will at least protect the reader against the impulse to simplify the situation for himself by accepting the Kroeber classification as "the true" one. As a matter of fact, such truth value as it has is bound to be largely proportionate to the degree in which it reflects a consensus of unprejudiced opinion in previous schemes. In the end, what is common to nearly all classifications can be accepted as very probably valid; but their idiosyncrasies must be examined with critical reserve.

The classification made in 1889 by the Russian-born French anthropologist Deniker is one of the most elaborate yet devised, and has stood the test of time remarkably, to judge by the degree to which other anthropologists build upon it. It recognizes 6 grand divisions, 17 minor divisions, and 29 separate races. The primary criterion of classification is hair texture. In the following list, the parenthetical forms at the right give the equivalent terms used in this book, whenever the difference is mainly one of name.

Perhaps this scheme subdivides the Mediterraneans and the native Ameri-cans overfinely, and the East Asiatics unduly little; but these are points of weighting rather than principle. The one point at which all subsequent opinion differs from Deniker's is in regard to race 8, his "Assyroid," obviously corre-sponding to our Armenoid, which he puts not into grand division C, Dark Caucasoids, but into B, along with Australoids, Veddoids, and East African dark-skins. This B group might be translated as "neither quite Caucasian nor

DENIKER'S CLASSIFICATION

A. Hair woolly, with broad nose　　　　　　　　(NEGROID)
　　I. 1. Bushman
　　II. Negroid
　　　　2. Negrito
　　　　3. Negro
　　　　4. Melanesian (including Papuan)
B. Hair curly to wavy　　　　(NEGROID TO CAUCASOID)
　　III. 5. Ethiopian (Sudan, etc.)　　　　(*East African*)
　　IV. 6. Australian
　　V. 7. Dravidian (southern India)　　　　(*Veddoid*)
　　VI. 8. Assyroid (Kurds, Armenians, Jews)　(*Armenoid!*)
C. Hair wavy　　　　　　　　(DARK CAUCASOID)
　　VII. 9. Indo-Afghan　　　　　　　　(*Hindu*)
　　VIII. North African
　　　　10. Arab or Semite　　　　(*East Mediterranean*)
　　　　11. Berber (North Africa)　　　(*Mediterranean*)
　　IX. Melanochroid
　　　　12. Littoral (Atlanto-Medit.)　　(*Mediterranean*)
　　　　13. Ibero-insular (Spain, Southern Italy)　(*Mediterranean*)
　　　　14. Western European　　　　　　(*Alpine*)
　　　　15. Adriatic (Northern Italy, Balkans)　(*Dinaric*)
D. Hair wavy to straight, with light eyes　(FAIR CAUCASOID)
　　X. Xanthochroid
　　　　16. North European　　　　　　(*Nordic*)
　　　　17. East European　　　　　*(*East Baltic*)
E. Hair wavy to straight, with dark eyes　(CAUCASOID TO MONGOLOID)
　　XI. 18. Ainu
　　XII. Oceanian
　　　　19. Polynesian
　　　　20. Indonesian (East Indies)
F. Hair straight　　　　　　　　(MONGOLOID)
　　XIII. American
　　　　21. South American
　　　　22. North American
　　　　23. Central American
　　　　24. Patagonian
　　XIV. 25. Eskimo
　　XV. 26. Lapp
　　XVI. Eurasian
　　　　27. Ugrian (eastern Russia)
　　　　28. Turco-Tartar (southwestern Siberia)
　　XVII. 29. Mongol (East Asia)

* "East Baltic" in the wider sense used in this book. Deniker called the peoples actually living on the East Baltic Sea "Sub-Nordics," and those farther inland, East Europeans or the "Eastern" race, with a "Vistulan" subrace.

Negroid," just as Deniker's E group consists of races not too certain as between Caucasian and Mongoloid affiliation. This leaves grand division A as Negroid, C and D Caucasoid, F Mongoloid. In other words, under Deniker's apparent complexity, there is the usual threefold primary classification, but with enough recognition of transitions to avoid any oversimplified rigidity.

Huxley's scheme recognizes four main races, or five including a transitional one. These are (1) "Australioids," including Dravidians and Egyptians (*sic*); (2) Negroids, and (3) Mongoloids, both as customarily accepted; (4) Xanthochroi, about equivalent to Nordics and Alpines; (5) Melanochroi, nearly the same as the Mediterraneans, but supposed by Huxley to be hybrid or intermediate between the Xanthochroi and the "Australioids." This classification in effect emphasizes the connection between Australoids and Caucasians, with the Negroids as a distinctive group on one side and the Mongoloids on the other.

Haeckel's classification is basically similar to Huxley's, in that besides the usual three primary stocks—which he elevates into species—he recognizes a separate group comprising Australians, Dravidians, and Vedda-like Indo-Australians.

Boas inclines to contrast Negroids, as one fundamental line of human development, with Caucasoids and Mongoloids joined in another line. In favor of this view is the fact that the Negro is an extreme type of *Homo sapiens* in hair form, pigmentation, nose breadth, prognathism, and lip eversion. Granting this distinctiveness, the East Asiatic Mongolian would have to be selected within the contrasting Caucaso-Mongoloid stock as its most specialized branch—and as on the whole most antithetical to the Negro—with his stiff, long hair, flat face, and epicanthic fold, extreme brachycephalization, and short limbs. In line with this finding is the fact that there are Negro-Caucasoid transitions just as there are Caucasoid-Mongoloid ones, but there are no races that seem clearly intermediate between Negroids and Mongoloids. However, it is evident that such a view as this must not be pressed too far, since the Caucasian also specializes in extreme features: light pigmentation, prominence of nose, orthognathism, and hairiness.

71. THE POLISH, VON EICKSTEDT, AND HOOTON CLASSIFICATIONS

A Polish school of physical anthropologists, under the leadership of Czekanowski, has developed a statistical technique of objectively sorting or factoring a given population into what it believes are its natural racial elements, components, or types: factoring it both qualitatively and quantitatively. The results are interesting to compare with those obtained through the more usual subjective inspectional approach secondarily validated by statistics. What follows is a condensation of Klimek's summary of the findings of the Polish school.

These are the racial types recognized, with the names, as far as possible, converted into those used in this book:

THE CZEKANOWSKI-KLIMEK SCHEME

Black Race

Pygmy
Bushman ("Negroidal")
Congo Negro ("Austro-African")
Sudan Negro ("Nigritian"): The most highly characterized Negro type
Australoid: Wavy-haired, with many primitive traits

White Race, Transitional to Black

Indic ("Mediterranoid"): Related to Mediterranean
East African ("Meridional"): Related to Oriental; perhaps a mixture of it
  with Sudan Negro

White Race

Oriental: East and south of the Mediterranean Sea
Mediterranean: North and west of the Mediterranean Sea
Armenoid
Nordic
(For additional European types resulting from crossing of the elemental
  types, see below.)

Yellow Race, Transitional to White

North Asiatic ("Palaeo-Asiatic"): Siberian sub-Mongoloids, including
  Ainu

Yellow Race

Lapponoid: Enters into several European crossed races; close to the next.
Central Asiatic: Difficult to distinguish from the last, when a component;
  Mongols, etc.; definitely brachycephalic
East Asiatic ("Pacific"): Taller than the last, less brachycephalic; Chinese,
  etc.
Eskimoid ("Arctic")
"Palaeo-American": A longheaded component, chiefly in South America,
  allied to the prehistoric Lagoa Santa skeletal type

In Europe, where analysis of data has been carried farthest, six additional
mixed or hybrid types are recognized by the Poles as due to crossing of four
basic types:
  Sub-Nordic, from Nordic and Lapponoid crossing (= East Baltic in the nar-
rower geographic sense)
  Northwestern, from Nordic and Mediterranean (= Irish, etc.)
  Dinaric, from Nordic and Armenoid [12]
  Littoral, from Mediterranean and Armenoid (a large Mediterranean type, Deni-
ker's Atlanto-Mediterranean subtype)
  Alpine, from Lapponoid and Armenoid [12]
  "Pre-Slavic," from Mediterranean and Lapponoid (Russia, etc. Similar to North
Asiatic)

[12] Thus after Klimek, 1932. Coon, *The Races of Europe*, basing on Czekanowski, 1928,
interchanges the parentage of Dinaric and Alpine from that given above.

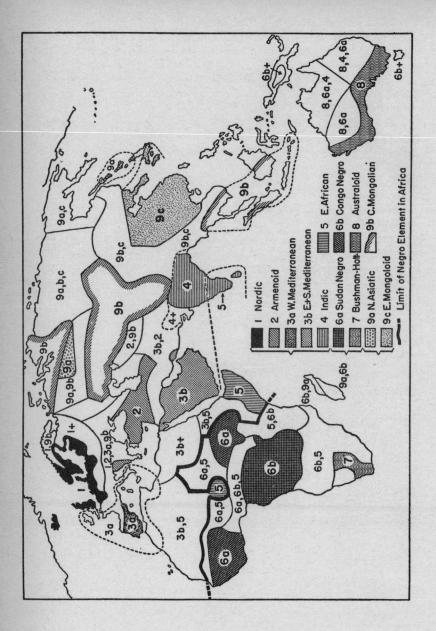

This last, European part of the classification is too schematic and diagrammatic to inspire much confidence that the six types actually did originate in the way stated as hybrids between four original ones. But the European classification is of interest because in the main much the same types are recognized under it as we have encountered before. Through the supposed Lapponoid ingredient in Pre-Slavic, Sub-Nordic, and Alpine, a Sub-Mongoloid element is recognized by the Polish school as stretching through Europe from Russia to France.

Not only Europe but the other continents are for the most part construed by this school as inhabited by populations that represent mixtures of from two to several of these seventeen primary racial components. The prevalence of such hybridization is almost certain, even if it should prove that the precise proportions of the constituent racial elements are not always as determined by the Polish school. Most of the world accordingly is mapped by them as an interdigitation of many colors. This complexity has been reduced in our map of their findings (Fig. 12), by plotting the shadings only on the areas of most definite dominance of the racial types—the areas of their purest characterization—in the Eastern Hemisphere.

The following may be added to supplement this map. An Indic element is recognized as present everywhere in Oceania except in southern Australia. It is strongest in Polynesia, where it seems equivalent to what is called Hindu in this book; elsewhere in Oceania, it is probably equivalent to Veddoid. The Mongoloid constituents in the Pacific are the "Central Asiatic," strongest in Sumatra, Java, and Borneo, and fading out southeastward; and the "East Asiatic," which appears in the Philippines and Celebes, and increasingly supplants the Central Asiatic toward Polynesia. New Guinea and Melanesia are attributed to the two African Negroid races, with varying admixtures of East African and Indic. The extinct Tasmanians are related to the Negroes more nearly than to the Australoids. The Madagascans are Congo Negroes with an infusion of western Indonesians, that is, "Central Asiatic" Mongoloids.

The aborigines of the New World are blends of four Mongoloid races. Of these, the "Palaeo-American" or Lagoa Santa has only slight local representation in North America, and none in the Eastern Hemisphere. The Eskimo survive dominant along the Arctic shores, but the presence of their type is affirmed to be traceable in South America, especially in Patagonia. The East and Central Asiatic types between them are found to have contributed most of the ancestry of the American Indians. The former is represented most strongly in the tall tribes east of the Mississippi, the latter, among rather short-statured, culturally advanced populations like the Maya, the Chibcha, and the Inca.

◄ FIG. 12.   CONCENTRATION AND DILUTION OF RACIAL TYPES

Areas of greatest concentration or purity of racial types (shaded) and of dilution or mixture (lettered only), according to the Polish school. (After Klimek)

So much for the views of the Polish school. The findings are not as clearly demonstrated as the members of the school believe; but most of them make considerable sense, especially if the basic racial "elements" or components are not adhered to too literally. And it is a virtue of the statistical method employed by the school that it emphasizes the mixtures and transitions which undoubtedly characterize much of humanity.

An elaborate classification, fuller even than that of Deniker, is the 1937 scheme of von Eickstedt, who recognizes three subspecies of man: the Albi or Europids, the Leiotrichi or Mongolids and Americanids, and the Afri or Negrids. These subdivide into 13 "series," 38 "varieties" or races, and about 40 additional subvarieties. Thus the Alpines belong, with Dinarids, Armenids, and Turanids, to the "Brachimorph series" of Europids, and subdivide into West Alpines and Lappids. The Melanochroic series of Europids comprises not only Mediterraneans, Orientalids, and Indids, but Polynesids. The "Protomorph" or primitive series of von Eickstedt's Europids contains Veddids and Ainuids. Under his Mongolids, von Eickstedt includes a "series" of "Subnigri" consisting of the "Khoisanid" variety, or the Bushmen and Hottentots. This placing at least emphasizes how aberrant and recalcitrant the Bushmen are. The Australids are degraded into mere East Negrids along with Neo- and Palae-Melanesids. A contact zone of transitional Europo-Afri is recognized; these consist of Aethiopids in East Africa and Indo-Melanids in India. This scheme gives the Hindus a triple racial origin: straight white allied to Mediterranean (Indid); primitive white (Veddid); and transitional black (Indo-Melanid).

The von Eickstedt classification presents several definite specialties or novelties, such as the placing of Polynesians, Bushmen, and Australians. But on the whole it obviously conforms to previous ones, the differences being mostly in degree of elaboration or weighting, and in the coinage of new and somewhat pedantic names.[13]

So as not to give the impression that all the more elaborate race classifications are by Europeans, an American one will also be summarized: Hooton's of 1946.

Hooton recognizes three "primary races" corresponding to the usual primary stocks. Under these he has 23 primary subraces, of which 8 are composite but predominantly White, Negroid, or Mongoloid. Certain of these subraces are again subdivided, sometimes into morphological types, sometimes into secondary subraces.

[13] Since about 1940, the von Eickstedt classification of North American Indians into Pacifids, Centralids, Silvids, and Margids has gained wide currency among archaeologists dealing with the eastern United States and Canada; and this without the von Eickstedt scheme as a whole appearing to be much known to them. Evidently physical anthropologists have so far failed to provide a classification of native types that meets the needs of the archaeologists in this area.

THE HOOTON CLASSIFICATION

I. *White or Caucasoid Primary Race*

1. Mediterranean
   a. Upper Palaeolithic survivals, chiefly in the British Isles
   b. Iranian Plateau
   c. Classic Mediterranean, in a hook-nosed and a straight-nosed subtype
2. Ainu
3. Keltic (light-eyed, dark or red haired, longheaded, mainly in the British Isles)
4. Nordic
5. Alpine
6. East Baltic (blond roundheads)
7. Armenoid (stabilized blend of Classic Mediterranean, Iranian Plateau, and Alpine)
8. Dinaric (stabilized blend of Upper Palaeolithic, Alpine, Armenoid, and Nordic)
9. Nordic-Alpine (individuals intermediate to 4 and 5; 23% of the U.S.)
10. Nordic-Mediterranean (intermediate to 1 and 4; 25% of the U.S.)

COMPOSITE, PREDOMINANTLY WHITE

11. Australian (Archaic White, Tasmanian, plus minor Melanesian)
    a. Murrian, most nearly White; specially in the southeast
    b. Carpentarian, Melanesian increment; in the north
    c. Tasmanoid; refuge areas in Queensland
12. Indo-Dravidian (Classic Mediterranean, Australoid, Negrito, plus varying minor fractions)
    a. Classic Indo-Dravidian: most of northern India; approaching Classic Mediterranean
    b. Armenoid-Iranian Plateau: western and northeastern India
    c. Indo-Nordic: northwestern Himalayas
    d. Australoid or Veddoid: central and southern India
    e. Negritoid: spots in southern India
13. Polynesian (mostly brunet White, plus Mongoloid, plus Melanesian)

II. *Negroid Primary Race*

14. African Negro or Negritian or Forest Negro
15. Nilotic Negro, probably with infusion of "Hamitic" Mediterranean
16. Negrito
    a. Infantile type: in all Negrito populations
    b. Adultiform: among all Negritos, except in the Andamans and the Philippines

COMPOSITE, PREDOMINANTLY NEGROID

17. Tasmanian: Negrito plus Australian
18. Melanesian-Papuan: Negrito, Australoid, hook-nosed Classic Mediterranean, plus fractions
    a. Papuan
    b. Melanesian
19. Bushman-Hottentot: Negrito plus Boskop (§ 51).
    a. Bushman
    b. Hottentot: Bushman plus Negro and Hamitic Mediterranean

III. *Mongoloid Primary Race*

20. Classic Mongoloid
21. Arctic Mongoloid or Eskimoid (including eastern Palaeo-Asiatic tribes)

COMPOSITE, PREDOMINANTLY MONGOLOID

22. Indonesian-Mongoloid or Indonesian-Malay (Mongoloid plus Mediterranean plus Ainu plus Negrito)
    a. Malay-Mongoloid (Indonesia and Farther India, including most Japanese)
    b. Indonesian (Pre-Mongoloid groups in South China, Farther India, and island interiors)
23. American Indian (Mongoloid plus Iranian Mediterranean plus Australoid plus a little Negritoid)
    a. Brachycephals, index 80 and up. Hawk-nosed and snub-nosed subtypes
    b. Dolichocephals, index under 80. Hawk-nosed and snub-nosed subtypes

A marked feature of this classification is the degree to which it admits mixture and makes use of it. The Polish school also holds most populations to be more or less mixed, but depends on statistical segregation of the ingredients. Hooton employs recognition, subsequently supported by sorting according to diagnostic criteria if individual measurements are available. In a simple situation, first judgment by visual observation is perhaps as effective and reliable a procedure as more elaborate and mechanical means; and it is certainly less pedantic. But when from three to six racial ingredients are recognized in a population, and these in different strengths and order of appearance, the majority of individuals are certain to show traits contributed by several of the racial components. One man's hair may derive from race A, his nose from B, his height from C. The next man examined may have the same features respectively from race components D, A, C. If features blend in heredity, as most of them do, many individuals will not even have clear A, B, C, or D hair, noses, or heights. In this event, most members of the population are likely to be indeterminate in most of their features as regards evidence of origin from A or B or C or D. In fact, such indeterminate features might logically be attributed to an infusion of race G, or H, if one had chosen to start with A, B, C, G, or A, B, H, D, instead of A, B, C, D. Everything accordingly depends on which racial ingredients one elects to start his hypothesis with, after inspection; and then, on how one defines the criteria or critical values for sorting out that ingredient. In short, the unscrambling of a composite race into its original pure-race constituents is a process that is far from simple and far from sure. No matter how quantitatively the constituents are defined, and how statistically validated the final analysis is, a subjective factor enters into the process. Consequently the findings are speculative in proportion as the population analyzed is complex in its origins.

So it comes about that some of the Hooton hypotheses are pretty finely spun. Some even seem circular. Thus he makes the Australians Archaic White plus a

Tasmanian and locally a minor Melanesian ingredient. The Tasmanians in turn he sees as predominantly Negrito, plus an Australian element—into which they have presumably already entered! Similarly with the Australoid or Veddoid type (12d) in India, which he evidently relates to the Australian types (11a, b, c) but in a manner of interdependence that is not clear.

Some of the admixtures are also pretty far-flung and ancient for their confident recognition today, especially when only small dosages of an ingredient are claimed. Thus the specific Iranian Plateau element in the American Indians! This appears to be invoked to account for the hawk noses in America. But how and when did Iranian-nosed ancestors travel from Afghanistan to America? And leave no traces along their route? It may be that hawk-nosedness has little probability of originating repeatedly in separate races through independent mutation, and that we must accordingly explain all its recurrences by connection through migration and mixture. But this is not proved; it is only an opinion.

The Negritos in particular are thought by Hooton to have left dashes of their type more or less all over the world. This might well be; but it involves a considerable hypothesis as to their origin and dispersal—considerable in the face of the very little we actually know about their past.

It is also necessary to realize that Hooton's subraces sometimes seem to be intended to account for all the people in an area, but in other areas they represent only a more or less pure morphological type, most of the population being mixed and not specially accounted for. Thus the type of the Classic Mongoloid subrace (20) is described as concentrated in eastern Siberia among tribes like the Tungus Gold and the Mongol Buriat, and also as occurring "frequently" among the northern Chinese. But what the other northern Chinese are, and their southern and central conationals, is not stated. Yet for India, where Guha's views are followed, the classification seems to be exhaustive.

There is also a seeming inconsistency, or at least ambiguity, between subraces such as 7, Armenoid, and 8, Dinaric, which are described as "stabilized blends due to interbreeding," and 9, Nordic-Alpine, and 10, Nordic-Mediterranean, which are "residual mixed types (interbreeds)" or "sortings-out" of individuals intermediate in characters. At any rate, the 23 Hooton subraces evidently are not all of them groups co-ordinate in kind or classificatory rank.

It will be noted that there are a number of traits which are shared by adjoining races: as blondness by East Baltic, Nordic, and partly by Keltic. Similarly with hawk or hook noses. These occur among one subtype of Classic Mediterraneans, among Iranian Plateau Mediterraneans, among Armenoids and Dinarics, and among Hamitic East African Negroes—all in a large continuous area where Europe, Africa, and Asia adjoin. Such continuity of occurrence within a single and freely interbreeding species would almost certainly mean a single origin for the trait, and its spread by mixture of populations. Hooton finds the origin of all hook noses among the Mediterraneans, and has the Armenoids and the Dinarics derive theirs from the more primary Mediterraneans. The view that one particular type of several was the one to have the hook nose first and then give it to the others—this is a finding that goes beyond description and has begun to enter the realm of hypothesis, or frank opinion. For instance, one might alternatively argue with equal logic that it was the Armenoids who first developed this feature and then transmitted it by admixture to the neighboring Iranian and eastern Classic Mediterraneans; for the western Mediterraneans are typically straight-nosed. When it comes to the remote Melanesian-Papuans and American Indians, the case for admixture of a Mediterranean element is obviously still weaker, in proportion to the distances and the long times involved in the view.

The Hooton scheme moves some of its ingredients and composite derivations about with a rather ingratiating insouciance. But once the degree of its speculativeness is recognized, the classification is unusually observant, original, vigorous, and stimulating.

72. BLOOD GROUPS AND GENES

Exceedingly interesting are the data accumulated in recent decades on the racial distribution of blood groups, a set of physiological phenomena of great medical importance in connection with blood transfusions. All human beings belong to one of four classes or "groups," AB, A, B, O, according as their blood serum and blood cells contain specific substances which cause clumping or agglutination of the cells when serum from individuals of certain classes is injected into the blood of other individuals. People of type AB possess two such substances, A and B; those of types A and B, one only; those of O, neither. Any one class is as healthy and viable as another. The difference between them seems not to be reflected in any other bodily trait, in fact can be ascertained only by a physiological test. Further, the factors determining the four classes are inherited by simple Mendelian rules of heredity, in distinction from most human traits, which are multifactor or hybridizing. However, the blood-group factors are triply allelomorphic—A and B both being dominant to O—instead of doubly allelomorphic or alternative—present or absent—as is usual.[14]

A special popular interest has attached to the blood groups because of their legal bearing in cases of disputed paternity. The most important fact in this connection is that individual paternity can never be positively proved by a blood test as such. A particular paternity may be disproved; as when the child is type B, the mother O, and the putative father A. Since A + O cannot yield B, this

[14] In fact, these blood "groups" or types are the first case of threefold allelomorphism established for man. The usual designation for the genes or heredity units in the chromosomes underlying the types of blood are: p for type A; q for B; both p and q for AB; and r for absence of both p and q, resulting in blood type O. The percentage frequency of these genes, which are the hereditary causal factors, is obtained from the frequency of blood types in any given population, by calculation. The formulas are: $r = \sqrt{O}$; $p = \sqrt{(O + A)} - \sqrt{O}$; $q = \sqrt{(O + B)} - \sqrt{O}$.

suspect is not the father of this B. Or again, if it is sure from other circumstances of the case that paternity must rest on one of two men only, one of these may be proved impossible by his blood type, and the other therefore be legally construable as the father. An indeterminate finding is much more frequent than a positive determination.

Finally, and most important for anthropology, many populations, both races and subraces, differ notably in the frequency proportion of individuals belonging to each of the four classes or types. Thus the percentages which the four types constitute of some sample populations is as follows:

BLOOD GROUP PERCENTAGES

Peoples	Type O	Type A	Type B	Type AB
A > 2B				
Swedes	34	51	10	5
English	46	43	7	2
Americans, white	46	41	8	4
Portuguese	38	52	6	3
Italians	36	51	9	4
Austrians	42	40	10	8
Greeks	38	42	16	4
Armenians	22	52	13	13
Philippine Negritos	48	33	14	4
A > B, < 2B				
Russians	41	31	22	6
Poles	32	38	21	9
Uzbek Turks	29	34	27	10
Japanese	31	38	22	8
South Chinese	32	39	19	10
A < B, O < B				
North Chinese	31	25	34	10
Manchus	27	27	38	8
Hindus	30	24	37	8
Gypsies	34	21	39	6
Philippine Moros	25	18	45	12
A± = B±, O > B				
Sumatrans	44	23	29	4
Annamese	42	22	28	7
Congo Negroes	46	22	24	8
Senegal Negroes	43	23	29	5
Madagascans	45	26	24	4
O > A + B + AB				
American Indians, full blood	91	8	1	0
Filipinos	65	15	20	1
Melanesians	54	27	16	3
Australians (natives)	57	38	3	1
Bechuana Negroes	53	19	24	4

The results in hand, which relate to several hundred thousand or millions of tested individuals from hundreds of racial, ethnic, or local populations, sometimes agree and sometimes disagree surprisingly with the usually accepted race classifications. Some East Asiatic Mongolians are thrown into a group with Hindus, others with Poles. The Mongoloid natives of America differ markedly from the Mongoloids of East Asia. The high-A peoples of Europe include Nordics, Mediterraneans, Armenoids, Alpines. The most extreme in low B are not Nordics but Iberian Mediterraneans. The most extreme high B's among whites are found in the Hindus—close racial relatives of the Mediterraneans. Senegal Negroes agree closely with brown Malaysians, but differ from the Negroid Melanesians.

It is clear that we have in these blood-group distributions an intriguing set of data, which crosscut ordinary race relationships. A reason for this irrelevance to race—perhaps the main one—is that we are dealing with a single trait, whereas a race is an expression of the total or average coherence of many traits. Head form, viewed by itself, is similarly irrelevant. Peoples as different as Negroes, Australoids, Hindus, Eskimo, and Spaniards all have long heads. The tallest of all populations are certain East Africans, northern Europeans, Polynesians, and Indians of the central United States—who are completely diverse racially. While some traits, like hair texture and nasal index, do occur in broad, approximate conformity with race, it is evident that many do not; and blood type happens to be one of these.

There is in fact a great deal more local variability among most populations than the few selected figures above show. However, they outline some interesting situations that on the whole are confirmed by fuller data. Thus the region of high frequency of type A is mainly that of southern and western Europe. Class A still exceeds B, but by a smaller ratio, among most of the peoples between western Russia and China and Japan. Type B is definitely in excess in India and again in the area about North China and Manchuria. Among most Negroes, Malaysians, and Farther Indians, A and B percentages are more evenly balanced, neither running very high, and both less than O. Peoples with high O frequency are often those of remote continents or islands or living in isolated groups.

All sorts of theories have been proposed to explain the populational distribution of the four blood types, ranging from hypotheses of very ancient inheritance [15] to development of certain factors in historic times. Thus it has been suggested that type O was the original one for mankind, and that then types A and B originated as separate mutations, A in Europe, B in India, and were subsequently spread by race mixture, persons of class AB having both A and B in their ancestry. However, it is hard to see how North China and Man-

[15] All four of the anthropoid apes show A; only the chimpanzee shows O; the other three, B. This does not get us very far in our human problem.

churia could derive much of their blood from India, and how if they did, South China and Japan could retain an excess of A in proportions almost identical with Russia and Poland. On the other hand, the Hungarian Gypsies, historically known as an emigrated group from India, do retain typical Hindu proportions.[16]

No general theory concerning blood-type distribution that will hold water has yet been found. Distributions are not even geographically clear-cut and consistent, but vary and wobble provincially very much as visible race features vary in subraces and local types. Thus, native America, when pureblood, mostly is very high in frequency of O, quite modest in A, extremely low or absent in B. Yet two Blackfoot tribes show 77 per cent A, the near-by Flatheads 42, the Dakota 29, British Columbia Indians 13. Evidently we have here a local center of A strength—but no explanation of the cause, whether by survival, selection, mutation, or mixture. The Eskimo of Greenland and Baffinland also run a rather heavy A, 13 to 56 per cent,[17] or more or less in the range of their O. To be sure, we could say about the Eskimo that they are otherwise marked off as a distinct American subrace. Also they may be relatively recent comers from Asia; with which there would be in accord the further fact of their containing a sprinkling of B—a characteristic Asiatic but un-American component.

In special cases the groupings do have bearing on racial purity or impurity of blood, as for the Gypsies in Hungary, and possibly a somewhat higher B for Jews in A-prevalent areas.[18] But such instances do not help at all to clear up the general problem of the origin and total history of the factors.

As a result of these blood-type findings, it has sometimes been suggested that the whole study of race by the usual methods was on a sterile track and out of date, because the bodies, skins, bones, and hair observed and measured by physical anthropologists were only compositely variable phenotypes—products of hereditary factors; and that what should be studied is these same causal factors of heredity as they appear in the genes in the chromosomes. At present, this is a pure wish-fulfillment proposal. We know hundreds of actual bodily traits or phenotype "appearances" for every known genetic unit character of heredity. In fact, the "laws" of heredity are every year themselves proving to be more ramified, even when we operate on problems simplified by breeding fruit flies in the laboratory. For man, on whom we cannot experiment, whom we have to take as he comes, the genetic situation is now almost as complex as the bodily zygotic one, but its data are far fewer. What evidence we have on human

[16] Thus, different lots of them run 26, 35, 37, 39% B, whereas six Hindu samples range between 32 and 41, but eight Hungarian groups only from 13 to 19.

[17] The center of third highest rank of A among Indians is Navaho 29-31; New Mexico Pueblo 12, 13; Papago 6. Elsewhere, A-frequencies of 5, 10, or 20% occur only where mixture with whites is known to have occurred among the Indians. A few South American cases of high B are probably due to the factor of chance in very small series, or to faulty technique; as Yahgan, 30 B out of 33 cases (!) and Caraja, 31 B out of 61.

[18] Thus, percentages of B respectively among Jews and Gentiles in: Rumania, 18, 14; Netherlands, 13, 10; U.S., 17, 9-14.

heredity to date that can be reduced to formulas, besides the A-B-AB-O blood types, is a few other blood groupings and a limited series of abnormalities. These, for what they are worth, will be further discussed in a moment. But for attacking the total problem of races and their origins and histories, these few present scraps of definite knowledge of human heredity are pitifully inadequate.

The blood types discovered subsequently to the original A-B-AB-O ones are subtypes of A; M-N; the Rh group; secreting factors—and there may be others.

Group A has recently been found really to consist of subgroups A_1 and A_2—which, incidentally, illustrates what was meant a moment back by the assertion that the genetics of unit characters has become ramifying: even the supposed irreducible factors decompose. Pertinent to race are the following observations, which will undoubtedly be added to from year to year. Among whites in Egypt, Russia, Finland, Sweden, Denmark, Germany, England, and the United States, the old A is found to break up into A_1 and A_2 in the ratio of from $3:1$ to $5:1$.[19] Among New York Negroes, the proportion was once $3:1$ and once $3:2$—that is, A_2 is fairly frequent—but the samples were small. Hawaiian Polynesians and the few American Indians tested show practically no A_2.

The M-N factors coexist alongside the A-B-AB-O factors, in the same blood but without relation to them. They do not affect transfusions, and have therefore been less studied. M and N are not in a dominant-recessive relation. Hence there are MN individuals; in fact, they are the most numerous. The most common percentage distribution, the world over to date, is around M 30, N 20, MN 50, corresponding to a gene frequency of m 55-60, n 40-45. This range of ratios holds for all European nationalities tested, for U.S. white Americans, Egyptians, Chinese, Japanese, Koreans, and for the one sample of Negroes tested in New York.[20] This suggests that the great majority of mankind adheres approximately to this pattern. Excess of N has been found only among the Ainu ($n = 57$) and Australian indigenes ($n = 82$). Unusual excess of M has to date appeared among Eskimo ($m = 91, 82$), U.S. Indians ($m = 78, 76, 75$), Hindus ($m = 76$), Arab Beduin ($m = 75, 62$). There is no explanation of why there are these uniformities and divergences. Data on more populations will illuminate the world status of this factor, but no doubt will also show up new problems.

The Rh factor was discovered in 1940, and is a gene unit causing presence or absence of an agglutinogen. Its practical importance lies in the fact that in a certain, but fortunately low, percentage of cases when an Rh-lacking woman carries a child by an Rh-positive man, the Rh element in the blood of the foetus sets up antibodies in the blood of the mother which in turn react destructively

[19] Except that among 400 Irish and 200 Welsh the ratio was about $2:1$.

[20] For 278 "Negroes" the M, N, MN percentages are 28, 22, 50; for 6129 U.S. whites 29, 21, 50!

on the blood of the foetus and may also prevent future live births. The Rh-male-present and female-absent mating thus has a slight negatively selective survival or perpetuation value. Soon however it was found that the Rh genetics were exceedingly ramifying, and by 1946 at least eight types of Rh blood and six or more allelic genes had been recognized. These complexities cannot be gone into here, except for the interesting fact of decisive racial variation. The salient features of the differentiation appear in this tabulation:

RH BLOOD TYPES
(Percentages)

	Rh_-	Rh_1	Rh_2	Rh_1Rh_2	Rh_0	Others
New York, Negroes	8	20	22	5	41	3
New York, whites	15	53	16	13	2	2
India	7	71	5	13	2	3
China	2	61	3	34	1	0
Japan	1	52	8	39	0	0
Mexico, Indians	0	48	9	42	1	0

The most aberrant from all, in this case, appear to be the Negroes, even though random samples of New York "Negroes" are bound to contain considerable white blood. The most alike are Chinese and Japanese; the Mexican Indians stand nearest them. Each racial group specializes in high and low frequency of one or more Rh types of blood.

Many individuals have their blood-type substances present also in other body juices, especially the saliva. Such "secretors" are genetically dominant, non-secretors recessive. The few data in hand indicate some difference in dominant-recessive frequency between Negroes and whites; and there may prove to be many other racial variations.

With all these genetically definite blood-serum types turning up, the prospect improves that we may ultimately be able to distinguish races at least partly by their genetic constitution as well as by the hitherto customary description of their phenotypes. With only the A-B-O genetics known, paternity could be determined, or rather eliminated, in only a minority of cases. But with the A_1-A_2, the M-N, the eight Rh types, and the secretion genetics also available, the determination is now possible, at least theoretically, in perhaps most cases. Turned around, the same applies to race distinctions. In their A-B-O blood grouping, Hindus and North Chinese, who are obviously very different racially, came out practically identical—through accident. So do Sumatrans and West African Negroes. It is however extremely unlikely that accident will make these pairs of peoples alike also in the wholly independent sub-A, M-N, Rh, and other frequencies. Conversely, the Gypsy-Hindu similarity in A-B-O frequency, though it looks good, might still be due to accident. If it is not accidental but based on connection by actual genetic descent, then it should show also in the M-N, Rh, and other frequencies. Or, if it should mainly hold, but with some deviations, then comparison, after data on enough populations are in hand, might indicate with what other racial ingredient the Gypsies had diluted their Hindu blood, or from which Hindu subrace or district they were chiefly sprung. All this future refinement of knowledge is conjectural, but it seems expectable.

These serological traits have been gone into here not because they are the most important in human genetics, but because they are the best known. They operate by the open-or-shut, present-or-absent, Mendelian method. Most human traits do not, or are not known to, operate so simply; or they have a genetic mechanism so complex that it has not been extricated. Skin color, eye color, hair color, hair form, and other visible traits show some approximation to genetic rules in their hereditary transmission, but the approximation is very loose. There may be many factors involved, some perhaps linked instead of independent. The hopes of three or four decades ago that all traits would soon be brought under simple allelomorphic rules have not been realized. Outside of blood characteristics, the human traits positively known to "Mendelize" are rather few, and they consist preponderantly of abnormalities and pathologies—fortunately for the most part infrequent ones. Some such are, or have been claimed to be:

MENDELIAN HUMAN TRAITS

Dominant	Dominant, Sex-linked or Probably So
Brachydactyly (short-fingeredness)	Mandibular prognathism (Hapsburg)
Local albinism	Basedow's disease
Absence of upper lateral incisors	Baldness (?)
Hypospadias	
Huntington's chorea	
Diabetes insipidus	

Recessive	Recessive, Sex-linked or Probably So
Total color-blindness	Red-green color-blindness
Nontasting of PTC *	Nonclotting of blood (haemophilia)
	Atrophy of the optic nerve
	Total albinism
	Addison's disease

* Paraethoxyphenyl thiocarbamide. It is very bitter to most people, but the nontasters do not get even a shred of taste from it. The frequency varies by race. Nontasting occurs in 37 per cent of Arabs, 30 per cent of United States whites, 6 per cent of Chinese, and 6 per cent of American Indians. Here, then, is another simple genetic trait to supplement blood types and subtypes in ultimately aiding us to verify racial connections or mixtures or their absence.

Most of these traits are altogether too rare to be of consequence as regards race. An exception is red-green color-blindness, which can appear in females only as the result of exceptional matings. Some frequencies for it are:

Eskimo, 1 per cent of male population; New Guinea Melanesians, 1 per cent; American Indians, 2; Chinese, 3; Japanese, 3; Chukchi of eastern Siberia, 3; Negroes, American, 4 (possibly raised by white-blood infusion); Egyptian, 5; Lapp, 6; white

American, 8. A high figure of 13 per cent of males for the Toda is almost certainly due to the inbreeding of this small caste-tribe of South India (§ 201). Analogously, there appears to be an unusually high frequency of total albinism, perhaps around .2 per cent, among the inbred and small Zuni and Hopi tribes, and again among the San Blas Indians of Panamá.

73. EFFECTS OF SELF-DOMESTICATION

Among the causal factors shaping races there is to be reckoned man's "domestication," already mentioned in § 34. Man is in certain senses a domesticated animal. Such a statement may at first sound like rank nonsense. We keep domestic animals for use or pleasure: who keeps us? As regards purposiveness, exploitation, and control, it is obvious that we are not tamed animals. It is only that as regards shelter, care, and regularly dependable food supply, men in general live more like their kept animals than like wild ones. We and our cattle both benefit from culture in our mode of living: wild beasts do not. It is a matter of a common protective "artificial" environment, as against a rigorous, competitive, and often harshly selective natural one. Such a change of environment from the feral state might, and actually does, induce changes of form and may induce changes of heredity. As regards the results of his mode of living, accordingly, man can legitimately be considered as the equivalent of a domesticated animal. Let us call him "self-domesticated," and avoid further quarreling about the implications of words.

Below are listed some of the traits that tend to develop in long-domesticated mammals; or, it might be said, have been preserved among them, whereas if they occurred in the wild state as occasional mutations, they would tend to be swamped out by crossbreeding, or to be lost by survival selection if disadvantageous.

1. Hairlessness, as in Chihuahua dogs.
2. Hair curliness or wool, as in sheep, poodles, and even some fowl. There seems to be no parallel in wild nature.
3. Depigmentation, either total as albinization or partial as blondism. Except in the snowy Arctic, there seem to be no albino species of wild mammals, but there are albino races of almost all domestic ones. There are "blond" or yellowish wild species, such as the weasel and the opossum, though there are not very many; but there are no wild blond cattle, horses, cats, or wolves, corresponding to the Jerseys, sorrels, buckskins, yellow dogs, and so on developed in breeding.
4. Overpigmentation or melanism occurs in nature as an alternative color phase in a few species, such as bears and panthers. There are black breeds of nearly all long-domesticated mammals and of some fowls.
5. Excessive fat deposits on rump or tail, as in some Asiatic breeds of sheep. The human equivalent is steatopygia.
6. Reduction of jaw length, as in most dogs compared with wolves and jackals. A further step is reduction of the nose and brachycephalization of the brain case, as in bulldogs, pugs, Pekinese, and some spaniels.

7. Droop ears. These do not occur in nature as a variant of erect ears.

8. A less compact cellular structure of bone has been alleged for some tame animals.

Of these traits, relative hairlessness is common to all living men, but Mongoloids and Negroids have evolved farther than Caucasians, Ainu, and Australoids. Woolly hair of course characterizes the Negroid. Probably the Bushmen are most extreme. They also show steatopygia, trait 5 in the list above. Depigmentation of skin, hair, and eyes is of course Caucasian, with the extreme in Nordics. Mongoloid head hair and eyes are melanized; the Negro adds considerable melanization of skin. Caucasian orthognathism is obviously a form of jaw reduction.

This seems a fair showing. We are unable to derive particular traits from particular conditions of "domesticated" living; but the total series is rather close to being parallel in man and in the animals he keeps. That there are more aberrant and fantastic forms among tame animals, such as tumbling pigeons, deformed and lap dogs, ponies and Percherons, is due to our controlling the heredity of some animals by selection and inbreeding in accord with our fancies or needs. By contrast, human breeding of human beings has often been wholly uncontrolled and apparently has never been really constructively controlled.

74. SELECTIVE FACTORS

It is remarkable how little is really known as to the causes of change of human type and race differentiation. Random genetic mutations, survival selection, adaptation to environment, domestication, may all have been at work; it is very difficult to say in what degree and at what points.

It is obvious that the native habitat of the darkest races, Negroids and Australoids, is in or near the tropics, and it has been thought that their extra melanin provided protection against solar actinic invasion. However, much of the tropics is occupied by brown races—the East Indies and native South America, for instance—and those races seem about as well adapted as the blacks in their tropical areas. The paler of the blond Caucasians perhaps survive less well in the tropics, as a race. Most of them certainly believe so; but then most of them certainly also prefer living in "God's country." It is clear that the prevalently blond populations originated in the cloudy and foggy parts of northern Europe (Figs. 9, 12; pages 145, 152). Possibly demelaninized mutations also occurred elsewhere, but had few or no survival chances except in this actinically protected area. However, even if this were so, it would not prove either that melanin was a handicap in a cool, foggy climate or that an ultraheavy dose of it was positively advantageous—either in low latitudes or in high altitudes.

A causal correlation has also been suggested between the prevalently broad noses of the tropics and the narrow ones of the Arctic—Negroes versus Eskimo and Nordics, for instance. Constricted inner nasal passages might conserve bodily heat in extremely low temperatures. But there is nothing as yet to show that a flat broad nose has any actual advantage in the tropics. Again, therefore, if there is a relation—and this is uncertain—it is only a one-way correlation.

All in all, man is such an unusually tough animal with such wide toleration of environment that it is difficult to pin special adaptive modifications on him. He is one of the very few successful omnivorous mammals—the bear and the pig being his most conspicuous compeers. He ranges from sea level to three-mile elevation of habitat, and from wholly arid to the most humid climates, which is true of almost no other mammal. In resistance to extremes of temperature, he makes up for lack of congenital fur by the cultural aids of clothing, housing, and fire; but at that his precultural range is likely to have been at least as wide as that of any primate. A total generalized habitus (§ 35) is so characteristic of the human species as to make rather improbable the explanation of many of the minor racial peculiarities by environmental adaptations of survival value. These peculiarities may often be due to gene mutations whose value for survival was indifferent. Especially would this be true after culture began to interfere with the rigor of purely organic selection.

75. PLASTICITY

Another human trait, which is perhaps a corollary of being generalized, is plasticity: the ability to change bodily form with environmental change, at least within limits. This was first demonstrated on a major scale by Boas in 1912 in regard to European immigrants in the United States, and has been spottily confirmed elsewhere. What Boas found was that the children of long-headed South Italians born in America were progressively broader-headed than their parents, and that the children of broad-headed Czechs and Jews from Central Europe were progressively longer-headed. Moreover, in all cases there was an increase of stature and a narrowing of face. Roughly, all these alterations were an approach toward the type of Anglo-Saxon descent most prevalent in the United States. A sample of the data follows:

CHANGE OF AMERICAN-BORN MALE DESCENDANTS OF EUROPEAN IMMIGRANTS INTO THE UNITED STATES FROM THE TYPE OF THE IMMIGRANTS (BOAS)

	Broad-headed Types		Narrow-headed Types	
	Bohemians	Jews	Sicilians	Neapolitans
Change in mm in				
Stature	29.0	17.0	1.0	6.0
Width of face	−2.1	−1.1	−1.2	−1.2
Length of head	−0.7	2.2	−2.4	−0.9
Breadth of head	−2.3	−1.8	1.3	0.9
Change in cephalic index	−1.0	−2.0	1.3	0.9
Number of cases	170	654	188	248

The changes in females were parallel. Moreover, American-born descendants differed from European-born descendants of immigrants in much the same way. And the results hold not only as between immigrants in the mass and immigrants' descendants as a mass or statistical average, but for specific immigrants and their own specific children. There can thus be no real question as to the validity of the findings. Above all, the changes of children from parents were greater in proportion as their parents had been longer in the United States. Moreover, analogous results have been obtained elsewhere, as by Shapiro and Hulse on Japanese settling in Hawaii. Roughly, the Hawaiian-born children of immigrants differed from the immigrants much as the immigrants differed—by selection—from the stay-at-home Japanese. Hrdlička found fourth-generation Americans narrower-faced than Europeans. It may therefore be concluded not only that there are certain unknown factors at work on race in the American environment, but, as a general principle, that heredity may be less fixed, less impermeable by outside influences, than had been supposed. As a result, the Boas findings produced considerable stir and some unnecessary controversy. There is nothing in the facts to show that the environment would continue indefinitely to alter the heredity. It might well dent it so far, but no farther. In other words, heredity must be construed as not absolutely rigid, but as plastic within certain presumably narrow limits. This seems reasonable enough.

Moreover, the immigrants to New York moved not only from one continent and climate to another, but from a social environment of country or small town to one of metropolitan congestion and industrial pressure, which would inevitably enforce an altered mode of living, a new set of physiological responses. That a move from rural to urban life brings with it slight modification of anatomical form had been previously found by observers in Germany and Italy (Ammon and Livi). To be exact, they showed that adjacent town and country populations differed; which means either that the very decision to move to cities constitutes a selection, or that those who move are subject to influences which modify their type—or rather, since adults are scarcely any longer modifiable, which modify the type of their children. Specific urban selection seems precluded in the case of American immigration, so that the environmental influence must be admitted. However, it is well to recognize that we do not yet know at all what the environmental factors at work are, nor how they themselves may vary.

In short, what these measurements and their statistical interpretation seem to establish is that hereditary racial types may possess a certain limited degree of plasticity, within the measure of which they can respond to alterations of environment. There is no indication that environment as such will alter a race progressively or cumulatively. If progressive adaptive alterations do occur, it is presumably through natural selection; that is, survival value of certain traits

76. THE HOLOGENETIC THEORY

The problems of the origin and the development of human races have attracted their full share of theories, ranging from more or less useful working hypotheses to fantasies. A few of these will be reviewed.

The principle of *hologenesis,* developed by Rosa in palaeontology, has been applied to man by Montandon. The theory holds that as evolutionary development begins in a certain direction, part of the organisms involved change rather rapidly; another part, more slowly. The former attain a *precocious* specialization but then stand still; the latter, at first *retarded* in their change, finally achieve a more balanced, successful, varied, and progressive development.

This is how the theory is applied to human racial history by Montandon. The first split of early recent man, he holds, was into a precocious Pygmoid and a more generalized branch. The Bushmen-Hottentots and the Pygmies remain as outdistanced, primitive survivors of their early specialization. The rest of mankind next divided into a precocious southern or Negroid branch and a generalized northern one. Within the southern branch, the Tasmanians split off from the other Negroids as the more precocious; that is, the more primitive. The northern or non-Negroid line of descent similarly divided into Veddoid-Australoids and less differentiated "Amer-Eur-Asiatics"; among these in turn the American Indians were set off as the more "precocious" against Eur-Asiatics. These last again divided into Asiatics, who branched into Eskimo and Mongoloids, and Europeans, who branched into Lapponoids and Europoids; the latter, in turn, apparently consisting of relatively precocious Ainu on the one hand and the Blonds, the Alpine-Armenoids, and the Browns (Mediterraneans) on the other. Including subdivisions not mentioned here, altogether 20 races are recognized.

This hologenetic theory thus boils down to a not very aberrant race classification, from the point of view of results; but it arrives at this goal by a method of its own. This method has something in its favor, but is also open to grave criticism. What it has in its favor is that the "precocious" Bushmen, Pygmies, Tasmanians, Veddoids, and Australoids are generally accepted as carrying primitive traits. The objections are, first, that it is far from sure that these races branched off early in the history of man—in other words, that they are really precocious. Some of them may represent late modifications of type in numerically small populations living in isolation. Second, there are places in the hologenetic system where it is the supposedly generalized "retarded" branch that in the end becomes specialized, as the bulk of the Negroids. Far from being primitive as against the more northerly remainder of humanity, they are now specialized also. In the same way, contrary to Montandon's supposition, the East Asiatic Mongoloids are certainly more differentiated or refined racially than the American Indians, who remain pretty generalized and free from primitive specialties such as Bushmen, Pygmies, Australians, and other supposedly pre-cocious groups show. The same thing can be said of Europoids: The phylo-genetically "retarded" Nordics are surely as highly characterized or specialized as the allegedly more precocious Lapps and Ainu. Finally, it is extremely un-likely that the actual evolution of races would rigidly proceed on a basis of merely a two-way split with that split always hinging on the same point of precocity. Nature is too full of conflicting and independent factors to work as simply as a piece of diagrammatic logic.

What the hologenetic scheme does do is to call attention to a series of small populations, usually surviving in the comparative protection of remoteness, iso-lation, or undesirable habitat, who show certain marked anatomical peculiari-ties. This holds for Eskimo, Ainu, and Lapps, as well as for the Bushman-Australoid series previously listed. Some of these aberrant types may really be survivals of very ancient and precocious modifications—"mistaken experiments" of evolution. But there is nothing to show that all these types are of this order: others quite possibly are relatively recent developments, connected with their special and isolating environments. In any event, the hologenetic theory makes a blanket assumption in advance instead of trying genuinely to investigate each case and then seeing whether there is a common principle in them all. Accepted not as an explanation, but as a point of view that raises some interesting un-solved problems, it has a certain value.

77. ENDOCRINE THEORIES OF RACE

Sir Arthur Keith has proposed that the origins of racial differences may be found in different functioning of the endocrine or ductless glands. For instance, thyroidal deficiency often makes for a flat face and nose but a bulging forehead; adrenal deficiency, for darkening of the skin; pituitary deficiency, for infantil-ism; while pituitary hyperfunction may cause acromegaly or enlargement of face and nose. These effects have been clinically determined in individuals. Keith's suggestion is that they were operative also in the formation of the races. Unfortunately, knowledge of racial endocrine differences, structural or func-tional, is still very fragmentary. Also, the exemplifications cited boil down to glandular deficiencies among Mongoloids and Negroids and to high activity in Caucasians. It seems theoretically improbable that the situation would be as simple as this: Caucasianism consistently due to a plus, other racial types to a minus. Thus Keith relates prominence of nose, chin, and brow ridges in Cau-casians to pituitary vigor akin to acromegaly; their higher sexual differentiation, or greater male robustness, to interstitial activity; their fairness, to a "virtue" or plus-functioning of the adrenals. Contrariwise, Mongolian shortness of limbs compared to trunk, and retraction of the nasal part of the face, are held to sug-gest a mild degree of achondroplasia or short-limbed dwarfism, of bulldog build or pug-facedness, such as is brought on in individuals by defects in the growth-regulating mechanism of the thyroid. Yet it would certainly be peculiar if the differentialism of Caucasians on one side from Mongoloids and Negroids on the other were regularly and one-sidedly due to the former having, in gland after gland, more endocrine activity, and the latter less—which is what the Keith explanation comes to.

Then, even were such racial deficiencies of function substantiated as facts, the first question would be whether they were not attributable to deficiencies in the standard or manner of living—in other words, to factors in the environment. For instance, goiter prevails in some areas adjacent to Switzerland, and in the north-central and western United States, because the soil and the drinking water contain insufficient iodine for the thyroid gland to build up its specific hormone. The lack of material forces many naturally normal thyroid glands to function subpar in these districts. Environmental factors like these would have to be eliminated before genuine hereditary differences characteristic of races were reached.

Finally, while we may grant the probability of some involvement of the endocrines in race differentiation, it appears arbitrary to single them out as a principal causative factor.

What does seem reasonable and sound in the endocrine approach is its *descriptive* application to racial types—a recognition in races of certain general conditions or features known clinically to have endocrine relations; but without an endeavor to pin the major *causation* of race on the glands. Thus there is undoubtedly a habitus or condition which can be called infantile-feminine, or even foetalized; and contrariwise, a masculine-senile habitus. The latter tends toward rugged features, prominent nose, chin, and brows, large hands and feet, long limbs, heavier pigmentation, hairiness, but also baldness. This complex of conditions is due, rather variably, to endocrine-caused acromegaly, to mere maleness, to age, or to combinations of all three factors. The infantile-feminine traits are a smooth face with low nose, high forehead and undeveloped chin, small hands and feet, tendency toward general fattiness, lighter pigmentation, and less hair except on the skull. This habitus, again, is variably due to youth, to femininity, and to thyroidal and pituitary deficiency.

It is evident that a number of races trend toward one or the other type. If the racial inclination is toward the infantile, men and women differ relatively little in appearance; if toward the senile, they differ considerably. In Europe, the Alpine type is infantile, on the whole; the Dinaric and the Nordic, especially of the so-called Palaeolithic Borreby-survival subtype, are senile. The East Asiatics, as exemplified by the Chinese and the Farther Indians, and again by most Malaysians, would be infantile-feminine. In Oceania, Micronesians are more feminine, Polynesians more masculine. Among American Mongoloids, the craggy, big-boned, large-handed, hawk-nosed Plains Indians are obviously senile, and contrast especially with the long-trunked, short-limbed tribes of the South American tropical forest, whose men and women are so strikingly alike in their

figures and faces. There is also little doubt which way the balance leans as between Australoids and Negroids: the Australoids have heavy supraorbital ridges,
gnarled and tense features, bushy beards; the Negro face by contrast has a
smooth forehead, relaxed features, loose lips, little beard.

These observations must not be stretched too far. Their value is essentially
descriptive, not explanatory. Both habituses are only polar extremes in a general
human range, most of which would be median or little differentiated.

Also, neither habitus should be assumed to be intrinsically correlated with
primitiveness. Rather it would appear that both senile-masculine and infantile-
feminine traits can occur in retardedly primitive and in secondarily specialized
races.

78. THE FINE-COARSE-TYPE THEORY

Less can be said for a bipolar differentiation into fine and coarse types,
which has sometimes been used to separate a given population into its supposed
racial constituents or origins, as by Baelz for the Japanese. There is no doubt
that there are in every population individuals with relatively narrow, high-
bridged noses, longer faces, slenderer bodies, tapering fingers; and others who
are comparatively short, broad, thickset, heavy, or muscular in the same features. The first will resemble aristocrats in their build; the second, peasants.
Moreover, if there are actual aristocrats and peasants in the population, we can
expect the aristocrats to lean on the whole more toward the first type, on account
of the ways each individual has preponderantly used his body since childhood,
and the peasants to the second type. Deft and graceful motions would be socially called for from members of one group; calluses, bulging muscles, and
heavy bones would be developed mostly by the other. All this can be anticipated
as the double result of individuals' differing from one another and of these particular differences also representing external modifications of heredity by somatic
habit functioning as directed by social-class environment. The case is no different in principle from the facts that every population contains both larger
and smaller individuals by heredity, and that in addition the best-nourished will
average bigger than the underprivileged. It would be an obvious and gratuitous
error to try regularly to establish separate racial origins for the large and the
small individuals in each population. Now and then a population may be found
to segregate into two indubitably separate types, as in East Africa, where the
very attenuated, tall, pastoral Bahima aristocracy rules over stockier farmers.
But here the differentiation is only incidentally into fine and coarse, primarily
into ultratall and leptosome as against a normal majority.

In the case of the Japanese, the fine or Choshiu and coarse or Satsuma
types, after having been tied up with the legendary history of Japan, are simply
derived, by the Baelz theory, from supposed original types on the East Asiatic
mainland. On this mainland the two types can undoubtedly be distinguished in
some individuals, as they can be in Japan; but they have there not been segre-

gated populationally, that is, areally or racially. The supposed foundation for the fine-coarse-race hypothesis in Japan therefore boils down to an equally hypothetical assumption made for China.

For China, however, Legendre, while following the essential Baelz logic, has preferred to make a guess of different content. He recognizes a larger, finer, more Europoid constituent, "Assyroid or.Aryan" in type and derived—hypothetically—from the West; and a darker, smaller, prognathous, flat-nosed, lower, and coarser Negritoid type, related to "Melanesians and Polynesians"! The great mass of the Chinese people are alleged to be hybrids of these two original elements. This last is of course pure preferential dogmatism. Granting that the total population could be ranged between the two extremes—and there is no effort made to show that quite differently chosen extremes would not fit the Chinese picture equally well—it remains to be proved that the extremes were really original. They might obviously just as well be rare specializations secondarily evolved out of a less-differentiated racial mass. It may be added that Legendre published his view under the sensational title *There Is No Yellow Race*. How hasty his basic race concepts are is evident from his allying his Negritos to Polynesians. Incidentally, Negritos considered as the original population of South China keep cropping up in print, because of references in ancient Chinese literature to aborigines of South China as small and dark— plus no doubt also because the far-fetched and unlikely has a dramatic appeal. With Negritos still in Malaya, Luzon, and the Andamans, it is wholly conceivable that there may also once have been tribes of them in China. But there does not seem to be any discovered evidence to that effect; and it is certainly at the very bounds of probability that a fertile tract like South China, now harboring many tens of millions of straight Mongoloids, should as recently as in the protohistoric period, only two or three thousand years ago, have been the haunt chiefly of scattered bands of Negroid Pygmies.

Views like these have a way of falling to pieces when they are really analyzed. Often, however, they live for two or three generations, either because no one troubles to make the analysis, or because of their appeal to our purely imaginative faculties. These particular theories have been dissected here chiefly as examples of uncritical thinking, of reasoning from arbitrary preferences. Thus the fine-coarse type of race explanation has by no means been limited to China and Japan, but has been applied again and again to racial origins elsewhere.

79. CONSTITUTIONAL TYPES

Constitutional types crosscut races in that they set up a classification of human physique in general, often with special reference to associated temperament, mental activity, and disease incidence. The majority of such typings are bipolar, and they amount in the last analysis to saying that there are broader-bodied and narrower-bodied individuals in every group. To put this simple and in itself harmless finding learnedly, we substitute the terms "eurysome" and "leptosome." Of course the middle majority of any population are not strictly either broad or narrow in physique, any more than they are definitely tall or short, phlegmatic or excitable, extravert or introvert, but are near-average or indeterminate. Interest picks up when associations are allied with a type of mind or liability to certain disease. Thus Kretschmer called the thickset, pyknics; the medium, athletics; and the ultraslender, asthenics; and found that when they go insane, pyknics are more likely to be manic-depressives and asthenics to be schizophrenics. This may well be: the ancients already recognized an apoplectic and a phthisic type whose somatic build is essentially identical with Kretschmer's extreme types. But probably a full half of any population cannot be assigned to either end-type without artificial forcing; nor is the average man in the middle markedly "athletic." On the other hand, concepts like leptosome and eurysome, or lineal and lateral, or for that matter pyknic and asthenic, do often have utility in descriptions of individual physiques or in other specific situations, when they are used without attempt at system-mongering.

Somewhat more varied than the bipolar theories is a fourfold scheme of constitutional types advocated by Sigaud and his followers: cerebral, muscular, respiratory, and digestive. The functional or physiological implications of these body forms are obvious. We can all think of individuals in our acquaintance who neatly fit into one or the other of these classes—also of a great number who fit badly or not at all.

The most recent classification of types, still partially in the mode as of 1948, is Sheldon's. He has somewhat reworked the older pyknic-digestive, muscular-respiratory-athletic, and cerebro-asthenic types, and has trapped them out in an impressive dress of endomorphs, mesomorphs, and ectomorphs on the basis of supposed dominance of the endo-, meso-, and ectoderm in their embryological development. He has also given them temperamental correspondences according as their tonus is dominantly visceral, muscular ("soma"), or neural. The definitions of the temperaments are incisive and characteristic. Thus, pyknic viscerotonics are described as relaxed, slow, complacent, even-tempered, tolerant, flabby, and without spark, but amiable and quietly sociable and dependent on people; they are fond of comfort, food, digestion, sleep, company, politeness, and affection. Somatotonics, with muscular physiques, are assertive, active, energetic, courageous, dominating, ruthless, callous, indifferent to pain, noisy, claustrophobic, and extravert; they seek adventure, risk, exercise, competition, and directness. Cerebrotonics, or ectomorphs, with neural loading, are restrained in posture and often in movement, but overresponsive and too fast in reactions. They are socially inhibited, apprehensive, hypersensitive, resistive to routine, unpredictable, secretive, solitary, agoraphobic and introvert, self-conscious. Also, they are poor sleepers, restless in their face and hands, oriented toward age but youthful in appearance. This last type pretty much adds up to a schizophrenically inclined temperament, as Kretschmer assigned it to his asthenics; just as the two other personality types of Sheldon approximate respectively the quiet and excited phases of cyclothymia. Nevertheless, the type characterizations are apt: we can all readily recognize individuals of our acquaintance. Sheldon is evidently a felicitous type-builder. The limitations of the scheme are first, that in spite of all elaboration of method, the type determinations themselves, plus the correspondence of anatomy with psychology, retain a subjective constituent. Secondly, all previous experience with types is to the effect that the majority of individuals are transitional or indefinite instead of clear-cut in type. The Sheldon scheme may be an exception, but it will have to prove itself.

In general, it must be remembered that successful instances of any type can always be found, but that the validity of a general explanation or system is proportionate to its success in accommodating the totality, or at least a near-totality, of cases without forcing or straining. To date, correlations between all constitutional somatic types and psychological or clinical types remain rather weak. This is not because psychosomatic correspondences are lacking, but because all types appear in series of living individuals with much less sharpness than they possess in the formulator's conception.

80. RACE, NATIONALITY, AND LANGUAGE

The term "race" has here been used in its biological sense, for a group united in blood or heredity. A race is a subdivision of a species and corresponds to a breed in domestic animals. Popularly, the word is used in a different sense; namely, that of a population having any traits in common, be they hereditary or nonhereditary, biological or sociocultural, organic or superorganic (§ 6). It is customary, but mainly inaccurate, to speak of the French race, the Anglo-Saxon race, the Gypsy race, the Jewish race. The French are a nation and a nationality, with a substantially common speech; biologically, they are three races considerably mixed, but still imperfectly blended (§ 62). "Anglo-Saxon" refers primarily to speech, incidentally to a set of customs, traditions, and points of view that are more or less associated with the language. The Gypsies are a self-constituted caste, with folkways, occupations, and at least Romany speech remnants of their own. They have mostly preserved their dark Mediterranoid type, as well as their high-B blood group, which they brought with them from India. The Jews, who were once a nationality, for a time even a state, at present of course form a religious body, which somewhat variably, in part from inner cohesion and in part from outer pressure, tends also to constitute a social caste within Western society. The degree to which they have and have not preserved a distinctive hereditary racial type has already been touched upon (§ 68, 72). At any rate, attitudes toward Jews obviously depend immeasurably more on emotional reaction to the social functioning of Jews than on their biology.

It may seem of little moment whether the word "race" is restricted to its strict biological sense or used more loosely. In fact, however, untold loose reasoning has resulted from the loose terminology. When one has spoken a dozen times of "the French race," one tends inevitably to think of the inhabitants of France as a biological unit, which they are not. The basis of the error is confusion of organic traits and processes with superorganic or cultural ones, of heredity with tradition or imitation. That civilizations, languages, and nationalities go on for generations is obviously a different thing from their being caused by generation. Slovenly thought, tending to deal with results rather than causes or processes, does not trouble to make this discrimination; and everyday speech, dating from a prescientific period, is ambiguous about it. We say not only "generation" when there is no intent to imply the reproductive process, but "good breeding" (literally, good brooding or hatching or birth) when we mean good home training or education; just as we "inherit" a fortune or a name—sociocultural things—as well as ineradicable traits such as brown eyecolor. Biology has secured for its processes the exclusive use of the term "heredity," and biologists employ the term "race" only with reference to a hereditary subdivision of a species. It is equally important that the word be used with the same exact denotation in anthropology, else all discussion of race degenerates irretrievably into illogical sliding in and out between organic and superorganic factors. The inherently great difficulties which beset the understanding and solution of what are generally called race problems, as discussed in the next chapter, are considerably increased by a confusion between what is and what is not racial, organic, and hereditary.

Problems of Race Difference

THIS CHAPTER deals with some aspects of the intricate question of just what are the differences between the functioning of the biological races of man and what they are due to. It tries to establish, not too successfully because of scarcity of conclusive evidence, how much of such differences is racially genetic—that is, organically hereditary—and how much due to historical, sociocultural conditioning; that is, environmental, superorganic causes. The argument therefore deals with one of the basic problems of fundamental science, as it has already been sketched in Chapter One. The present chapter does not deal with what are popularly called "race problems"—which in most cases are not racial but ethnic—namely, the troubles of minority groups and the troubles they give to majorities. The concern is rather with some of the underlying facts and principles in those cases where biological race is really involved.

81. QUESTIONS OF ENDOWMENT AND THEIR VALIDITY

Are the human races alike or dissimilar in mentality and character? Are some lower than others, or are they all on a plane as regards potentiality? The answers to these questions are of theoretical import, and naturally also bear on the solution of the practical and often crucial race problems with which some nations are confronted. The word "race" is here used in its strict or biological sense, as denoting a subspecies or other group set off by heredity (§ 80), not in the loose popular sense of a group set off by speech, religion, or social consciousness.

As long as an inquiry remains sufficiently abstract or remote, the desirability of such inquiry is likely to go unquestioned. As soon, however, as investigation touches conduct—for instance actual relations with other races—sentiment has a way of rising to the effect that perhaps after all the problem does not so much call for understanding as for decision. Thus, in regard to the Negro problem in the United States, it is likely to be said that the immediate issue is what may be the best attitude toward Jim Crow cars and other forms of segregation. Are these desirable or undesirable, fair or unfair? Here are specific problems to which actual conditions press for an answer. Under the circumstances, it will be said, is not an inquiry into the innate capacity of the Negro rather remote, especially when everyone can see by a thousand examples that the Negro is obviously inferior to the Caucasian? He is poorer, more shiftless, less successful. He has made no inventions, produced no great geniuses. He clearly feels himself inferior and comports himself accordingly. Why then raise the issue of capacity at all, unless from a desire to befog the question, to subvert the conclusions of common sense and everyday experience by special pleading that substitutes adroitness for sincerity? In some such form as this, objections may rise in the minds of some.

The answer to such criticism is first of all that racial inferiority and superiority are by no means self-evident truths. Secondly, the belief in race inequalities is founded in emotion and action and then justified by reasoning. That is, the belief is rationalized after it is held, not primarily inferred by pure reason. It may be true, but it is not proved true.

As to what is self-evident, there is nothing so misleading as direct observation. We see the sun move and the earth stand still. It is "self-evident" that the sun revolves around the earth. Yet after thousands of years the civilized portion of mankind finally came to believe that it is the earth that spins. Science had no perverse interest, no insidious motive, in advocating the Copernican instead of the Ptolemaic system; in fact, it was driven to its new belief gradually and reluctantly. It was prescientific humanity, with its direct, homespun, everyday observation, which had really prejudged the matter, and which, because it had always assumed that the earth was stationary, and because every idiot could see that it was so, long combated the idea that it could be otherwise.

As for beliefs founded in emotion and subsequently rationalized, it may suffice to quote from a once famous book by Trotter on mass opinion:

When, therefore, we find ourselves entertaining an opinion about the basis of which there is a quality of feeling which tells us that to inquire into it would be absurd, obviously unnecessary, unprofitable, undesirable, bad form or wicked, we may know that that opinion is a non-rational one, and probably, therefore, founded upon inadequate evidence. Opinions, on the other hand, which are acquired as the result of experience alone do not possess this quality of primary certitude. They are true in the sense of being verifiable, but they are unaccompanied by that profound feeling of truth which belief possesses, and, therefore, we have no sense of reluctance in admitting inquiry into them.

Take the attitude of many a Californian or Australian about the Mongolian; of the average Texan about the Mexican; of the run-of-the-mill Southerner about he Negro; of the Westerner about the local tribes of Indians; of the English-man about the Hindu; of the German even about the Poles and Russians who racially are only barely distinguishable from himself—is not their feeling pretty fairly described by the statement that inquiry into the possibility of racial equal-ity would be "unnecessary," "absurd," or evilly motivated, and that their belief in race superiority rests on an "a-priori synthesis of the most perfect sort," and possesses "the quality of primary certitude"?

In short, the apparently theoretical beliefs held as to race capacity by people who are confronted by an actual race conflict or problem are by no means the outcome of impartial examination and verification, but are the result of the decisions taken and the emotions experienced in the course of acts performed toward the other race. The beliefs rest ultimately on impulse and feeling; their reasoned support is a subsequent bolstering-up. Of course, the fact that a belief springs from emotion does not render that belief untrue; but it does leave the belief scientifically unproved, and calling for investigation.

These conclusions may vindicate inquiry into the relative capacity of races from the charge of being finespun, insidious, impractical, or loaded with bias.

In an approach to the problem, one consideration stands out. If the human races are identical in capacity, or if, though not absolutely alike, they average substantially the same in the sum total of their capacities, then such differences as they have shown in their history or show in their present condition must evidently be the result mainly of circumstances external to heredity. In that case, knowledge of the historical or environmental circumstances, and analysis of the latter, become all-important to understanding. On the other hand, if hereditary racial inequalities exist, one can expect that the historical or cultural influences, however great they may be, will nevertheless tend to have their origin in the hereditary factors and to reinforce them. In that case, differences between two groups would be due partly to underlying heredity and partly to overlying cultural forces tending on the whole in the same direction. Yet even in that case, before one could begin to estimate the strength of the true racial factors, the historical ones would have to be subtracted. Thus, in either event, the first crux of the problem lies in the recognition and stripping-off of cultural, social, or environmental factors, so far as possible, from the complex mass of phenomena which living human groups present. In proportion as these social or acquired traits can be determined and discounted, the innate and truly racial ones will be isolated, and can then be examined, weighed, and compared. Such, at any rate, is a reasonable plan of procedure. We are looking for the inherent, ineradicable elements in a social animal that has everywhere built up around himself an environment—namely, his culture—in which he mentally lives and breathes. It is precisely because in the present inquiry we wish to get below the effects of culture that we must be ready to concern ourselves considerably with these effects, actual or possible.

82. ANATOMICAL EVIDENCE ON EVOLUTIONARY RANK

But first of all it may be well to consider the relatively simple evidence that has to do with the physical form and structure of race types. If one human race should prove definitely nearer to the apes in its anatomy than the other races, there would be reason to believe that it had lagged in evolution. Also there would be some presumption that its arrears were mental as well as physical.

But the facts do not run consistently. One thinks of the Negro as simian. His jaws are prognathous; his forehead recedes; his nose is both broad and low. Further, it is among Caucasians that the antithetical traits occur. In straightness of jaws and forehead, prominence and narrowness of nose, Caucasians in general exceed the Mongoloids. Thus the order as regards these particular traits is: ape, Negroid, Mongoloid, Caucasian. With ourselves at one end and the monkey at the other, the scale somehow seems right. It appeals, and seems significant. Facts of this sort are therefore readily observed, come to be remembered, and rise spontaneously to mind in an argument.

However, there are numerous items that conflict with this sequence. For instance, one of the most conspicuous differences of man from the apes is his relative hairlessness. Of the three main stocks, however, it is the Caucasian that is the most hairy on both face and body.

In texture of hair, as well as sparseness on the body, the Negroid is the most "domesticated" (§ 73) and the most characteristically human.

Ape lips are grayish, thin, but mobile and extrudable almost to being prehensile. Among men, Mongolian lips are perhaps thinnest and Negro ones the most specializedly full and everted.

It is unnecessary to multiply examples. If one human racial stock falls below others in certain traits, it rises above them in other features, insofar as "below" and "above" may be measurable in terms of degree of resemblance to the apes.

It is also clear that some traits may have been acquired independently, may have been secondarily evolved over again. Thus the supraorbital ridges. When one observes the consistency with which these are heavy in most Pleistocene specimens—Pithecanthropus, Sinanthropus, Neandertal, and Rhodesian man—and how the male gorilla shows them enormously developed; and that among living races they are perhaps strongest in the lowly cultured Australian, it is tempting to look upon this bony development as a sign of primitiveness. Yet there is an array of contradicting facts. The youthful gorilla and the adult orang are without supraorbital development. The male gorilla has his powerful brows for the same reason that he has the crests along the top of his skull: they are needed as attachments for his powerful musculature. They are evidently a secondary sex character developed within the species. So among fossil men there were two strains: the second one, represented by the Piltdown, Steinheim,

Swanscombe, and other finds (§ 45, 54), being smooth of forehead. Among living races the Asiatic Mongoloids lack marked supraorbital development; the closely related American Indians possess it rather strongly; some Caucasians and many Negroes show little of the feature; Australians have it most of all. Evidently it would be unsafe to build many conclusions on either the presence or the absence of supraorbital ridges.

Perhaps these instances will suffice to show that even the mere anatomical rating of human races is far from a simple or an easy task. It is doubtful whether as yet it is valid to speak of one race as physically higher or more advanced, or more human and less brutish, than another. This is not an outright denial of the possibility of such differential ratings: it is a denial only of the belief that such differentials have been established.

83. PHYSIOLOGICAL DIFFERENCES

In gross physiology, all human races are much alike. The simpler measures like pulse and respiration rates and body temperatures come out remarkably uniform in group averages, considering how much these features vary between individuals, and in individuals according to momentary activity and health. There appear to be almost no significant racial differences. On temperature, the figures given by Hooton and von Eickstedt differ only slightly, but are in contradiction. If whites have a higher normal temperature than Negroes and American Indians, the difference does not exceed .01 or .02 of a degree Centigrade. Among some 700 Indians of the southwestern United States and northwestern Mexico, Hrdlička found the pulse to average about 60 per minute, in place of the usual 70 or 72. These are mostly high-plateau dwellers; but a small sample of lowland Maya also showed a rate 10 lower than the compared whites. Pulses around 60 have been recorded also for Japanese and for Mongols. This may accordingly prove to be a Mongoloid propensity.

There are a few records on blood pressure. These suggest the seriation: Europeans, Negroes, Chinese, Cuna Indians of Panama, Hindus, Japanese—which does not make too much racial sense. The Japanese are cited at 90-105, Cuna at 105, the Chinese 101-115, as against a white "norm" of 128 for systolic pressure. On the contrary, Adams found an average of only 121 over 81 for American whites, but 128 over 85 for American Negroes in several thousand cases, with the Negro excess increasing with age. There is undoubtedly more hypertension—excessive blood pressure—in American Negroes than in whites, but this falls in the realm of pathology (§ 85) and its cause is in dispute.

Basal metabolism was first worked out on whites, and is rated by formulas that usually include body weight and skin surface as estimated from height. The height-surface ratio may vary racially, and the readings for metabolism of nonwhites may accordingly be somewhat inaccurate. White or nonwhite or both in Cuba, Brazil, Syria, Java, Singapore, and Queensland run below the American-European standard. Some of this deficiency is attributed to climate; quantity and kind of food may also be factors. The principal observations that as of 1946 looked as if they might have racial significance are the following:

Eskimo (4 series), plus 15-26 per cent
Maya and Quiché Indians (4 series), plus 5-8
Araucanian Indians of Chile, plus 10-15
India (7 series), minus 11-18
Chinese outside of China (3 series), minus 12-15
Miao of Kweichou, China, plus 16
Australian aborigines (2 series), minus 11-13
Pureblood Negroes, no satisfactory figures available

The thyroid gland is most directly involved in basal metabolism. This gland is larger in Europeans than in Chinese; larger also in white than in Negro Americans, relatively to the total body. In Europeans the thyroid weighs a bit more than one-two-thousandth of the body, in Javanese less than one-three-thousandth.

Of internal organs, the spleen seems definitely smaller in American Negroes than in whites, also the liver; and the intestines are shorter, but heart and kidneys are about the same. The physiological significance of these differences is not clear.

84. INCIDENCE OF DISEASES

Pathology might seem to promise more than normal physiology. So far as mortality goes, there are enormous differences between races. And the mortality may be largely the result of particular diseases. Measles, for instance, has often been a deadly epidemic to uncivilized peoples, and smallpox has in some regions at times taken toll of a quarter of the population in a year or two. Yet it is shortsighted to infer from such cases any permanent racial predisposition or lack of resistance. The peoples in question have been free for generations from these diseases, and have therefore not maintained or acquired immunity. Their difference from us is thus essentially in environmental experience, not hereditary or racial. This is confirmed by the fact that after a generation or two the same epidemics that at first were so deadly to Polynesians or American Indians sink to almost the same level of mild virulence that they show among ourselves. Up to about 1900-10, most tribes in the United States decreased progressively in numbers. Since that decade, nearly all have first held their own and then increased. They had then been exposed for several generations to our diseases, or to our special strains of them, and had built up partial immunities and resistances more or less like our own.

Then too, immediate environment plays a part. The nonliterate often has no idea of contagion, and still less of guarding against it; he thinks in terms of magic instead of physiology. His remedial treatment is likely to be by a mixture of guesswork, empiricism, magic, and spiritualism. He knows nothing of sepsis, vaccinations, or preventive medicine.

It may be worth while to consider briefly the facts as to mortality from cancer. This dread disease appears to be not contagious, so that the factor of acquired immunity is eliminated. It is regarded as incurable, except by operation or radium or X ray, so that differences in treatment become relatively unimportant. If therefore significant differences in racial liability to cancer exist, they should emerge clearly. There do seem to be such differences. But they are overlaid by other factors external to the organism as it is inherited.

The raw statistics uniformly make cancer seem an overwhelmingly Caucasian disease. Thus, some comparative samples of cancer deaths per 100,000 population in various places within the period 1905-15 run as follows:

DEATHS FROM CANCER, 1905-1915

Johannesburg: whites, 52; Negroes, 14
Natal: whites, 56; Hindus, 11
Hong Kong: Europeans, 53; Chinese, 5
Manila: whites, 51; Filipinos, 27; Chinese, 19
East Indies: Dutch, 81; Singapore and Straits Settlements: natives, 13, 10;
  Ceylon, Calcutta: natives, 5, 11
United States: whites, 77; Indians, 4

However, for some unknown reason climate, as expressed grossly by latitude, is also a factor. Thus for large cities, in the same period:

CANCER IN LATITUDES
(Large cities)

60°-50° N.	106	30° N.-30° S.	38-42
50°-40° N.	92	30°-40° S.	90
40°-30° N.	78		

In some cases occupation is a direct or indirect cause. It was long ago noted that chimney sweeps were particularly liable to cancer. Thus as far back as 1890 they suffered in England, among males of 45-54, 532 cancer deaths a year per 100,000 population, as against an average for all occupations of 118. It is now known that the coal tars in soot are irritants that may stimulate cancerous growths. There are other vocation-frequency differences that remain wholly unexplained—perhaps being due to an indirect functional relation—but which recur decade after decade, so that the fact must be accepted. Thus British gardeners have twice as good a chance of not dying of cancer as brewers, and clergymen as lawyers. And this in spite of gardening and the clerical profession being long-lived occupations with high survival into the old age when cancer is most frequent.

This suggests a third factor besides latitude-climate and occupation; namely, a low general death rate and a consequent large proportion of aged people in the population. In a backward population in the modern world—they need not be primitive, only a couple of generations hygienically behind the times—so many children and young people die of preventable or curable disease that there are relatively few survivors to die of cancer, nephritis, or heart ailments as they become aged. All these latter diseases have in fact shot upward in the last century, and especially in the past fifty years, wherever sanitation and hygiene have been most advanced. This has been in proportion to the marked reduction of deaths from infantile dysentery, diphtheria, smallpox, typhoid, tuberculosis, and pneumonia. Most medical authorities believe that there is an intrinsic increase of both cancer and heart disease among ourselves in contemporary decades. But the eminent medical statistician Dublin believes that for cancer the increase is probably not real. It is obvious that there is a statistical increase due to the change in age distribution; and until this can be reliably computed, the size of the genuine increase will remain in doubt. The influence of the age factor holds for all populations, but it will be particularly strong, as regards an age-weighted disease like cancer, among the economically and medically backward, where most nonwhite peoples find themselves at present.

A fourth factor is the degree of medical observation and treatment. Where there are no X-ray laboratories or examinations, where hospitals or operations are not available or where patients fear or avoid them, and autopsies are not made, cancer deaths may be high, but diagnoses and death certifications will be low. Thus in Hungary, from 1901 to 1904, the reported cancer deaths were 239 per 100,000 among the owners of large farms, 41 among the owners of small farms; 108 among employing blacksmiths, 25 among their employees; 114 among employing tailors, 32 among employed tailors. Obviously, these pairs of groups differed in their economic status and therewith in the degree of their exposure to medical diagnosis.

Here too may be the explanation of why the South African Negro showed a rate of only 14 per 100,000 in the period that the United States Negro showed 56; also why the Chinese rate was as low as 5 in Hong Kong, rose to 19 in Manila and to 26 in Hawaii, while the average for the racially similar Japanese was 62 for the whole of Japan—as compared with 50 for Spain, which is pure Caucasian, but has been economically and medically one of the more backward countries of Europe. In Tokyo and Kyoto the rate soared to 73 and 90 respectively, just as in the United States it is considerably higher for the urban than for the rural population.

Within the United States, also, the rate rises and falls almost parallel for whites and Negroes according to locality; as,

CANCER DEATHS 1906-1910
(per 100,000)

Place	White	Negro
Memphis	59	34
Charleston	73	37
Nashville	74	55
New Orleans	86	73

If allowance is made for the facts that the Negro population of the United States is poorer and less educated than the white; that diagnosis or authentic medical certification of cause of death for the Negro population is more likely to be haphazard; that most Negroes live mainly in low-latitude southern states, the majority of whites in northern states; and that Negroes tend to be rural rather than urban—we derive from this that a considerable differential cancer death rate, such as a third more for the white than the colored, might be reasonably accounted for without bringing race into consideration. More on this in the next section.

In short, what superficially seems to be a notable race difference in cancer liability and mortality turns out to be at least in part due to natural and socio-cultural environment. This is not an assertion that race has nothing to do with the disease—only that the degree of influence of race has not yet been reliably defined and is difficult to define. The variable x of race and the variable y of environment both remain undetermined; but until we can strip off a fairly determinate result of y influence, we are not even coming to grips with the x factor.

Cancer has here served as an illustration only because there are analyzable data available and because the environmental factor of communicability seems to be ruled out, strengthening the first-blush case for its apparent dependence on race. Each separate disease has of course to be examined independently both as to its racial frequency and as to all the factors possibly involved.

Malaria, for instance, has been depicted as a scourge of the light-skinned races, against which Negroids have a large degree of racial—that is, genetic—resistance. Historical theories have been built upon this assumption. For example, there is an attractive hypothesis as to why Madagascar, especially in its coastal lowlands, is prevalently Negro in race but Indonesian in culture. The light-skinned invading people and their descendants were said to die off from fevers, but to leave their culture to the Negroids. Yet where malaria is endemic in Africa, and whites tend to die off from it while black natives flourish, it is reasonably clear that this is because childhood infections have built up the individual Negro's resistance—that is, the resistance of those who survive this rough process of exposure and immunization. In the United States the position of the Negro is superficially the opposite from that in Africa. The Negro death rate from malaria the United States over is eight times higher than that of whites! The reason is, first, that most of the United States no longer has very many deaths from malaria. There being much less malaria around, Negroes on the average acquire less immunity than in Africa. But, second, a much larger proportion of the total Negro population than of the total white population lives in the malarious districts of our South, in rural districts containing undrained areas, in poverty, without screens and sometimes without enough quinine. Hence there is enough infection in and around the lower Mississippi Valley to bring malaria mortality up to an appreciable figure in the Negro total, but only to an inconsiderable proportion of the ten times larger and more widespread white total. In being transported to the United States, the Negro has lost the protection of the childhood immunization of each new generation, but has not gained the white American's protection derived from mostly living in healthy districts and from maximum medical prevention and care. In a sense he has got caught in the middle.

The diagram in Figure 13, illustrating the variations in the history of malaria in the Romagna, proves that factors other than race must often be at work. With the incidence and the severity of the disease changing markedly through the centuries among the members of the same population in the same district of Italy, it is clear that either the malaria amoeba has varied in virulence; or that *Anopheles* mosquitoes have varied in numbers; or that economic or other cultural circumstances have had an effect; or possibly that immunity gets lost and has to be reacquired within the same racial strain. In short, the malaria-to-race relation ends up by once more presenting us with a single equation containing several unknowns.

The eminent bacteriologist and immunologist Zinsser sums up the situation as to racial immunity in the statement that it is most often attributable to indi-vidually acquired resistance: genetic factors may occasionally be involved. Even with experimentation on animals, he says, it is hard to determine which kind of immunity—racial or environmental, hereditary or acquired—one is dealing with. Pinner, speaking of tuberculosis, says that a true inheritance of acquired immunity has never been demonstrated. Well, what is difficult for a laboratory

B.C.   A.C.   Centuries
8 7 6 5 4 3 2 1   1 2 3 4 5 6 7 8 9 10 11 12 13 14 15 16 17 18 19 20

FIG. 13.   MALARIA FREQUENCY

Curve of malaria incidence and virulence through twenty-seven hundred years in the Italian Romagna. (From Ackerknecht after Hackett after Celli)

worker, who can set his conditions and controls for animals, is obviously going to be more difficult for the anthropologist, who has to take his facts on man raw as nature and history feed them to him.

85. SPECIALTIES OF NEGRO PATHOLOGY

For some diseases the United States Negro offers a better field for interracial comparison than the African, because in spite of social disadvantages, he lives at least roughly in the same environment as the whites he is compared with, or we know enough about his circumstances to make some estimate of his environmental difference. It is true that the statistics would be worth considerably more if the mostly-Negro and the mostly-white in blood had been distinguished instead of being lumped as "colored"; but the future may bring that improvement. The data that follow—and that are tabulated overleaf—are based mainly on what Lewis has brought together.

So as not to pluck perpetually at the one string of difficulty of obtaining positive findings, let us begin with those diseases in which it is most likely, perhaps as good as certain, that Negroes and whites do show genuinely racial—that is, genetic—differences; go on from these to those which can be debated; and end with commentary.

Sickle-cell anemia is virtually confined to Negroes, perhaps wholly so. Some think there is no clear occurrence of it in any individual demonstrably free of suspicion of Negro blood. The anemia occurs as a relapsing disease in a very small proportion of a group of colored people whose blood normally and in health contains "sickle"-shaped cells. This condition is called sicklemia and is shown by about one American Negro in fifteen. It appears not yet to have been proved Mendelian, but is generally considered to be a unit factor of heredity. It may therefore be a race-limited mutation.

Negro resistance to trachoma is high in Africa as well as America, and contrasts with the prevalence of this eye infection in India and the susceptibility of the American Indian.

Hookworm resistance also is marked in Africa. Hospital records and autopsies in Africa confirm also the American experience of relative scarcity of peptic ulcer and urinary stones in Negroes. Gallstone infrequency is likewise established for Trinidad and Jamaican Negroes as well as those in the United States. The high Negro incidence of nephritis is allied to that of hypertension.

Negro resistance to measles and infantile paralysis has a slight statistical doubt cast on it by the fact that both are less common in southern than in northern states.

As to cancer, early records show a greater difference between the two populations than recent ones. The creeping-up presumably means that the Negro now has more diagnosis and treatment than he used to get. The total present rate

COMPARATIVE PATHOLOGY OF NEGROES AND WHITES IN THE UNITED STATES

DIFFERENCE DEFINITE AND MARKED, ALMOST CERTAINLY RACIAL

Lower Incidence for Negroes	*Higher Incidence for Negroes*
Diphtheria	Sickle-cell anemia
Yellow fever	Whooping cough (frequency × 3)
Haemophilia (nonclotting)	Fibroids in womb (× 5±)
Peptic ulcer	Keloid tumors (× 15±)
Psoriasis	Nephritis
Lupus	
Trachoma	
Surgical suppuration	

DIFFERENCE PERCEPTIBLE, SOME PROBABILITY OF BEING RACIAL

Lower Incidence for Negroes	*Higher Incidence for Negroes*
Scarlet fever	Lobar pneumonia
Measles	Hypertension
Infantile paralysis	Cerebral hemorrhage
Angina pectoris	Syphilitic heart disease
Arteriosclerosis	Cancer of female genitalia
Coronary occlusion	
Peptic ulcer	
Gallstones	
Urinary stones	
Most cancers	

FACT OR CAUSE OF DIFFERENCE IN DISPUTE

Lower Incidence for Negroes	*Higher Incidence for Negroes*
Pernicious anemia	Tuberculosis
Diabetes	Syphilis
	Typhoid fever
	Malaria

FACT OF DIFFERENCE WHOLLY UNCERTAIN

Smallpox	Rickets	Mongolian idiocy
Influenza	Epilepsy	Appendicitis
Pellagra		Hypertrophy of prostate

is around two-thirds that of the white; but for women of childbearing age there are more deaths from cancer among Negroes. The differences are perhaps greater qualitatively than in frequency: sarcoma, epithelioma, melanoma are particularly uncommon in Negroes. For the Negro in Africa the situation is pictured somewhat differently. Though the total incidence there is also less, primary carcinoma of the liver, skin cancer, and melanoma are relatively conspicuous, carcinoma of the stomach rare. But, as in America, a larger proportion of all Negro cancers come in middle life. This may mean a racial difference or only that fewer Negroes survive other diseases to die of cancer when they are old.

The records reveal fewer Negro than white diabetes admissions and deaths. But that this is a disease largely of diet and habits is shown by the fact that Frankfort Jews compared with Gentiles—from whom they certainly were not markedly different racially—had a diabetes incidence more than six times as high.

As for tuberculosis, some authorities believe and some disbelieve that there is a racial basis for the admitted difference in virulence. Tuberculosis ranks second in mortality for American Negroes, sixth for whites; fifty years ago it stood highest for both. The clinical descriptions for Negroes still frequently read like those for nineteenth-century whites, among whom a milder fibroid form has now come to be usual. Up to the age of twenty, the colored death rate runs at least three or four times higher. At ten to fourteen years, it is nearly eight times higher. After twenty-five, Negro and white rates more and more approximate. Tuberculosis is obviously a disease in which early diagnosis and persistent, prolonged treatment are of utmost importance, and these in turn are bound to be functions of educational and economic level. In parts of tropical Africa, French reports indicate a "virgin-soil" type of tuberculosis similar to that of previously unexposed American Indians or Polynesians. A fair summing-up for the United States situation seems to be Pinner's, that most of the tuberculosis frequency and mortality of the Negro is probably due to social conditions, but that the form of the disease, and the Negro's lower resistance to it, especially in youth, are probably at least partly founded on a genetic racial difference.

Syphilis is of course par excellence a social disease, and therefore one of the most difficult really to prove a racial basis for. Between 1915 and 1935, the reported death rate for whites increased 44 per cent; for Negroes it increased 38 per cent. Several plausible cultural explanations suggest themselves for this change, or apparent change. But it seems inconceivable that the germ plasm or the hereditary constitution, the genetic basis of the races, could have altered so much in 20 years. There is an old medical problem about yaws, which whites rarely get but many colored peoples in the tropics have frequently. It and syphilis may be two diseases or two "forms" of one disease. There may also be cross-immunity between them.

Smallpox, like typhoid fever, seems to be endemically old and mild in Africa. Pellagra in the United States has a curious distribution. Its reported occurrence is given as from two to five times less common among Negroes, its mortality as two to five times as great. This might mean that, being poor, the Southern Negro actually gets pellagra, which is a diet disease, oftener than do whites, but neither he nor anyone else is likely to pay attention to it till he is on the point of death. For appendicitis, Negro deaths run higher; but here the cure is by surgery, for which Negroes presumably possess both less willingness and less opportunity.

These brief analyses will serve to show that while it is as good as certain that races differ genetically in their pathology, as in other traits, the problem is beset by so many contingencies and pitfalls that exact proof can be brought only rarely, and in general we are lucky if reasonable probabilities can be determined.

86. ACHIEVEMENT AND SOCIAL ENVIRONMENT

One point will have become clear in the course of the foregoing discussion; namely, that the difficulty of coming to positive conclusions is due to two sets of interacting causal factors, the given hereditary ones and the environmental ones that play upon heredity. The environmental factors are themselves a composite of geographical influences and of the economic, emotional, and other social influences that human beings exert upon each other.

If this intermingling of distinct kinds of causes is true of races when considered from the side of physiology and medicine, it is evident that the intermingling will be even more intricate in the mental sphere. After all, bodily functioning varies only within fairly definite limits: when external influences press too strongly upon the innate nature of the organism, the latter ceases to function and dies. The personality, on the other hand, however much its organic structure is given by heredity, depends for its content wholly on experience; and this experience can be thoroughly varied. Individuals of the same organic endowment may conceivably be born either in the uppermost stratum of a highly refined civilization or among backward peasants and remote tribes. Whether this actually happens, and to what degree, is of course precisely the problem we are trying to solve. But that it is theoretically and logically possible cannot be denied. And here a vicious circle of reasoning begins. One argument says: There have been no recognized geniuses among peoples like the Hottentots, and the sum total of their group achievement is ridiculously small; therefore it is clear that the Hottentot mind must be inferior. The opposite argument runs: Hottentot cultural environment is so poor and limited that the finest mind in the world reared under its influence would grow up relatively sterile and atrophied; therefore even if the mind of the Hottentot is intrinsically identical with our own, or at least of equivalent capacity, and Hottentot geniuses have actually been born, they have nevertheless been unable to flourish as geniuses.

Evidently the same facts are before those who advocate these opposite views, but these facts are viewed from diametrically opposite sides. If one starts to travel around the logical circle in one direction, one can keep revolving indefinitely and find ever fresh supporting evidence. If, however, one begins to revolve around the same circle of opinion in the opposite direction, it is just as easy and just as compelling to continue to think in this fashion and to find all testimony corroborative.

In such a situation it is possible to realize that from the point of view of proof, or objective truth, one view is worth as much as the other—which is nothing. It is an emotional bias that inclines one man toward the conviction of race superiority and another toward that of race equality. The proofs in either case are for the most part a mere assembling of ex-parte testimony. It is easy enough to advocate impartiality. The difficulty is in being impartial; because both the hereditary and the environmental factors are in reality unknown quantities. What we have objectively before us is such and such a race or group of people, with such and such present traits and historical record. These phenomena being the product of the interaction of the two sets of causes, we could of course, if we knew the strength of one, compute the strength of the other. But as we have isolated neither, we are dealing with two indeterminate variables. Evidently the only way out of the dilemma, at any rate the only scientific way, is to find situations in which one of the factors is, for the time being, fixed. In that case the strength of the other factor will of course be proportionate to the attainments of the groups.

Actually, such instances are excessively difficult to find. There are occasional individuals with identical heredity; namely, identical twins, produced from the division of a single ovum. In such twins, the strength of environmental influences can theoretically be gauged by the difference in their careers and achievements. Yet such twins are only individuals, and it is risky to make inferences from them to racial groups. It is conceivable that heredity might on the whole be a more powerful cause than environment, but that racial groups would still average substantially alike in their heredity. Because a natively gifted and a natively stunted individual within the group vary conspicuously in achievement, even under similar environment, it does not follow compellingly that races differ in germ plasm because they differ in achievements.

If, on the other hand, one sets out to discover cases of identical environment for distinct racial strains, it becomes apparent that this task is impossible. Analysis quickly shows that the environment is identical only up to a certain point, and that beyond this point important social and cultural divergences begin. Thus, so far as geographical environment goes, the Negro and the white in the southern United States are under the same conditions. There is also uniformity of some of the gross externals of cultural environment. Both Negroes and whites speak English; are Christians; wear store clothes; go to the movies; and so on. But, just as obviously, there are aspects in which their social environment differs profoundly. Educational opportunities are widely different. The opportunity of attaining leadership or otherwise satisfying ambition is wide-open to the white, and practically closed to the Negro. The "color line" inevitably cuts across the social environment and makes of it two different environments.

It might be said that the southern United States furnishes an extreme case of a sharply drawn color line. That is true. But on the other hand there is perhaps no place on earth where something corresponding to a color line is not drawn, some distinction or preference is not made, between two distinguishably different populations occupying the same territory. It sometimes happens that distinctions are diminished and only faintly or subtly enforced, as in modern Hawaii or Brazil, where to outward appearances many racially different populations dwell together without discrimination. Yet examination reveals that the absence of discrimination is rather nominal. As regards the relations and associations of human beings, the welcome they extend or the aloofness that they show to one another, there are always lines drawn. This means not only difference in opportunity, but difference in experience, habit formation, practices, and interests.

87. TESTS ON THE SENSE FACULTIES

This factor of experience enters even into what appear to be the simplest mental operations, the sensory ones. The scant data available from experimental tests indicate that a variety of dark-skinned or uncivilized peoples, including Oceanic and African Negroids, Negritos, Ainus, and American Indians, on the whole slightly surpass civilized whites in keenness of vision and fineness of touch discrimination, whereas the whites are somewhat superior in acuity of hearing and sensitiveness to pain. Yet what do these results of measurements mean?

Vision is tested for its distance ability. The farther off one can distinguish objects or marks, the higher one's rating. Civilized man reads—normally—at fourteen inches. He works with sharp knives, with machines that are exact; he is surrounded by things made with such exact machines; he handles thin paper and filmy fabrics. His women sew and embroider with the sharpest of needles, the finest of thread. Everything about us tends toward close accuracy and away from the haziness of distant observation. The savage, on the other hand, the half-civilized person even, inspects the horizon, watches for game or its dim tracks, tries to peer to the bottom of streams for fish. He does not read, his needles are blunt, his thread is cord, his carving is without precision even though decorative, the lines he makes are freehand and far apart. He has been trained all his life, as it were, for the usual vision tests. If the psychologist reversed his experiment and sought the degree of power to see fine differences at close range, it is possible that the savage might prove inferior.

The whole act of vision in fact involves more than we ordinarily think. After all, seeing is done with the mind as well as with the eye. There is the retinal image, but there is also the interpretation of this image. A sailor descries the distant shore, whereas the landsman sees only a haze on the horizon. To the city dweller a horse and a cow a mile off are indistinguishable. Not so to the rancher. There is something almost imperceptible about the profile of the feeding end of the animal, about its movement, that promptly and surely classes it. He sees the total configuration of the object—dimly perhaps, but he knows what it means. At still longer ranges, where the individual animals have wholly faded from sight, a herd of cattle may perhaps be told from one of horses, by the plainsman, through the different clouds of dust they kick up, or the rate of motion of the cloud. An hour later when the herd is reached and proves to be as said, the astonished traveler from the metropolis is likely to credit his guide's eyes with an intrinsic power greater than that of his own field glasses—forgetting the influence of experience and training.

In keenness of hearing, on the contrary, one would expect the civilized white to come out ahead, as in fact he does; not because he is Caucasian, but because he is civilized, and because the instruments of experimentation, be they tuning forks or ticking watches or balls dropped on metal plates, are implements of civilization. Make the test the howl of a distant wolf, or the snapping of a twig as the boughs bend in the wind, and the college student's hearing might prove duller than that of the Indian or the Ainu. There is a story of a woodsman on a busy thoroughfare, amid the roar of traffic and multifarious noise of a great city, hearing a cricket chirp. When the cricket was actually discovered in a near-by cellar opening and the man in the fur cap was extolled for his miraculous keenness of audition, he dropped a dime on the pavement: at the clink, all the city passers-by stopped and looked around.

As to the pain sense, an introspective, interpretative element necessarily enters into experiments. What constitutes pain? When the trial becomes disagreeable? When it hurts? When it is excruciating? The savage may physiologically feel with his nerve ends precisely as we do. But being reared to a life of chronic slight discomforts, he is likely to think nothing of the sensation until it hurts sharply; whereas we signal as soon as we are sure that the experience is becoming perceptibly unpleasant.

In short, until there shall have been more numerous, balanced, and searching tests made, it must be considered that nothing positive has been established as to the respective sensory faculties of the several human races. The experiments performed are tests not so much of race as of the average experience and habits of groups of different culture.

88. INTELLIGENCE TESTS

If inconclusiveness holds as regards the sense faculties, it might be expected to hold to a greater degree of those higher faculties which we call intelligence; and such is the case. For some decades, intelligence tests have been gradually evolved and improved and standardized, and they are now routine in much personnel selection. During World War I, psychological examinations were introduced in the United States Army on a scale unheard of before. More testing, and more effective testing, was done in World War II; but it was directed rather at sifting out aptitudes or special kinds of ability, and the results have not been classified and published. The same is true of the personnel testing that has become so highly developed in civilian education and industry. The modern techniques are far more refined. But the old World War I draft results still focus better on the comparative race problem because of their very breadth and the sweep of their unselected range.

The purpose of these examinations was to assign men to the tasks best commensurate with their true abilities; especially to prevent the unfit from being entrusted with responsibility under which they would break down and bring failure on larger undertakings. Men subject to dizziness were to be kept from flying; those unable to understand orders, out of active line service. The tests throughout were practical. They were meant to determine whether a given man was fit or unfit. They did not pretend to go into the causes of his fitness or unfitness. This is an important point. Whatever illumination the army intelligence tests shed on the problem of race intelligence is therefore indirect. Different racial or national groups represented in the examinations attain different capacity ratings, but there is nothing in the results themselves to show whether they are due to racial or to environmental factors. Evidence on this point, if it can be derived at all from the tests, has to be analyzed out.

In general, examinees in the United States were rated by being assigned, on the basis of their scores, to grades lettered from A to E, with plus and minus subgrades. The most comprehensive presentation of results is to express the percentage of individuals in each group that made the middle grade C, better than C, and worse than C. On this basis we find:

RESULTS OF ARMY INTELLIGENCE TESTS

Group and Number of Individuals	Below C	C	Above C
Englishmen, 411	9	71	20
White draft generally, 93,973	24	64	12
Italians, 4,007	63	36	1
Poles, 382	70	30	(.5)
Negroes generally, 18,891	79	20	1

These figures at face value seem to show deep group differences in intelligence; and these face values were at first accepted in some quarters. The reason is that they flatter national and race egotism. To be sure, the Englishmen in the American draft make a better showing than the drafted men at large; but this would be complacently explained by saying that the English represent in comparative purity the Anglo-Saxon or Nordic stock which is also the dominant strain among Americans, but which has been somewhat contaminated in their case by the immigration of Latins and Slavs, who rate much lower, as is shown by the Italians and Poles tested. Lowest of all, as might be expected, is the Negro. So runs the superficial but satisfying interpretation of the figures—satisfying if one happens to be of northern-European ancestry.

But there is one feature that raises suspicion. The Italians and the Poles are too close to the Negroes. They stand much nearer to them in intelligence, according to these figures, than they do to the white Americans. Can this be so— at least, can it have racial significance? Are these Mediterranean-Alpines, descendants of the Romans, and these East Baltic-Alpines, so large a strain of whose blood flows in the veins of many white Americans, only a shade superior to the Negro? It sounds like a Nazi opinion. Something must be "wrong" with the figures; that is, they must contain another factor besides race.

A little further dissection of the lump results reveals this factor. The northern Negro far surpasses the southern in his showing. He gets ten times as high a proportion of individuals into the above-average grades, only half as many into the below-average. Evidently the difference is due to increased schooling, improved earning capacity, larger opportunity and incentive: sociocultural environment, in short. So strong is the influence of the environment that the northern Negro—born English-speaking, of course—easily surpassed the foreign-languaged, immigrant-descended Italian in the United States.

FURTHER RESULTS OF ARMY TESTS

Negroes, 5 northern states, 4705	46	51	3
Italians in the U.S. 4007	63	36	1
Negroes, 4 southern states, 6846	86	14	(.3)

Evidently the psychological tests are more a gauge of educational and social opportunity than of race, since the Italian, although brunet, is of course a pure Caucasian.

This conclusion is reinforced by another consideration. The type of test first used in the army had been built up for reasonably literate people speaking English. Among such people it discriminated successfully between the more and the less fit. But the illiterate and the foreigner knowing no English failed completely—not because their intelligence was zero, but because the test involved the use of noncongenital abilities which they had not acquired. A second set of tests, known as Beta, was evolved for those who were obviously ineligible, or proved themselves so, for the old style of test, which was designated as Alpha. The illiteracy of the subjects given the Beta test was in most cases not an absolute one. Men who could not write an intelligible letter or read the newspaper or who had had only half or less of the ordinary grammar-school education, together with aliens whose comprehension of English remained imperfect, were put in the group of "illiterates" or badly educated. Separating now the literates from the illiterates among a number of racial, national, or sectional groups, we find:

ALPHA TEST: LITERATES

Englishmen, 374	5	74	21
White draft generally, 72,618	16	69	15
Alabama whites, 697	19	72	9
New York Negroes, 1021	21	72	7
Italians, 575	33	64	3
Negroes generally, 5681	54	44	2
Alabama Negroes, 262	56	44	(.4)

BETA TEST: "ILLITERATES"

White draft generally, 26,012	58	41	1
Italians, 2888	64	35	1
New York Negroes, 440	72	28	0
Poles, 263	76	24	(.4)
Alabama whites, 384	80	20	0
Negroes generally, 11,633	91	9	(.2)
Alabama Negroes, 1043	97	3	(.1)

It must be borne in mind that the two groups were not set apart as the result of tests, but that the two tests were devised to meet the problem of treating the two groups with reasonable uniformity. The point was to find the excellent man, and the unfit man, with the same degree of accuracy whether he was literate or illiterate. When found, he was assigned to the same grade, such as A, or D minus, whether his examination had been Alpha or Beta.

Now let us observe some of the figures. In 1917, the New York Negro was nearly on a par with the Alabama white among literates, and a bit ahead of him among illiterates. Approximately the two groups came out the same; which means that growing up in a certain part of the country has as much to do with' intelligence, even in the rough, as has Caucasian or colored parentage.

The literate Negroes of the draft, irrespective of section, slightly surpassed the illiterate whites.

In every case the literate members of a race or a nationality made a far better showing than the illiterate.

It is now clear also that the important factor of education enters so heavily into the first figures cited that they can mean little if anything as to inherent capacity. Of the Englishmen tested, nine-tenths fell in the literate group; of the Poles, a fifth; of the Italians, a seventh. In the draft generally, nearly three-fourths of the whites were literate; of the Negroes, less than a third.

In short, in spite of the fact that the Beta test was intended to equalize conditions for the illiterate and the semi-illiterate, the outstanding conclusion of the army examinations seems to be that education—cultural advantage—enormously develops faculty. Which is no wonder.

Is there anything left that can positively be assigned to race causation? It may be alleged that within the same section the white recruits regularly surpass the colored. Alabama whites may rate disappointingly, but they do better than Alabama Negroes; New York Negroes show surprisingly well, but they are inferior to New York whites; illiterate whites from the whole country definitely surpass illiterate Negroes; and among literates the difference is still more pronounced. But is this residuum of difference surely racial? As long as the color line remains drawn, a differential factor of cultural advantage is included; and how strong this is there is no present means of knowing. It is possible that some of the difference between sectionally and educationally equalized groups of whites and Negroes is really innate and racial. But it is also possible that most or all of it is environmental. Neither possibility can be demonstrated from the unrefined data available.

Of definite bearing on the cause of part of the differential are some tests cited by Klineberg. These were given in New York to twelve-year-old Negro children, most of whom were born in the South. They were grouped according to how long they had lived in Harlem.

DEVELOPMENT OF NEW YORK CITY NEGRO CHILDREN

Years in New York City	Average I.Q.
1 or 2	72
3 or 4	76
5 or 6	84
7, 8, or 9	92
Born in the North	92

How far the higher I.Q. was due to living in the somewhat less harshly discriminating North, and how far to the stimulating effect of big-city environment, is not known. But, caught at the most susceptible age, these children in a few years made up more than two-thirds of the lag behind whites with which they came North.

That city life with its pace, abundance of contacts, and competitive aspects sharpens native wits—at any rate for good scores in tests—has been known to psychologists. It is presumably one factor in the better rating of northern Negroes, who are largely urban, over southern and mainly rural Negroes. Klineberg ingeniously combined measure of rural-urban difference and racial difference in a series of tests he gave to schoolchildren in Europe. In Hamburg, Paris, and Rome he took average samples, which of course were far from racially pure, but which at least represented respective Nordic, Alpine, and Mediterranean predominance. The tests were the same, except for being administered in German, French, and Italian. The results came out essentially identical: between 212 and 219 by the particular score used. Klineberg also gave the same test to seven lots of rural children in the three countries. In each place, he made sure that not only each child but both its parents were born in the province. Also he accepted for testing only children who visibly conformed in their physique to one of the three basic European racial types. These are the results, by the same scale:

SCORES OF COUNTRY CHILDREN OF THREE RACIAL TYPES

Nordic	Germany	Hanover	198
Mediterranean	France	Pyrenees	197
Alpine	Germany	Baden	194
Alpine	Italy	Piedmont	189
Alpine	France	Auvergne	180
Nordic	France	Flanders	174
Mediterranean	Italy	Sicily	173

First and outstanding, all the yokel groups are behind all the city slickers. It is clear that the urban-rural mode of life has far more influence than intra-white racial membership on the sort of intelligence that is tested by tests. As between the three races, Nordics and Mediterraneans come out a bit on top in the countryside, but also at the bottom; the Alpines hold all the middle places. That Sicily trails the others is very likely due to the fact that Sicilians are the poorest and historically most retarded of the seven groups. Their fellow Mediterraneans in France are relatively high up among the rurals. This set of tests certainly emphasizes the influence of group exposure to conditioning over that of genetic constitution of racial groups.

The influence of the linguistic factor, well recognized by psychologists since the Beta tests, has also been neatly brought out by Klineberg with reference to so-called race. The figures speak for themselves.

VERBAL AND PERFORMANCE SCORES

	Verbal Test Score	Performance Test Score	Superiority in Performance Score
Italians	85	93	8
Chinese, Japanese	89	102	13
U.S. Indians	75	92	17
Mexicans	82	92	10
New York City Jews	96	82	−14

The taciturn, inarticulate Indian made the greatest improvement as soon as he was put to using his brain, eye, and hands instead of brain, ear, and tongue. The Jews were East Side New York City, and therefore mainly children of immigrants from towns; and they were themselves raised not only in the metropolis but in the environment of a group that practices and esteems verbalism. So they came out easy tops in that and a bad last where eyes and hands were involved.

89. STATUS OF HYBRIDS

In nearly all tests of the American Negro, full-bloods and mixed bloods have not been discriminated. It is usually difficult to do so. Yet if races have distinctive endowments, the nature of these is not cleared up so long as individuals who biologically are seven-eighths Caucasian are included with pure Negroes merely because in this country we have the social habitude of reckoning them all as "colored."

In the World War I army examinations an attempt was made to separate one group of colored recruits into darker-skinned and lighter-skinned sub-groups, the latter containing those estimated to be mulattoes or less than half Negro. The light group made the better scores: in the Alpha test for literates, 50, the dark Negroes only 30; in the Beta tests for illiterates, the respective figures were 36 and 29.

But is the mulatto subject to any more advantageous environment than the full-blooded Negro? So far as voting and officeholding in the Deep South, riding in Pullman cars, and occupying orchestra seats in theaters are concerned, there is no difference: both are colored and therefore beyond the Jim Crow barrier. But the mulattoes of slavery days were likely to be house servants, brought up with the master's family, absorbing manners, information, perhaps education; their black half-brothers and half-sisters stayed out in the plantation shacks. Several generations have elapsed since those days, but it is probable that the descendants of mulattoes have kept a step or two ahead of the descendants of the pure blacks in literacy, range of experience, and the like. It is well known that modern American Negroes tend to accord higher status among themselves to the lighter-skinned and Caucasian-featured individuals. Successful Negroes tend to marry light-colored spouses. A light skin and a convex nose count for almost as much as a good education or successful parents—both among Negroes themselves in their internal social cleavages, and in getting jobs or other opportunities from whites. To be sure, which is cause and which effect here? Quite likely, our x is both cause and effect, and our y likewise. But all that is being contended for is that any judgment is more or less dogmatic when the causality in the phenomena is surely complex and probably circular.

It is impossible to predict what the social effect of miscegenation will be. The effect undoubtedly varies and must be examined in each case. Thus, Indian half-breeds in one tribe may usually be the result of wholly transient or mercenary unions between inferior whites and the more promiscuous native women and may therefore grow up in an atmosphere of demoralization to which the full-blooded Indian is less exposed. This demoralization would, to be sure, affect character and not intelligence as such; but it might stand in the way of schooling, stability, or sense of security. In another tribe, to the contrary, the half-breed might normally grow up in the house of a permanently settled white father, a squaw man, and in that event would learn English better, go to school earlier and longer, and in the case of a test therefore achieve a higher rating than the full-blood. Where the infusion of white blood, with accompanying economic, literate, and technological benefits, happened a couple of centuries ago, as among the Iroquois, it might have possessed an advantage for a while and then gradually have lost it again.

For Indians, Garth has made a serious endeavor to correlate intelligence rating with proportion of blood. Among 1400 Indian schoolchildren he got results as follows:

TESTS ON INDIANS BY PROPORTION OF BLOOD

	Average I.Q.
4/4 Indian	72
3/4 Indian	74
1/2 Indian	75
1/4 Indian	78

This looks like something. But if we project the series of figures one step farther on, to no-Indian blood, it should come out around 80 for all-white; whereas of course the mean for whites is 100, the scale being based on that as standard. One might predict then that full-whites brought up wholly under the social conditions of American reservation Indians would score 80. Or, to put it differently, two-thirds of the test inferiority of Indians is presumably due to their conditioning environment. The other third may be racial, or it may not, subject to the cautions in the last paragraph.

Perhaps the most elaborate investigation of the relative capacity of hybrids was made by Davenport and Steggerda on race crosses in Jamaica, where Negroes and part-Negroes ("browns") outnumber whites, and where social discrimination is unusually mild for an English-speaking community. The findings were far from clear-cut, though the number of individuals measured seemed reasonably adequate—up to 400 adults and 300 subadults. As almost always, the variability within any one race group was consistently found to be greater than the difference between its average and that of the two other groups.

Thus in musical capacity, six different traits were tested in three age groups—children, adolescents, and adults—and hence there is a total of 54 comparisons among blacks, hybrids, and whites. Only six of these 54 were statistically significant by the formula in customary use among psychologists. Four of these were the average differences by which black children surpassed white children in pitch, time, and rhythm perception, and adult blacks surpassed adult whites in rhythm. But the two other instances of "sureness"— really it is only a very high probability—showed the superiority of white adolescents over both black and brown in perception of intensity of tone, even though among both children and adults the blacks came out first in this trait. In time sense, the surely superior black children lost their supremacy to whites among adolescents, and in both time and pitch they lost it to brown adults. The results point in too many different directions to make much sense. It does look as if in Jamaica at least full-Negroes were perhaps superior in most musical faculties in childhood, but that the mulattoes and the whites drew abreast of them after about age thirteen.

The appended tabular summary of scored "firsts" or superiorities shows clearly this apparent and unexplained age shift in musical ability. But it also shows that when all tests and all ages are taken together, while the whites score tops oftener than do the blacks, the hybrid browns are *not* intermediate but beat them both out—29 as against 24 and 17! However, even a mere dip below the surface of the grand total reveals the cause of this strange result: the investigators happened to get hold of an unusually bright sample of brown fourteen-to-sixteen-year-olds. Thus they carried off 11 firsts in all nonmusical tests as against only 5 by blacks and whites combined. Brown children also led: 9 nonmusical firsts against 7. But brown adults did badly: 3 firsts against 5 by blacks and 8 by whites; or counting in a few additional tests not given to children, the

NUMBER OF "FIRSTS" OR HIGHEST TEST SCORES IN JAMAICA

	Blacks	Browns	Whites
Children			
A. Musical capacity	5	0	1
B. Miscellaneous performance	3	4	1
C. Army Alpha intelligence	0	5	3
TOTAL	8	9	5
Adolescents			
A. Musical capacity	1	2	3
B. Miscellaneous performance	1	5	2
C. Army Alpha intelligence	0	6	2
TOTAL	2	13	7
Adults			
A. Musical capacity	2	3	1
B. Miscellaneous performance	1	3	4
C. Army Alpha intelligence	4	0	4
TOTAL	7	6	9
All Age Total			
A. Musical capacity	8	5	5
B. Miscellaneous performance	5	12	7
C. Army Alpha intelligence	4	11	9
TOTAL	17	28	21
Additional miscellaneous, adults only	0	1	3
TOTAL	17	29	24

score was blacks 5, browns 4, whites 11, in nonmusical superiorities. It is conceivable that one race might show precocious ability compared with another and then lose its edge again. But it is hardly conceivable that a hybrid stock should first surpass both the races of which it was a blend, and then fall behind both of them! We can only conclude that the age and race samples tested were insufficient in size or unevenly selected.

The reliable results of this intriguing investigation accordingly are, first, a fair probability that blacks show a slight early musical superiority over whites and possibly maintain it. Second, in general intelligence the browns are by no means a mere intermediate between Negroes and whites, but show a surprisingly independent and variable superiority and inferiority to both. This last condition can easily be accounted for by irregularities of sampling, or of social condition, but scarcely by genetic hybridity. In short, our principal results are again negative.

90. EVIDENCE FROM THE CULTURAL RECORD OF RACES

An entirely different method of approach to the problem of race capacity is that of examining the cultural record, the achievements in civilization, of groups. While this approach is theoretically possible, and while it is often attempted, it is subject to little control and therefore unlikely to yield dependable conclusions.

First of all, the cultural history of a people must be known for considerable periods before one can validly think of inferring therefrom anything as to the faculties of that people. The reason is that active civilization, as a productive process, is slow to grow up, slow to be acquired. Mere momentum would normally keep the more advanced of two peoples ahead of the other for a long time. In proportion as not nations but groups of nations were involved, the momentum would continue for still longer periods. Civilization flourished for some thousands of years in the Near East, and then about the Mediterranean, before it became established with equal vigor and success in northern Europe. Had Julius Caesar or one of his contemporaries been asked whether by any sane stretch of fantasy he could imagine the Britons and the Germans as inherently the equals of Romans and Greeks, he would probably have replied that if these Northerners possessed the ability of the Mediterraneans they would long since have given vent to it, instead of continuing to live in disorganization, poverty, ignorance, rudeness, and without great men or products of the spirit. And, within limits, Caesar would have been right, since more than a thousand years passed before northern Europe began to draw abreast of Italy in degree and productivity of civilization. Two thousand years before Christ, a well-informed Egyptian might reasonably have disposed in the same sweeping way of the possibility of Greeks and Italians being the equals of his own people in capacity. What had these barbarians ever done to lead one to think that they might yet do great things? Today we brush Negroes and American Indians out of the reckoning with the same offhandedness. And enough of us let slip the same sentiments about Asiatics to antagonize whole great nations like the Chinese and the East Indians, and therewith help to conjure up or to perpetuate difficult international problems.

In general, arguing from performance to potentiality, from accomplishment to achievement, is valid under conditions of set experiment—such as are impossible for races—or in proportion as the number and the variety of observations is large. A single matched competition may decide pretty reliably as between the respective speed capacities of two runners for a given distance. But it would be hazardous to form an opinion from a casual glimpse of them in action while one might happen to be hastening and the other dallying. Least of all would it be sound to infer that essential superiority rested with the one in advance at the moment of observation, without knowledge of their starting points, the difficulty of their routes, the motive or goal of their courses. It is only as the number of circumstances grows from which observations are available that judgment begins to have any weight. The runner who has led for a long time and is increasing his lead, or who has repeatedly passed others, or who carries a load and yet gains ground, may lay some claim to superiority. In the same way, as between human races, a long and intimate historical record, objectively analyzed, gives some legitimate basis for tentative conclusions as to their natural endowment. But how long the record must be is suggested by the example already cited of Mediterranean versus Nordic cultural pre-eminence.

The fallacy that is most commonly committed is to argue from what in the history of great groups is only an instant—the instant at which one's own race or nationality is dominant. The Anglo-Saxon's moment is the present; the Italian's, the Renaissance; the Greek's, the age of Pericles. Usually, too, the dominance holds only for certain aspects: military or economic or aesthetic superiority, as the case may be; inferiorities on other sides are merely overlooked. The Greek knew his own venality and mendacity, but looked down on the barbarian nevertheless. Anglo-Saxon comparative backwardness in the plastic and musical arts is notorious, but does not deter most Anglo-Saxons from believing that they are the elect in quality, and from buttressing this conviction with the evidences of present industrial, economic, and political achievements—and perhaps past literary ones.

91. EMOTIONAL BIAS AGAIN

Inference from record to potentiality where the record of one's own group is favorable, and failure to draw such inference where the achievement of other groups is superior, is a combination of mental operations that is widespread because it arises spontaneously in minds not critically trained. Here is an instance:

One of the great achievements of science in the nineteenth century was Galton's demonstration, in a series of works beginning with *Hereditary Genius,* that the laws of heredity apply to the mind in the same manner and to the same degree as to the body. On the whole this proof has failed to be recognized at its true importance, perhaps because it inclines adversely to popular presuppositions of the independence of the soul and mind from the body, propositions to which many men still adhere emotionally or unconsciously.

From this perfectly valid demonstration, which has been confirmed by other methods, Galton went on to rate the hereditary worth of various races according to the number of their men of genius. Here a fallacy enters: the assumption that all geniuses born are recognized as such. A great work naturally requires a great man, but it presupposes also a great culture. It may be that, historically speaking, a great genius cannot arise in a primitive degree of civilization. That is, the kind of concentrated accomplishment which alone we recognize as a work of genius is culturally impossible below a certain level. Biologically the individual of genius may be there; civilizationally he is not called forth, and so does not get into the record. Consequently it is unsound to argue from the historical record to biological worth. However, this Galton did; and his method led him to the conclusion that the Negro rates two grades lower than the Englishman, on a total scale of fourteen grades, and the Englishman two lower than the fifth-century Athenian.

This conclusion has never been popular. Most people, on becoming familiar with Galton's argument, resist it. Its fallacy is not easy to perceive—if it were, Galton would not have committed it—and the average person is habitually so vague-minded upon what is organic and what is sociocultural or historical that the determination of the fallacy would be well beyond him. His opposition to Galton's conclusion is therefore emotionally and not rationally founded, and his arguments against the conclusion are presumably also called forth by emotional stimulus.

On the other hand, some individuals of this day and land do habitually infer, like Galton, from cultural status to biological worth, so far as the Negro is concerned. The same persons who might eagerly accept the demonstration of a flaw in Galton's argument in favor of Athenian superiority would often become skeptical and resistive to the exposition of the same flaw in the current belief as to Negro inferiority. It is remarkable how frequently and how soon, in making this exposition, one becomes aware of some hearers' feeling that one's attitude is sophistical, unreal, insincere, or motivated by something concealed.

The drift of this discussion may seem to be an unavowed argument in favor of race equality. It is not that. As a matter of fact, the anatomical differences between races would appear to render it likely that at least some corresponding congenital differences of psychological quality exist. These differences might not be profound, compared with the sum total of common human faculties, much as the physical variations of mankind fall within the limits of a single species. Yet they would preclude identity. As for the vexed question of superiority, lack of identity would involve at least some degree of greater power in certain respects in some races. These pre-eminences might be rather evenly distributed, so that no one race would notably excel the others in the sum total or average of its capacities; or they might show some minor tendency to cluster on one rather than on another race. In either event, however, race difference, moderate or minimal, qualitative if not quantitative, would remain as something that could perhaps be ultimately determined.

But it is one thing to admit this theoretical probability and then stop through ignorance of what the differences are, and another to construe the admission as justification of mental attitudes that may be well grounded in historical conditioning but are in considerable measure unfounded objectively.

In short, it is a difficult task to establish any race as either superior or inferior to another, but relatively easy to prove that we entertain a strong prejudice in favor of our own racial superiority.

92. SUMMARY

It would seem that the subject of basic race problems—that is, of the natural endowment of true human races—can be summarized as follows:

The essential difficulty of these problems lies in the fact that the performance of groups is the product of two sets of factors, biological and cultural, both of which are variable and usually not readily separable.

Progress in solution of the problems will be made gradually, and will be hastened by recognition of how few positive determinations have yet been made.

Most of the alleged existing evidence on race endowment is probably worthless.

The remainder probably has some value, but to what degree, and what it demonstrates, cannot yet be asserted.

The most definite determinations promise to eventuate from experiment. If fully controlled experiments in breeding and rearing human beings could be carried out, the problems would soon begin to be solved. Experiments on animals would prove practically nothing, because animals are cultureless—uninfluenced by environment of their own making.

Progress will be aided by increasing shift of attention from the crude consideration of comparative lump rating of the races—that is, as to their gross superiority or inferiority—to a consideration of such specific qualitative differences as they may prove to show. The question of finding the race in which the greatest number of qualitative excellences may be concentrated is subsequent and of much less scientific importance.

Scientific inquiries into race are for the present best kept apart from so-called actual race problems. These problems inevitably involve feeling, usually of considerable strength, which tends to vitiate objective approach. On the other hand, practical problems will no doubt continue to be met practically; that is, morally and emotionally. Whether the Japanese should be forbidden to hold land in California and the Negro be de-facto disfranchised in the Deep South are problems of economics and of group ethics, which unfortunately will probably for some time to come be disposed of emotionally, as at present, irrespective of the possible findings of science upon the innate endowment of the Caucasoid, Mongoloid, and Negroid strains and substrains.

All that has been said here of course applies with even more force to what is miscalled the problem of "racial minorities" when these minorities, such as Poles or Italians or French Canadians or Irish in the United States, or Germans in Alsace or Czechoslovakia, are not racial groups at all but are set apart ethnically or socially or culturally, as by their speech, religion, customs, traditions, or cohesive group loyalties.

Cultural Psychology

241. PSYCHIC UNITY OF MANKIND

IT IS self-evident that in every cultural situation there also necessarily inheres biopsychic activity: without men and minds there would be no cultural forms, activities, or changes. Cultural activity might be described as bodily-mental activity—"psychological" functioning—specially directed and shaped by impinging past and present culture. Students of cultural phenomena, whether anthropologists, sociologists, or historians, have always recognized that their material contains psychological aspects. But they leave these implicit, or make them explicit only at points; at any rate, they do not reduce their data to psychology. Reciprocally, all modern psychologists recognize that the total picture of any natural or spontaneous human situation always contains a cultural ingredient. They never actually encounter a "pure" unconditioned mind; that is a concept or abstraction: culture has always affected human minds—before the psychologist can examine them. The business of psychologists, however, is to try to hold this cultural factor constant in a given situation, to account for or to equalize it, and then to proceed to their own specific problems of investigating the mind *as if* it were "pure," of investigating the psychic aspects of the behavior of individual human beings, and after that of man in general.

In a corresponding way, anthropologists and historians normally begin with the tacit assumption that human nature,[1] in the gross and in the mass as it

---

[1] "Human nature" is here understood in its everyday sense, not with the technical sense—almost the opposite meaning—which some psychologists give it, of that which is

occurs in societies, is sufficiently uniform to allow of its being treated as a constant. Transmission of culture from generation to generation could not take place without loss or serious modification if the hereditary strain of the human culture-carriers varied considerably. Nor could culture material be diffused in space from population to population, often with ease and rapidity and sometimes with very little modification, if in its spread it encountered fundamentally diverse genetic strains, races with definitely distinctive endowments of faculty. We can infer from one human society to another, as regards capacity for essential interchange of their cultural functioning, as we cannot infer about capacities or behavior from dogs to cats or from cats to sheep.

The involved doctrine is the famous "psychic unity of man." This cannot be considered to be either a proved fact or an axiomatic principle; but it is so overwhelmingly borne out by the run of total experience that the anthropologist or the sociologist feels warranted in assuming the principle of essential psychic unity as at least a sufficient approximation to truth, and to employ it as a working hypothesis, or at any rate as a convenient symbol. He proceeds *as if* the principle were proved. He may be not conscious of this, just as the average historian constantly makes the assumption implicitly but might balk at an explicit avowal of it. The anthropologist continues to make the assumption because if he is impartial he finds that with it his work on culture leads to coherent and productive conclusions, but without it he bogs down before he has begun.

This does not mean that the question of panhuman psychic unity or equivalence is a settled one. For biology and psychology it remains a very real problem, and one of great interest. Only, it is a difficult and a complex problem because of the cultural factors that also enter it; and anthropologists obviously cannot suspend all study of culture until this tough nut has been cracked to their complete satisfaction, as well as to that of biologists and psychologists. It is indeed probable that the groups of men we call races are not absolutely identical in their make-up and faculties (§ 91). But it is clear from a great preponderance of the evidence that the differences between races are sufficiently minor to allow the essentially free flow of culture from one population and one generation to another, and to permit us to study the nature of these flows, and the nonracial changes and permanences of culture, with reasonable reliability. If this were not so, we should have to consign most of history, anthropology, and sociology to the scrap heap and begin over again with a psychosomatic genetic interpretation of man and his varieties.

Here, then, we have right at the outset a point where psychology and anthropology are in contact and in reciprocal interrelation.

---

wider or more common than the uniquely individual, but narrower than the universal (see § 246). This strange usage appears to be due to an ultrascientific leaning-back of some psychologists against the imputation of naïvely believing that we know anything about unconditioned human nature or that they would derive anything from it.

242. PERSONALITY IN CULTURE

Recognition of interpersonal relations, and hand in hand with them the recognition of individual personality qualities and differences, also have an important function in anthropology. Interpersonal relations may refer to the competitions and co-operations and adjustments between individuals in the same social group. In that event the term refers to a particular kind of psychology that emphasizes interindividual relations under proper consideration of the cultural frame. But again, study may be directed toward the effect that different kinds of culture have in producing different kinds of personalities and therewith coloring the interrelations of individuals in their societies; plus the reciprocal influence of such personalities on the maintenance or exaggeration or modification of their culture.

The recognition of personality and personality relations is of real significance in enhancing the understanding of culture by giving it body and reality—a stereoscopic sense of depth. We have seen (§ 6) that in one sense culture is an abstraction, a generalization inferred from many individual behaviors, statements, and happenings. One might query, if so minded, whether reality of existence can properly be ascribed to such an institution as marriage. One might say that the institution is a concept, only particular marriages between individual men and women possessing actual reality as phenomena. The "institution" comprises a set of rules and folkways, or laws and expectations, which rarely occur quite identically as we pass from one specific instance to the next. Among ourselves, among the rules or expectations are monogamy, being of age, the license, the wedding, its registry, the obligation to support, property claims, contingent rights to divorce; plus the expectation of love, fidelity, children, and so on. No deep argument is needed to prove that the expectations as well as the outcomes vary from couple to couple, from person to person; and that there are options or alternative choices at a great many points—whether to have a church or home or justice-of-the-peace wedding, or whether one bequeaths to his wife the legal minimum or his whole estate.

Any broad account of the institution is bound to suppress as much as possible the highly variable roles of the actual individual men or women concerned, and to become a catalogue of institutional features. It can even become a dry and lifeless listing, a bit like a law code. A half-dozen case histories of marriages are much more interesting, especially if the personalities are seized and rendered with spirit—why he married Joan and not Marjorie, and why then and not a couple of years before. Such anecdotes not only are vivid; they can also be extremely illuminating, like most gossip by intelligent people. But they are obviously not going to be very informative scientifically unless one compiles a great many cases and generalizes them.

To one who does want to learn about a custom, in order to compare it with the corresponding customs of other societies on the way to arriving at an inductive generalization of customs and culture, too much case history can be interminably delaying. It is a question of how far our interests are purely intellectual, or are diluted with aesthetic proclivities that insist on tempering the abstractions of science with portrayal of concrete, gossipy particulars. It is evident that an institution yields more of the "feel" of living reality when it is merely a background for the interplay of persons; but that it serves generalized understanding usefully in proportion as the colorful individualities and personalities are subsumed in the socially common features involved. It is much the same in history: the essentially literary historian puts us in constant touch with lifelike people; the profoundly intellectual one reveals rather the underlying drifts and major forces, and brings in personalities much less, and chiefly as exemplifications of situations and trends rather than as primary moving forces.

A less rigid construction is also possible: to see anthropology as dealing with culture expressed through and in persons. On this view, the subject matter of anthropology would be not merely culture as an abstraction, as a set of rules, as a series of depersonalized events, but culture with human beings living under and through it, conditioned by culture, adjusting to it, trying to manipulate it, now and then influencing and changing it a bit. From this angle, the skeleton of culture may be said to function, and to be fully understood, only as it is clothed by the flesh and blood of living personalities. This is an attractive way of presenting the situation: particularly to the outsider and the program-maker.

The working anthropologist is likely to receive it with a certain caution. He will ask himself whether we would know the larger things that we do know about the development of culture, about its processes and patterns, about the broad outlines of its history, if we had at every point tried to bring into the picture the fluctuations and clashes, the motives and variabilities, of the personalities concerned. Is it not essentially because on the whole anthropologists have abstracted from these individuals, have risen above them to a more generalized level, that we do know something of the forms and mechanisms of culture? The answer on the whole is Yes. If we had tried to bring in the full psychology of all the human beings involved in culture, we should have bogged in their endless welter. Specific progress in organized understanding is normally made by singling out certain aspects of the phenomena being studied and concentrating on these; by selective strategy rather than by an over-all, indiscriminate rush at the objective. After results have been attained, going back for reintegration and consolidation is in order. Anthropology is now in a position to call such a halt and review the tie-up with psychology. That is why this chapter is here. But it would hardly be in the book, or would be pretty empty talk, if anthropologists had not for the past generation or two pretty much forgone the temptation to psychologize, and had thereby discovered culture as such and piled up a gratifying amount of understanding of it.

The separateness of the two aspects—cultural forces and personalities—has been illustrated in a previous chapter, where the invention of the steamboat as a culture historical event has been outlined in § 185 and then followed in § 186 by a sketch of the personalities of the inventors. And, conversely, the interplay of the two is exemplified by the account in § 201 of how the Kota got themselves new gods.

The whole problem of the double aspect of our phenomena can also be seen as hingeing on how far we wish, in any given study, to carry or not to carry what might be called intellectual reductionism. In so far as we construe cultural happenings as personal ones, we explain them in psychological terms or "reduce" them to psychology. In the same way psychological happenings in individuals can be explained—actually only in part, but in theory and expectation wholly so—in physiological and biochemical terms, and psychology thereby reduced to physiology and biochemistry. One step further, and our physiological-biochemical findings are translated, or are theoretically translatable, into straight physicochemical factors. Such a reduction to the more underlying set of explanations has a great fascination for some minds, because it leads to the picture—or vision—of a seemingly unitary and simplified universe. The other side of the matter is that direct explanations regularly account for more phenomena than the reducing ones; and that they preserve certain qualities which get lost in the reduction process. Anger and fear can both be produced by adrenalin effecting vasomotor constriction. But anger and fear are actually quite different experiences, and can lead to opposite behaviors—without these differences' being explainable by the biochemistry of adrenalin. And so psychology can perhaps help us understand Fitch and Rumsey and Fulton, but it can never explain why France had the best roads, England the canals and good engines, but the United States the big empty rivers crying to be navigated. Reductionism is fine in its place. It interrelates the sciences, gives us a view of them as a larger whole, holds out the prospect of a grand unification. But it will not do the separate business of the several sciences, will not carry on their daily work. Reductionism is science straining at an ultimate philosophy, not a science doing its job. That is why psychologists continue to study anger and fear and other emotions in life histories, or by experiments, or with animals, instead of rushing to give adrenalin injections. And it is why anthropologists analyze cultural events and situations first of all in cultural terms—but remember always that cultural happenings are also personal and psychological happenings.

The ability to comprehend character and personal motivation is of course a psychological gift. But it is not necessarily formal scientific psychology: it may be allied rather to Thackeray or Shakespeare or Gibbon. It can plant the more arid stretches of the presentation of cultures with refreshing trees, and dot them with oases for which we must be grateful. But it is not in itself a theoretically intellectual activity. The intellectual discipline charged with dealing with personality and motivation and behavior is the science of psychology; and that is by no means a continuously lush oasis. Perhaps the strongest insistence yet made in anthropology on the "rights of the individual" was by Sapir, who was unusually sensitive aesthetically. But Sapir was and remained a superb ethnologist and contributor to the theory of culture, as well as one of the all-time great scholars in linguistics; and he who studies language inevitably deals with its patterns as a sociocultural phenomenon. Language, serving intercommunication, must be superpersonal to function at all. Language allows a final, slight personal touch of nuance, of style; but a greater injection of individuality than this cannot but lead to increasing unintelligibility and malfunction of speech. The linguist studies something that is in its nature overwhelmingly superindividual and anonymous.

Occasional anthropologists, inclined to anticipate the future by putting main emphasis on personality, may be assumed to be de-facto psychologists satiated with culture or uninterested in it from the beginning, so that they use it chiefly as a springboard. They are like the occasional psychological-laboratory workers specializing in brain anatomy or fatigue poisons who are actually doing physiology.

It is true, as Linton points out, that at present it is equally impossible to explain culture in terms of individual psychology and to understand it without some reference to psychology. After all, culture exists only through persons, in or by their behavior. Yet when we study culture, we concern ourselves primarily with those aspects of their behavior which are more than individual. Our generalizations, and therefore our specific scientific findings, are obviously on a more-than-individual level. But the individual and personalized substratum is still there. So far as we remain aware of the substratum, our depictions and analyses of culture retain a certain color and body and impression of life. So far as we are unaware of the underlying psychology, or indifferent to its suffusion, our cultural findings may be exact, but they tend to be arid, mechanical, and lacking in interest.

243. PSYCHOLOGICAL CONSIDERATIONS ALREADY ENCOUNTERED

Before proceeding farther into the psychology of culture, let us draw together in review the principal instances that have already been touched on in the course of this book.

Tradition on which culture rests for its continuance, and diffusion by which it spreads, viewed psychologically, are of course only imitation and learning (§ 123, 142). Imitation can be conscious or unconscious; learning, taught or untaught. Modern psychology gives much attention to learning, both animal and human. Imitation, and the related function of suggestion, were more in vogue a couple of generations ago, when the jurist-historian-philosopher Gabriel Tarde wrote his famous *Laws of Imitation*. Tarde is rich in illustrative cultural data, was translated into English by a social anthropologist, and his influence seems to have been greater on sociologists and anthropologists than on formal psychologists. Contemporary social psychologists appear to think that Tarde only described when he thought he explained—not realizing that this is characteristic of the historical as distinct from the experimental approach. Some of them say that the word "imitation" has become a cloak for ignorance, and ought to be replaced by "learning by human example." This sounds a bit like the corrective the ancient Chinese philosophers used to call rectification of names. Whatever we call it, we have here a good illustration of the relation of psychology and anthropology. The psychologist studies the mechanism of learning or imitation, as such. The anthropologist deals with what is learned or not learned; to wit, culture, and its structure or patterning, and the interrelations of cultures.

Since psychology entered its stimulus-response phase, it has been so concerned with conditioning, so impressed by its total influence on the plastic personality, that it is difficult to get psychologists to admit any genetic—inborn—differences between individuals; at any rate, any specific congenital differences. It is not that they deny the potential existence of such differences. But they cannot establish them with certainty; yet they can prove and measure a great deal of conditioning. The result is that they often proceed professionally *as if* individuals differed only in their environmental exposure and life experiences and not in their genes. This is a striking parallel to the attitude and procedure of anthropologists on race differences, as set forth in Chapter Five. Races may differ in their heredity, but the indubitable and ever present overlay of conditioning prevents us from proving it. So we proceed—must proceed when driven to it—*as if* race differences were wholly due to their historical conditioning.

Physiological needs and psychological "derived imperatives," already touched on in § 130, have been emphasized among anthropologists especially by Malinowski in an attempt to construct once and for all a complete and final theory of culture. It is now pretty well recognized that it is a perpetual snare to try to account causally for the endlessly varied forms of culture by tracing them back to a few organic needs or drives. Everyone agrees that physiological sex impulses underlie love and marriage. We even know something of the biochemistry as well as the effects of sex hormones. The real problem involved begins to be faced when it is realized that on the fairly simple sex-hormone situation there rest thousands of diverse forms of marriage and nonmarital sex customs, as just pointed out in § 242; much as there are hundreds of cuisines and kinds of table manners which obviously cannot be accounted for from the fact that all people have to eat to live and therefore get hungry. Even below the level of socialized culture, psychologists long since realized that the erotic psychic life of individuals varies enormously according to the conditioning and experience to which they have been exposed, and that only the simplest denominators of the phenomena can be explained by the organic sex equipment. A fortiori for the cultural phenomena.

Similarly, to account for, say, the art production of men under culture by invoking the "derived imperative" of an "aesthetic impulse" is a mere restatement of the facts, and barren except verbally.

The theoretical weakness of this position is revealed by the fact that at the same time that Malinowski thought he could derive culture from physiological needs and psychic imperatives, he was proclaiming culture "a reality *sui generis*" —as having an independent existence.

Conscious need of self-perpetuation as a basic drive of societies and cultures has been discounted in § 142. Not that societies do not wish to survive; but ordinarily they take for granted that they will. The whole matter of security about which we hear so much these days, both in psychology and in world affairs, has been tremendously magnified in our awareness as compared with our grandfathers. Perhaps our ancestors felt equally insecure, but they certainly let on about it less. The shift looks like a fashion change in social feeling that has invaded scientific thinking.

Psychological bases for certain specific and recurring cultural inventions have been invoked for: difficulty in invention of a zero sign (§ 189); tendency toward syllabic writing (§ 219); and doubt whether pictographic representation arises spontaneously (§ 202). These bases are not findings by psychologists but psychological inferences by anthropologists and historians from the forms and circumstances of the inventions.

Folkways (§ 116) underlie institutions and are customs, and customs may be called social habits. Social habits are also habits shared by individuals, and like these are acquired by conditioning, which in turn is a matter of repeated stimuli resulting in channeled responses.

Technologies involve manual or bodily activities, usually repeated, which establish motor habits (§ 143), which are perfectible to the point of virtuosity. Reciprocally, an extinction of technicians, or the enforced suspension of certain motor habits and skills for a generation, can lead to the loss of arts and technologies by a society (§ 157).

Several psychological factors enter into invention. On the primate level, control of emotion is of great importance in inventive problem-solving; but so is competition (§ 28); and impulses to destroy must be taken into account. The quality of insight, and of ability to profit by fortunate accident, which are recognized as close to the core of cultural invention (§ 147-148, 187), are sometimes perceptible among the more gifted anthropoids (§ 28). Play activity (§ 15, 29), direct or rechanneled, unquestionably enters into human inventing: occasionally perhaps into mechanical devices such as the bow and the wheel (§ 148); certainly at times into customs and institutions such as animal domestication (§ 165) and labile social and religious superstructures (§ 166-167).

The whole range of fashion, in style, in dress, and otherwise, not only crystallizes play impulses but undoubtedly expresses restlessness, tensions, surplus of energy, desire for change rather than for security (§ 137, 164). The cultural "fatigue" manifested by the pagan Hawaiians about their religion (§ 168) may be a metaphor, but it undoubtedly refers to an instability of attitudes.

Historical ambivalence of attitudes in intrinsically border-line situations is illustrated by the discussion of stepdaughter marriage (§ 167), both in primitive societies and in the contemporary United States.

Related to the changeableness of fashion is the sense of pride in the fleeting moment which in metropolitan and urban populations cumulatively replaces the pride of spot felt by peasant and rural peoples (§ 121). This change in turn involves a weakening of the strong sense of apartness and potential hostility that primitive and retarded groups regularly feel between their in-group and all out-groups, and which is an expression of strong identification with the in-group. This identification with a group, at any rate with a locally limited group, is what the cosmopolite and the sophisticate tend to replace by sense of immersion in a mass, with consequent loss of affective participation, of rooted attachment (§ 124). This matter will be touched on again in § 253.

This loss of the sophisticate is a loss of social attachments. There is an opposite condition, in which attachment to the group and to persons is strong, but attachment to possessions weak. The freedom of being unencumbered is prized, as among Australoids and Negritos (§ 120, 146). These attitudes in turn lead to a lack of interest and stunting of technologies which serve to manufacture possessions; and to a hand-to-mouth, reserveless subsistence economy.

The degree to which populations—and individuals too, mostly—are unconscious of their culture and take it for granted, or are only "foreconscious" or potentially conscious of it, has been stressed particularly in regard to language (§ 110). In language, sharply patterned form structure and unconsciousness of this structure coexist to a remarkable degree. In the fashionable terminology of the day, grammar is covert in speech. To a somewhat less marked and variable degree, the same holds for the other manifestations of culture (§ 116, 215).

Allied are the sensitive blind spots often covered by false rationalizations, in which societies indulge much like individuals (§ 116, 212, 216). Related to these, in turn, is the tendency of societies to forget the increments to and the changes made in their culture, largely even those occurring within living experience, and almost wholly as regards the farther past. This convenient forgetting makes possible a strong conviction of the functional integration of the culture. Such a conviction is evidently more useful to the society—as well as more pleasant—than active historical-mindedness. Folk history and popular history regularly minimize change and overemphasize integration and stability.

In proportion as stability is actual, especially in those parts of culture which necessarily function best as closed systems, like calendars and alphabets, strains sooner or later arise as other parts of the culture or the language change. "Reform"—that is, adjustment of the lag—is difficult in proportion as the system is tightly knit. Resistance to reform is in part affective attachment to habits; in part, realistic perception that the cost of change will fall largely on the present generation, its benefits accrue to future ones. False rationalizations find a favorable breeding-ground here, as well as subterfuges to cushion change that cannot be avoided. Sometimes conservatism is so entrenched in ramifications of sentiment that the violence of revolution or total authority is needed to break its resistance (§ 151, 170, 212, 216).

The dominance of social conditioning also accounts for the slowness with which certain inventions have been made whose essence is simplification of method or "reduction segregation"—Toynbee's etherialization (§ 155, 206-207). As might be expected, the reduction is more easily made by a population coming fresh to the problem than by the one that has accumulated and lived with the unnecessary accretions.

By no means all prohibiting puritanism of cultures is due to such tendency to innovate by reduction; but that it can be a factor seems to be established by the case of Islam (§ 172, 199).

Prestige considerations can be powerful advancing and retarding agencies in culture dynamics, as is evident from the competition of alphabetic and ideographic writing in Korea (§ 221) and of changes in Kota worship (§ 201).

The heart of the quality of culture resides in its patterns (§ 132-139), which represent its structuring or organization with relation to values (§ 125). The term "values" is here used in its current sense, which however also has some philosophical usage. It corresponds pretty well with "human values," provided that phrase is employed without its usual primary emphasis on common or universal values as if culture were uniform or consisted largely of common denominators. The common denominators are there, but all cultures also have particular qualities, and to allow for these we would have to expand our popular-term definition to "human values, both common and distinctive." To every value there is attached, or there corresponds, as Thomas long since pointed out, an attitude; and an attitude is an organization of responsiveness, an orientation of interest. At any rate, with attitudes we are admittedly in psychological territory: psychologists recognize and deal with them.

This whole important subject has only recently moved into the conscious consideration of students of culture and psychology, and will undoubtedly be developed further. Some exemplifications of its nature and scope have been given in § 125, 136-139.

Finally, there are the outright endeavors to represent whole cultures qualitatively by organizing them around the focus of a psychological or psychiatric concept, such as Apollinian or Dionysiac orientation, megalomania or paranoia. The virtues and limitations of this particular approach have been discussed in § 135.

The foregoing constitutes an unsystematic array, because the various psychological considerations have come up incidentally during a more or less orderly presentation of the nature and behavior of culture. From here on we can proceed somewhat more systematically in considering psychology.

244. NATIONAL TEMPERAMENTS OR TYPES

First of all, it is possible to take societies and cultures as they come, leave them whole, but try to characterize or describe their total cast or ethos in psychological instead of cultural terms. The terms or concepts would necessarily be those of individual psychology—at any rate in the beginning of our consideration.

Beyond this descriptive procedure, it is possible to try to seek out the psychological mechanisms at work in sociocultural situations in general; or to trace them comparatively as they appear in varying strength in the array of cultures that have existed in the world. These later procedures will be followed beginning with § 246, whereas the present section and the next will be concerned with characterizing descriptions.

Such characterizing descriptions can take two principal forms. Either a system of psychological types is set up, and cultures are fitted to these; or cultures may be empirically evaluated for the strength with which particular psychic factors or traits are represented in them. Both methods, as just admitted, involve a transfer from individuals to social groups. But this transferring should have validity, at least up to a certain point, because of the strong molding effect the culture of any social group has on its members, and because in turn the group consists of individual men.

We shall consider first the characterization by psychological types.

A number of type classifications devised for individuals are available: into extravert and introvert; into reasoning, feeling, intuitive, and sensory, according to Jung; into Dionysiac and Apollinian as taken over from Nietzsche; and so on. Scientifically, these types rate much like the constitutional bodily types discussed in § 79. They are open to the same limitation, that only a minority of cases correspond neatly to any conceptual type; the majority are intermediate or typologically indefinite. In short, there are good fits to the typological scheme, but they are only part of the total. With transfer of the method to the psychology of societies, this defect may be somewhat accentuated, and is certainly not removed.

The oldest of the type classifications—for individuals—interestingly enough is a strictly psychosomatic one. It is the famous classification according to "humors" by Hippocrates, the father of medicine, in the fifth century B.C. Bodily fluids and secretions, such as blood, mucus, bile, were supposed to give rise to dispositions or characters, of which four were recognized: sanguine, phlegmatic, choleric, melancholic. Methodologically, these four types are perhaps as arbitrary, and certainly as speculative, as the contemporary Greek selection of fire, air, water, and earth as the four "elements" of which everything material was thought to be composed. But chemistry has progressed farther than psychology, and the Greek elements are superseded by a set of 92 or more of a wholly different nature; whereas the Hippocratic characters are indeed sedulously avoided by modern professional psychologists, but without psychology's having evolved a notably better scheme for replacing them. Also, prescientific as both the Hippocratic dispositions and their supposedly causative humors are, the dispositions at any rate possess a degree of shrewd, empirical validity. We all can think of individuals who are splendid exemplifications of the sanguine or melancholic or choleric or phlegmatic type; though there are always more individuals who are only partial fits, or nondescript.

The types can of course also be applied nationally as well as individually, and sometimes have been so applied: though not, to be sure, by modern professional psychologists. Thus, the French and the Italians and the Irish would generally be described as sanguine; Scandinavians, Poles, and perhaps Russians as melancholic; Spaniards would probably come nearest to being choleric; Dutchmen and Germans are considered phlegmatic in Britain, whereas continental Europeans would put the same label on the British. Note however that these are all peoples belonging to one and the same larger society and civilization; they appear to differentiate sharply in temperament for the very reason that they are compared within the same European frame of reference, like the members of a family, a club, or other limited group. Americans might be harder to tag appropriately with one of the four labels, presumably because, though adhering to the same culture as Europeans, they live under new circumstances in another continent. Nations of antiquity, such as Romans, Greeks, and Hebrews, are also hard to characterize, and so are peoples of basically different cultures, such as Arabs, Hindus, Chinese, Japanese.

The philosopher Kant—for whose empirical characterizations in his *Anthropologie* see the next section—still accepted and dealt with the four Hippocratian temperaments, and grouped them. The sanguine and melancholic are temperaments of feeling, he says; the choleric and phlegmatic refer primarily to tension and action. In cross grouping, sanguine and choleric go together in that the affect or emotion comes and goes rapidly, melancholic and phlegmatic in that it rises slowly but persists. Kant denies composite temperaments; but he is silent on what to do about the temperamentally undifferentiated or subdifferentiated whom we would today assume to be in a majority.

Sapir has suggested applying Jung's individual personality types to nations. Apart from a primary division into extravert and introvert, which is now generally familiar through having seeped down to the man on the street, Jung recognizes four types prevailingly dominated by sensation, intuition, feeling,[2] or reason. The first two, in Sapir's translation, are considered less organized and the last two more organized. Feeling is thus as systematizing an activity as reason. Jung himself classed intuition along with sensation as "unorganized"—

---

[2] "Sensation" refers to sensory experience, "feeling" to emotion—cf. "feeling fine."

what is here called unsystematic. This was because he considered intuition as a mechanism for solving suspense by "irrational" or blind guessing; whereas Sapir construed intuition rather as a telescoped or stenogram-outline form of reasoning, the formal successive steps of demonstration being subconsciously perceived but overtly leaped over.

In this modified version of the fourfold Jung classification, Sapir sees the Latin nations as more sensory than northern Europeans. They indulge and cultivate their senses; their ready aesthetic sensibility is due to the weighting with sensation. It might be added that they are often passionate in their actions because they have few inhibitions; but they distrust and dislike prolonged feeling as a means of formulating thought. By contrast, Germans and Russians live much more largely in feeling, and much of their thinking is done essentially through it. In Americans the sensory elements are again lightly stressed; but intuitional propensities are strongly developed as compared with feeling. This of course would not mean that the characteristic American is callous, but that he is not at home with feelings and prefers not to operate with them if avoidable. Like the Britisher, he is afraid to be thought guilty of gush and is uncomfortable in the presence of it. He certainly tends to refrain from the uninhibited and immediate expression of feeling, and is averse also to prolonged reveling in it, to the *Duselei* of the German, or the "mooning" of the pre-Soviet Russian.[3]

Appraisals by this approach also become more difficult when extended to cultures different from our own. The ancient Hebrews were pretty surely of feeling type; but what were the Greeks and Romans? And how about still more remote India, China, Japan? Even there some measure of general agreement might perhaps be reached. The ascetic Hindu is presumably not sensory; or is his asceticism really a reaction formation to strong sensational development? As a mystic and a romantic he might be classed as of feeling type; but he is also an inveterate rationalist and arguer. And mysticism participates in intuition as well as in feeling. By common consent the Chinese are more sensory than the Hindus, and they tend to distrust feeling somewhat like Anglo-Saxons. But what is their basic ingredient? And how do they differ from the Japanese?

245. EMPIRICAL DESCRIPTIONS OF NATIONAL CHARACTERS

Perhaps one gets farther in these matters of national characters and cultural temperaments if one operates pragmatically from case to case with all the variable resources of description, instead of trying to force a fit to a scheme. Thus the Spaniard is individualistic and proud; the Frenchman has a passion

[3] How much national dispositions depend on culture is shown by this example. With the Bolsheviki coming into power, Russian culture was deliberately reoriented, and Russian temperament with it. One would not describe the contemporary Soviet character as a mooning one.

for clarity, reason, and money; the German alternates between sentimentality and throwing his weight around; the Russian is fatalistically resigned but cheerful and dogged. Of this nature, too, is the old Arab saying, seemingly first Englished by Gibbon, that God endowed the Arabs with excellence in the tongue, the Greeks in the brain, the Chinese (whom the Arabs knew better from their manufactures than in their institutions) in the. hands.

Such appraisals may look like the "stereotypes" or derogatory labelings of ethnic groups about which modern social psychologists (§ 246), following the publicists on current affairs, have so much to say. But these appraisals differ from stereotypes in that they attempt an answer to a genuine intellectual problem, whereas stereotypes are emotional expressions of self-superiority used as substitutes for ascertaining the facts. That certain adjectives have now and then been applied in abuse does not remove them from scientific vocabulary. Anthropologists need hardly feel that they are going to be confused with hate-inciters because they see a problem in these matters of cultural and national psychology.

Popularly, national dispositions tend to be assumed as innate, but it is evident from the discussion of race in Chapter Five that heredity cannot be the principal factor, and that the dispositions must be due largely to cultural and historical causes. Thus, there is no doubt a temperamental difference between Englishmen and Americans as a whole, with Canadians pretty fairly intermediate. Yet Americans are descended in the main from Britons, and the non-British constituents in the American populational make-up are so diverse, and each of them is such a minor element in the total, that it is hard to see how these non-Anglo-Saxon elements could have pushed us away from the British prototype in any one consistent direction. They would rather neutralize one another and therewith leave Americans as slightly less characterized Britishers. That is certainly not the whole story of what happened. The typical Britisher appears to Americans slow in thought, speech, and action, and they in reverse seem volatile and vehement to him. There can be little doubt that Americans in general enjoy concentration of effort, instant decisions, quick mobilization, and all-out effort, even to exaggeration, where the English want to take their time, drift into commitments, and resent being hurried. The difference shows even in such supposedly physical activities as athletic sports: Americans excel in sprints and in field events that call for the crowding of supreme effort into a moment, whereas the British tend to surpass them in the grind of long-distance runs.

Many such appraisals, nonprofessional though they be, seem to rest on sound observation. The differentiations spring in the main from varying total-culture patterns that tend to impose different attitudes and habit formations on the majority of individuals of the population. The difficulty with the subject is that we cannot yet satisfactorily deal with it by accurate methods. To date, the approach has remained essentially subjective, intuitional, and common-sense. There is neither check of measurement nor control of experiment; and it is notorious that the topic can hardly be approached without a bit of coloring by our prejudices. This does not mean that considerations of the sort should be tabooed. They possess an undying interest for the student of man, and rightly so, because they touch what is supremely important in culture, its basic patterns and the value systems and orientations of these. It is better to proceed to some psychology by intuition than to have no psychological ideas at all—provided we realize our stabs and guesses to be only such.

Formal social science tends to be averse, as Sapir said, to characterizations of culture in psychological terms, but in the long run they are inevitable and necessary. They will no doubt continue to be made until some more verifiable approach is devised. Mostly, too, separately formed judgments agree surprisingly. For instance, in 1789 the greatest modern philosopher, Immanuel Kant, published his last work, which dealt with psychology, as we should call it, but which in line with the usage of the times he called *Anthropologie*. One of the final sections of this deals with the "character of peoples"—or as we might translate it, ethnic psychology.

His characterization of his own German countrymen remains of interest today. The German, he says, is home-loving; solid but not brilliant; industrious, thrifty, cleanly, without much flash of genius; phlegmatic, tough in endurance, persistent in reasoning; intelligent, capable, but lacking in wit or taste; modest, without confidence in his own originality, therefore imitative; overmethodical, pedantic; without impulse toward equality, but addicted to a painstaking hierarchical grading of society that sets title and rank above natural talent; docile under government, accepting despotism rather than resisting or altering the established order of authority. This was written more than a century and a half ago, when Germany was politically divided and impotent; but even after World War II most of it is still a surprisingly happy diagnosis. Or take this sketch of the Spaniard: ceremonious, grave, imbued with a sense of personal dignity and national nobility, though cruel; grandiloquent, but temperate in habits; devout and legalistic; unwilling to learn, resistive to reform; behindhand in the sciences; looking upon work as an evil or a misfortune. It is evident that these characterizations are made far more in terms of psychology than of institutions or culture. Nevertheless, Kant derives national temperaments partly from "culture," and partly from the diversity of ethnic origins. In this distinction he seems to be referring respectively to somewhat consciously directed cultivation, and to relatively spontaneous growth, both of them being within what we today call culture.

Characterizations or physiognomic judgments such as these may be regarded as attempted shorthand translations of the more general patterns of a culture, and especially of its ethos or values and standards, into terms of the psychological behavior of the generalized or averaged individual of the society to which the culture belongs. The judgments are subjective, but reasonably unprejudiced observers arrive at fairly concordant descriptions.

The following is what Morley of Chichen Itzá has to say on the modern Maya of the Yucatán Peninsula. They are industrious and hard-working even on a poor diet; cleanly in their persons but untidy with belongings; seemingly insensitive to suffering, fatalistic, and unafraid of death. They are conservative, and disinclined to lead or to assume public responsibility, but individualistically independent, though not at all competitive. They are talkative, sociable, cheerful, fond of practical jokes; are not highly sexed, but inclined to promiscuity; are strong on family ties, but not given to showing their affection. They have respect for law and a sense of justice; are honest, averse to thieving and begging; are not quarrelsome but do harbor revenge. And they are not religious, but strongly "superstitious"—which probably means that they do not bring much piety or feeling to their religion except the emotion of fear.

This characterization is based on thirty years of acquaintance. How much of a picture or conviction does it give to anyone who does not know the Maya or other American Indians? To the writer it seems an adequate rough description of Indians in general, even as far away as the United States, except for being somewhat sunnier; and this last characterization might be due to the fact that the Maya are a long-adjusted and a majority population, as compared with our Indians. Yet the question arises: How far would Morley's total characterization have applied also to the Maya of a thousand years ago, when their indigenous religion, art, architecture, astronomy, and hierarchy were flourishing? Most of the characterization perhaps would have held good at that time also, though both the content of the culture and its orientation would have been very different from that of today, when the Maya in effect are Catholic peasants or peons.

And that fact brings us to a consideration of some consequence. It seems possible, theoretically, for two peoples to show much the same psychological character or temperament and yet to have different cultures. The reverse seems also to hold: namely, that culture can be nearly uniform while national character differs. Western Europe, for instance, has basically much the same civilization all over, yet the temperaments of its peoples are sharply distinguishable. At any rate we are in the habit of distinguishing British, French, Spanish, Italian, and German national characters; even the smaller Irish, Dutch, Swiss, Portuguese, have their recognized distinctiveness in typical personality response. And to those who know Scandinavia, the Danes, the Norwegians, and the Swedes certainly present different temperaments. So do South English, North English, Welsh, and Scots among Britons. Are all these distinctions only the stereotypes of prejudice? Or mere conventional badinage? That hardly seems possible. And if so, then the normal or typical personalities of these several nations appear often to be more distinct than the cultures of these same nations. Or at least, to put it with less assumption, the psychologies seem in part to vary independently of the cultures.

If this is correct, then recent attempts to assign each culture a strict counterpart in a "basic personality structure" or "modal personality" type (§ 135) go too far. There can be little doubt that some kind of personality corresponds to each kind of culture; but evidently the correspondence is not one-to-one: it is partial. If this is so, we are not yet quite ready to describe exactly how a culture forces into a narrow mold each of its individual members, who then, in growing up, reperpetuate the culture. There is probably more play, more give, than that in the process. And part of our problem thus would be to ascertain how much of such give there is, how close the correspondence of culture and psychology is or is not, rather than to assume the correspondence as complete and confine ourselves to tracing out its detailed workings.

Let us consider some further cases.

Among the Papuanoid Indonesians of Alor in the Lesser Sunda Islands, the modal personality is described as that of teased, frightened, tolerated, half-abused children who have become adults full of fear, suspicion, spite, and trickiness. According to DuBois, the Alorese are wary, aggressive, touchy, given to chicane and hard dealing, but basically frustrated and confused. They are also greedily hopeful of people and always disappointed in them; this is inevitable, since they are ever exploiting them. They dispute with acrimony, shout, grasp weapons, swear curses—as readily toward spouses, affinals, or kin as to others. Then they sulk; but soon they eat together again or remove the curse by a sacrifice: they have no reserves of deep hate. Violence is feared, fortitude not highly prized, war carried on chiefly by treachery, bravery reckoned by success. Only lack of assurance and self-reliance keeps them from ruthlessness. There are no outstanding successes or accepted heroes in their society. Lacking internal conscience, they are sensitive to ridicule and derogation, and shame becomes the chief social sanction. Lying is taken for granted. A neighbor's disaster provokes pilfering of his effects. All skills, technological, ritual, or social, are at a low level for lack of prestige recompense; their execution is slovenly and slight; training for them is as inconsistent as their reward. When sick, the Alorese become depressed and give up; they have impulses toward suicide but rarely commit it and have not devised any institution for its occasions or forms. They are uninterested in intoxicants. All this suggests low and prevalently negativistic toning of affects. The chief symbol of euphoria is feeding: and that in supernatural as well as social relations. Women's power lies in control of food, which is grown chiefly by them; but they receive no corresponding status. Men have the status, but lack power and security. And as the children are exposed to whims instead of steady affection, everyone manages to seem chronically unhappy. The Alorese are discontent, distrustful, and exploitive of human beings and spirits alike; only danger makes them placatory.

This characterization seems one-sidedly repellent. Can any people actually be so unmitigatedly disagreeable and contemptible? The appraising observer comes from a culture that values internalization, conscience, reliance, scruple, courage, consistency of feeling and relations, dignity, and achievement—qualities that are underdeveloped in Alor. Hence the picture is black. We see no positive values in the culture, and therefore no virtues of character in the typical personality. So far as the culture seems to have values, it is for food, power, and prestige on a wholly infantile or even primate level—irrespective of how they are acquired. That the prevailing slants of behavior in Alor are as represented can hardly be doubted; but a more picaresque-minded observer might have drawn a somewhat more sympathetic portrait of Alorese personality. Subjectivity is difficult to eliminate wholly from these psychological characterizations of cultures.

It will be of interest to compare recent temperament characterizations for two neighboring nationalities of very similar culture, the Burmese and the Siamese.

Among the Burmese, according to Gorer, who moved from psychoanalysis into anthropology, women are good-humored, cool, impersonal, kindly, firm, efficient, and helpful. They manage the household, do most of the business, control the family money, and generally dominate, but without claiming dominance. As girls they act coy, but as wives and mothers they take the initiative in teasing, loving, and protecting.

By contrast, Burmese men are described as vain, lazy, pampered, primping, and gossipy; generally passive and unmanned, but when active, destructively violent. They fly into uncontrolled rages in which they are cruel and criminal: temptation is felt as something irresistible. Acts like arson, murder, and looting are common and are not causes for shame, but are freely confessed and are thought wiped clean by punishment. Such violences do not deprave Burmese men, nor lead to professional criminality. There is a similar irresponsibility toward money, which is prized as the means of adornment, indulgence, and social show, and is sought after without compunction through the easy ways of bribes, gambling, and confidence tricks. Excitement is found in competitive games like cockfights and boat races. Then too, men are vain of their bodies and dress, though boyishly so rather than effeminately. They are also theatrical, given to strutting in public; they are fond of professional plays and of amateur acting. In public station they are irresponsible and capricious. Sexually, they seem puritanical, or at least given to extreme bodily modesty. They use almost no opium, and alcohol infrequently, but drunkenness tends to be pursued to stupefaction. The quality in which men consistently claim to surpass women is "patience"!

According to Benedict, whom we have already encountered in § 135, Thai or Siamese women possess their own property, are more purposive than men in acquiring and retaining it, handle the day-by-day family money. They go in more than men for jewelry and display. Ideal wives are thought to be like sisters or mothers, cherishing and submissive; others are considered contentious or even "audacious."

Thai men are cheerful, easy-going, jolly, gay, indolent. They accept subordination to higher rank or power without either resentment or servility; they do not cringe. They respect and obey authority without demanding return or assistance from it. There is a minimum of discipline in the family, as in public relations: the Thai are a quiet people; their gatherings are convivial instead of unruly. They are self-reliant in a quiet, careless way—without much sense of responsibility for others. They enjoy resting unworried, at ease, preferably eating, chewing, drinking, or smoking. They like gambling; they trouble little over laying by money, but are fond of spending it. They dislike quarrels, rarely offer violence, are not easily irritated; in disputes, the better man tends to leave off first; anger is felt to be disadvantageous; and they incline to be forgiving. There is much festive drinking, which renders them happy and noisy, but releases no hostile aggressions, nor do they often continue to the stage of passing out; drunkenness is not a serious social problem, nor is opium. They tend to disregard property rights as children might, evade debts, do much petty pilfering, but commit few crimes of violence. Sincere in their Buddhism, they however practice no asceticisms and seek no mysticism or Nirvana, but aim to achieve merit in this life, which they appreciate as good. With all their gentleness, they are worldly-minded. Anger heats the heart, they say, disturbs life by leading to grudges and foolish actions, is disadvantageous; it should be curbed while still small. The "cool heart" is without anxiety, rests at ease, surveys and weighs the situation, accepts cheerfully what it must, and takes advantage of circumstances, including the stupidity or the emotion of others. Successful guile is admired, as successful force is not. Security is achieved through patience and in not being duped. "Patience"—of which women pass as having less than men, though they are more reckless—involves calm circumspection and acting with worldly wisdom; it gives peace as well as success. Patience really is self-control over disturbing emotion, and leads to a species of self-reliance.

Psychoanalytically, the Siamese are obviously "oral" in type (§ 255).

It is evident that the Burmese and Siamese cultures not only tend to mold their members alike by custom, as in making women the family budget managers, but are alike in their value appraisals, as in judging men more "patient" than women, contrary to ourselves. In contrast, it is evident from the foregoing accounts that there are indubitable differences between the two nationalities in their modal temperaments. This holds even if we allow for some degree of subjective difference between the two judgments cited. Other observers corroborate that the Burmese are relatively touchy, proud, theatrical, and violent; the Siamese relaxed, amiable, easy in their dignity, pleasure-loving, and serene. The normal degrees of tension differ, as do the "personas" assumed, the roles one tries to play. This reinforces at least that part of our previous finding which said that modal personalities or temperaments may vary characteristically while cultures remain much alike.

Indeed, national temperaments evidently become most distinctive when peoples are contrasted whose cultures are basically alike: such as Frenchmen, British, Germans, Scandinavians, Spaniards, whose cultures are only subvarieties of the general European phase of Occidental civilization. By contrast, to compare French national character with Chinese, or Italian with Japanese, seems random and somewhat futile. Part of the futility would appear to be due to a fact already noted; namely, that the categories of psychological characterization developed among Occidentals for Occidentals break down, tend to lose their meaning, when applied to Asiatics. A counterpart of this fact is the highly characteristic special meaning which Siamese and Burmese evidently give to their words for "patience"—and Chinese and Japanese to "sincerity"—meanings that obviously include a lot that our translating terms do not cover.

We may conclude therefore that the most fruitful and sound way in which national temperaments can be studied is as between related groups partaking of the same basic culture. Wherever the modal personalities of two such groups differ, there will expectably also be some subcultural differences in customs and institutions. But these will be known or readily ascertainable, and should be measurable or definable. Therewith the accompanying psychological differences may perhaps be explained. At any rate their associated variables will be clear. When this sort of systematic and partly controlled study has been made, say for Europe and another for East Asia, comparisons of a higher order should be successful: for instance, inquiry into how far the common denominators within European and within East Asiatic basic civilizations agree or differ.

The investigation could then be extended to the psychological aspects of the indigenous American cultures, the Negro African ones, the Islamic peoples, and so on. When Maya, Otomí, Yaqui, Navaho, Zuni, Yurok, Shoshone, Dakota, and Eskimo psychologies have been investigated for their common qualities as well as their distinctivenesses, and the relation of these to their cultural uniformities and peculiarities is known—when all this has been done, then comparison with the results of similar studies on the interrelations of, for example, Burma, Siam, Annam, Java, Bali, and Tagalog, and of China, Korea, and Japan, ought to be extremely illuminating. At present, while we are still limited to the matching of Zuni with Bali, of Samoa with the United States, of the Lepcha with the Navaho, of Germany to Japan, the situation is really pretty haphazard and random.

It is probable that we already possess a good many valid findings in this field of the psychological physiognomies that correspond to cultural physiognomies. But until the field is more systematically organized, there is little way of knowing which of the findings are relatively sound and secure and which represent chiefly personalized reactions of observers. With organization once achieved, it is also to be presumed that the validity and the limits of the concepts and categories used will become defined—whether these be "patience" or "aggression," "sincerity" or "frustration." And finally, it should then be possible to answer the further question of how far genuinely similar or homologous psychologies can appear in peoples of different cultures, either through accidental convergence or through recurrence of stages, castes, or classes.

246. SOCIAL PSYCHOLOGY AND CULTURAL PSYCHOLOGY

Social psychology began to develop soon after 1900, largely through sociologists who had been influenced by Tarde's *Laws of Imitation* (1890), and also by Le Bon's *Psychology of the Crowd* (1895), which in turn reflected the findings of the psychiatrists Charcot and Janet on suggestion. Professional psychologists, until then, had been essentially concerned with the individual. As they gradually took over social psychology from the sociologists and the philosophers, they gradually increased emphasis on critical caution, definition, and experiment. Social psychology is now a fairly well delimited subject. Among its specialties are in-groups and out-groups, social adjustment, attitudes, dominance, leadership, audiences, morale, public opinion, group prejudice including stereotypes, propaganda, revolution.

Personality is recognized as acquired, as being a product of socialization. Its consideration therefore falls within the scope of social psychology. Some go so far as to distinguish between "inherent nature," which refers to what is universal in men; socially conditioned "human nature," or the qualities of the personality that make it like other personalities within the same society; and individuality, or qualities that make it unlike others. Thus Japanese and Americans have differently conditioned "human natures." Apart from this special and somewhat confusing usage, it is evident that social psychologists recognize culture for what it is. But they scarcely deal with it as such, as something having a specific content. Instead, they deal with certain generalized or abstracted psychological processes operative in culture, such as drives; factors in learning, formal education; overt versus covert responses and symbolic versus direct behaviors; prestige influences; conventional, institutional, or formal situations; pressurings; and the like.

It will be seen from this that social psychology does not explain or even touch any concrete existing culture or part of a culture—which it would call "a cultural situation." It deals only with certain abstracted psychological mechanisms or attributes that are or can be operative in culture. In fact, what we have just considered as psychologically expressible types of culture or national temperaments (§ 245) social psychology tends to dismiss as unscientific, linking them with emotional "stereotypes" of ethnocentric, depreciatory, or abusive origin. Then, social psychology is more specific about society than about culture, and deals at length, and sometimes concretely, with interpersonal relations, such as social adjustment, leadership, propaganda; and interpersonal relations as such of course are social relations.

It is evident that social psychology deals consistently with what its name implies; but also that it scarcely touches culture as the anthropologist ordinarily concerns himself with it. Since about 1935 some anthropological work has been increasingly and avowedly aware of a number of the concepts of social psychology, such as covertness, prestige, symbolism, socialization of the individual. This widening is all to the good. Yet any attempt to consider culture only or primarily through the medium of concepts such as these would mean that the specific field of anthropology—culture content and cultural form and pattern—was being virtually abandoned for psychologizing. It does remain true that all the knowledge in the world about who influences whom, and how, tells us nothing of what people are influenced to—of their culture. And culture—pure culture as distinct from that mixture of persons, events, and institutions which is called history, and distinct also from the part-culture manifestations with which economics and government are concerned—culture is the specific subject of all the nonbiological part of anthropology, and of no other study or science, except perhaps sociology if it chooses to make the choice. If anthropologists do not study cultural manifestations as such, no one else will.

In short, social psychology is a developed and still developing field of importance, adjacent to that of anthropology and related to it, dealing with the interactions of human beings as social animals and therefore as culture producers and carriers. But to date this psychology has not been seriously concerned with the *different* behaviors of men under different cultures, nor with the explanation or even the characterization of different cultures in psychological terms. So far as this latter task has been undertaken—namely, what we might call the psychology of cultures, or of culture as such—it has been attempted, though as yet in piecemeal fashion, chiefly either by anthropologists or by inquirers influenced by psychoanalysis. The psychological description of cultures would necessarily underlie their psychological explanation. Such description would comprise, first, the characterization of whole cultures in terms of psychological attributes; and second, it would go on to comparison of the degree of development of such attributes in a variety of cultures. Neither line appears to have been developed very far, else we should presumably be recognizing a subscience or field of cultural psychology comparable to social psychology.

In the last two sections (§ 244-245) we have reviewed some of the endeavors at psychological characterizations of whole cultures. The eight sections which follow (§ 247-254) will pursue the complementary approach: namely, that of examining certain psychological qualities or attributes as they manifest varying strength and varying relationships in diverse cultures. It will be found that both approaches reveal quickly that cultures differ strikingly if somewhat elusively in their psychological qualities or physiognomies. But neither approach can yet be said to have yielded a notable body of theoretical conclusions. This means that such a field as cultural psychology evidently exists, but that it has not yet been developed and organized into an autonomous branch of science. If what follows, or in fact if this whole chapter, appears unsystematic, it is due to this condition of immaturity of the subject; this however may be partly compensated for by the stimulus inherent in the very awkwardnesses of youth.

The qualities or proclivities of cultures with which we shall from here on be dealing are evidently similar to the special orientations, attitudes, or weightings, the interests and preoccupations, that all cultures manifest and which have been discussed in connection with culture and its patterns in Chapters Seven and Eight. The difference from these patterns is that an orientation or an interest involves preoccupation with something specific, like horse-racing, or cattle, or dreams, or legal procedures, or funerals, and can therefore be described as cultural. But the psychological bents we shall be concerned with from here on are in themselves devoid of concrete cultural content: for instance, co-operativeness, or cleanliness, or aggression. While no wholly sharp line can be drawn between the two approaches, the cultural one is the more behavioristically descriptive as well as more concrete; the psychological one, the more dynamic and concerned with abstracted process.

247. CO-OPERATION, COMPETITION, AND INDIVIDUALISM

We have one comparative study, instigated by Mead, which classifies a series of nonliterate cultures as to their co-operative, competitive, and individualistic orientations, and inquires how far these may correlate with other trends in the same cultures. The individualistic category was introduced secondarily to cover certain cultures, such as the Eskimo, which are not organized co-operatively but at the same time hold out no social rewards for competitive success. It is a case, in them, mainly of each man for himself, or at any rate for his biological family group. In genuinely competitive societies, such as the Ifugao and the Kwakiutl, the social premiums definitely go to those who can outdo or outclimb others. Co-operative cultures tend to accord prestige in proportion as the individual's efforts benefit the lineage, the village, or the community. Thus there is little credit accorded him for acquiring property, but much for giving it away with honor. In extreme cases, as with the Zuni, the communal sense is so strong as to set public opinion against endeavors at leadership or conspicuous personal success as presumptuous and presumably antisocial. The diagram shows the grouping of the cultures (Fig. 29).

Certain traits, which were found by Mead to correlate pretty regularly with either predominantly co-operative or competitive tendencies, may be eliminated at the outset because they are implicit in the concepts of co-operation and competition. Thus "emphasis on rising in status" and "interest in property for personal ends" are contained in the definition of social competition; similarly,

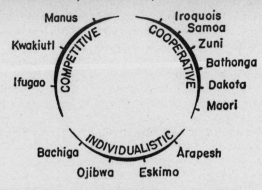

FIG. 29. STRENGTH OF CO-OPERATIVE, COMPETITIVE, AND INDI-
VIDUALISTIC ATTITUDES IN 13 TRIBES
(After Mead)

"closed social system," "high security for the individual," and perhaps "faith in an ordered universe" are implied in co-operativeness. These come near to being verbal or spurious correlations.

There remain several other traits that either are outrightly cultural, like agriculture and institutionalized suicide, or which are at least culturally deter-mined, like conscience and ego development. The distribution of these traits is shown in the tabulation; and it is evident that none of them evinces any very close correlation with any of the three orientations.

First of all, geography, a people's particular place in the world, has nothing to do with competitive, co-operative, or individualistic trends. The six American cultures examined, and the five Oceanic ones, belong to all three types. This rules out any major historical developments characteristic of grand areas. A given culture is, say, co-operative not because all the cultures in its continent have had a common development toward co-operation, but because of particular circumstances experienced in its peculiar national history. To put it the other way around, any one culture in an area may gradually become increasingly co-operative or competitive or individualistic. On the basis of probability, therefore, some cultures are likely to have changed at some time from one class to another. This in turn indicates that sets toward co-operation, competition, and individual-ism are not necessarily among the more permanent trends of development; and this suggests that they are secondary rather than deep-seated characteristics. Our own society has undergone considerable shift from a competitive-individ-ualistic to a co-operative orientation in the last forty years, without fully equivalent change in the basic content of its culture.

One might expect that agriculture, with its settled life and its numerous tasks best performed by people working together, would induce co-operative attitudes. There probably is such a trend, but it is not wholly determinative. The co-operative Dakota were nonagricultural; and on the other side, there are three farming tribes among seven individualistic or competitive ones.

CORRESPONDENCES OF CULTURE TRAITS TO THE TOTAL SET OF CULTURE

Based on Mead

(All capital letters denote the presence of the trait in question; dashes, its absence)

Type	Tribe	Continent	Agriculture	Institu- tionalized Suicide	Forcing Education	Ego Development	Status Emphasis	Conscience (Internal Sanction)
Competitive	Manus	Oc	—	—	F	E	S	C
	Kwakiutl	Am	—	I	F	E	S	
	Ifugao	Oc	A	I	F	E	S	—
Individual	Bachiga	Afr	A	—	—	—	S	C
	Ojibwa	Am	—	I	F	E	—	C
	Eskimo	Am	—	I	F	—	—	C
	Arapesh	Oc	A	—	—	—	—	—
Co-operative	Maori	Oc	A	I	—	E	S	C
	Dakota	Am	—	I	F	—	S	—
	Bathonga	Afr	A	I	—	—	S	—
	Zuni	Am	A	—	F	—	—	—
	Samoa	Oc	A	—	—	—	S	—
	Iroquois	Am	A	I	—	E	S	—

Institutionalized suicide (§ 254) means that occasions and forms for it— such as hara-kiri—are provided by the society. This trait shows so even a scatter as to indicate that it lacks correlation.

"Forcing or hastening education," to prod the young toward adulthood as fast as possible, is one of a set of habits that expectably would be well developed in definitely competitive societies. So would ego development. A boy that remained immature, yielding, docile, unstrenuous—given to play instead of work after he was able-bodied—would get off to a bad start in his career of living in such a society. It will be seen that all the frankly competitive societies do speed up education and instill self-regard. On the contrary, six of the ten noncompetitive cultures also show at least one or the other of this pair of traits; so that the correlation may be described as lopsided, complete for one kind of culture, partial for the other kind.

Status emphasis occurs in all three competitive cultures, and in five of the six co-operative ones—all but super-Apollinian Zuni (§ 135). This is no doubt because competition and co-operation both are concerned with interpersonal relations, and thus are sensitive of them, though with opposite weighting—one positively, the other negatively. The contrast accordingly should be between the two types jointly as against the individualistic type in which by definition people are attuned to self-sufficiency rather than to their relations with others. It does work out this way. Three of the four individualistic societies are classed as uninterested in status. The East African Bachiga are rated as status-concerned; but they are on the edge of the individualistic type, verging toward the competitive; and they are described as anarchistic, touchy, and contentious.

Five of the thirteen cultures are judged as showing definite development of "feelings of internal sanction"; that is, conscience. Three of these five are from the individualistic class. This is as might be expected, since when competition is accepted as the normal way of living, it will tend to stifle certain kinds of scruple; whereas in a co-operative setup, it would seem natural for internal sanctions to be replaced by social approvals. Nevertheless, the correlation is not complete, since one of the individualistic cultures fails to develop conscience, whereas one each of the co-operative and competitive ones does develop it. The latter, Manus, probably owes its conscientiousness to its puritanism (§ 248). It is interesting that the faraway Yurok of California also can be described as characterized by competitiveness, shrinking puritanism, conscience (sense of sin relieved by confession), strong emphasis on status, and a sensitive ego. In fact, except perhaps for less speeding of their children into adulthood, the Yurok psychological profile, in terms of the traits here dealt with, simply repeats the Manus one; and certainly without any specific historical connection between the two cultures.[4]

In summary, it appears that where the present set of correlations are not spurious through being implicit, they mostly are only partial. There seems to be surprisingly little tendency for broad psychological trends to co-occur regularly with either specific personality traits or with cultural institutions. This in turn suggests that cultures, like personalities, are psychologically plastic. They probably do not often permanently harbor directly conflicting trends; but they may and do include almost any combination of compatible trends. Thus the psychological structure of cultures, as of individuals, may be complex, and perhaps normally is complex, in the sense of being a composite, a more or less successful or viable integration, of factors that have no intimate or necessary relation to one another, but which do possess the faculty of working out an adjustment and being able to co-exist.

It is evident that we need more studies of the type of this one by Mead.

248. INHIBITION AND PURITANISM

Inhibition, asceticism, and puritanism can be recognized in societies as well as in individuals. Inhibition is the impeding of the free flow of expression, the checking or blocking of one impulse by another and contrary one. The blocking may be conscious and voluntary, in which case it may approach closely to the guiding power of "control"; although inhibiting definitely involves the halting

---

[4] This reinforces what has been said in § 245 on the possibility that cultures of unlike content can be alike psychologically; or their content may be similar but their psychology dissimilar. In other words, eidos and ethos (§ 125) may go together but do not have to.

or suppression of an impulse, whereas control, fundamentally, steers or directs without the implication of check or conflict. But the blocking may also gradually become habitual and unconscious, as well as widely spread or chronic in the personality, as when we speak of someone as an inhibited individual. This passive sense is the one most to the fore in recent psychological thinking.

Asceticism is always an act of will: the deliberate practice of austerity, abstinence, and self-mortification. It is the sensory gratifications of one's own body that are suppressed by asceticism in the interest of some standard of morals, religion, or inner development. Puritanism got its name from a cultural phenomenon, the ethics of a British group of sects three centuries ago, and it carries connotations varying from commendatory to adverse, with the latter gaining ground in contemporary usage. Puritanical aims are also ascetic; but the special quality of puritanism seems to be the wish to apply asceticism to others as well as to oneself, to enforce it socially. The Hindu prizes asceticism, the New Englander was a puritan. Continued puritanism tends to build up inhibitory systems, thus completing a circle of linkage; though puritanism and asceticism primarily prohibit and punish—others or oneself—while inhibition is basically protective and is derived from caution or fear rather than from misprizal or hate.

Not only Anglo-Saxons are puritanical: Protestantism in general inclines that way, and its strongest inclinations to puritanism seem to have developed under the influence of Calvinism, which originated on the continent of Europe. Early Christianity and then mediaeval Christianity put a high value on asceticism, at first for hermits and later for monks, but did not exact it of laymen; they cannot properly be described as puritanical. India, seat of asceticism, past and present, developed Buddhism and Brahminism; but like early and mediaeval Christianity, these religions asked asceticism only of their clergy, the monks or priests. With the laity exempt from mortification, and with abstinences such as from eating flesh being only recommended, Buddhism as a whole, though ascetically inclined, cannot be classed as puritanical. On the contrary, the third world religion, Mohammedanism, contains a definite puritanical element, and that in spite of its permitted four wives and promised houris which loom so large in our popular conception of it. Alcohol in any form, the eating of pork, gambling, representation of men and animals in art, are all forbidden in Islam; even coffee and tobacco had a hard time getting by, and are discountenanced by the strict, who also long opposed fire insurance and life insurance as being a form of gambling on decisions made by God, and who denounced printing as an unauthorized innovation (§ 172, 199). It is interesting, psychologically as well as culture-historically, that sex, on which later Protestant puritanism perhaps centered its repressive interests—"immorality" means nonmarital sexual indulgence in ordinary American English, as "passion" is coming to mean sex appetite—this same sex is the principal field of activity which Mohammedanism excepts from its puritanism.

Ascetic practices of one sort or another are widely spread among non-literate peoples also. Chiefly this is in connection with acquiring supernatural power or mana, which is conceived of as nonsensory, spiritual, and mental, and thus somehow to be heightened by repression or punishment of the body. The means of ascetic practice vary from abstentions—from food, drink, sleep, sexual gratification—to inflictions of pain—winter bathing, whipping, piercing, blood-letting. Some measure of asceticism in religious situations is so nearly universal as to need no further comment; variation is chiefly in kind.

Now and then a primitive people goes on beyond self-asceticism and becomes puritanical in its generic attitudes. The Melanesians of Manus are so described: censorious, joyless, vindictive, burdened with a sense of the world's wickedness. Something of this temperament is discernible among most Melanesians, though often it is difficult to be sure just how much of the quality inheres in the society or enters through the observers' eyes. Two things give Melanesian puritanism a special interest. It is not founded on well-developed religious practices of asceticism, such as punishing one's body; and it seems wholly lacking from the national temperament of the Polynesians farther out in the Pacific, as well as among the Indonesians on the other side of Melanesia. It seems to spring from a sense of sin rampant in the world and necessary to guard against.

A sense of something akin to sin appears to be involved wherever a regulated confession mechanism occurs. But it is clear that peoples can feel themselves guilt-ridden or sin-ridden without setting up confession as an institution. The Melanesians are a case in point: Manus has confession, near-by Dobu and Trobriand do not. Protestant denominations unanimously and strongly turned against confession when they broke away from Roman Catholicism; but in most of them sin was probably more to the forefront of consciousness than it had previously been in Catholicism (§ 253). The occurrence of institutionalized confession among nonliterate peoples the world over is spotty. Thus in North America it is a well-developed practice with Eskimo, Yurok, Aztec, and Maya, who certainly differ drastically among themselves in culture as well as temperament; besides, it occurs more incidentally among Carrier, Iroquois, Pueblo, and others. The acts confessed may range from breach of taboo to malevolent witchcraft, as at Zuni, or incest as at Manus. This variety, together with the distribution, indicates more or less parallel, separate developments for many of the institutions of confession. Common primitive features are that retribution for wrongdoing may befall the sinner's children or kinsfolk rather than himself; that the confession neutralizes the evil; but that to be effective it must be made publicly.

A generic inclination toward an inhibited temperament seems to characterize most the Mongoloids of Asia and America, but with definite exceptions, such as Eskimo and Polynesians and perhaps Indonesians. American Indians certainly cultivate restraint. They preach self-control, as well as constant pleasantness of manner to others. When they erupt into anger or cruelty, it is in the manner of the inhibited: with a break, or jerk. Negroids in Africa would probably be classed among the noninhibited, but in Oceania among the inhibited. Australians also would be on the noninhibited side. Accordingly there is the usual lack of clear-cut correlation with hereditary race.

249. CLEANLINESS AND ORDER

One attitude in which cultures differ is that toward bodily cleanliness. Allied to this is the sense of neatness and order in dress and personal effects and surroundings. There is immense variation in these matters, both between different nations and in the same nation at different times.

The Greeks built no great baths, but they did build gymnasia and they did prize athletic sports. In these they stripped: the word "gymnasium" originally meant a place in which one went naked, *gymnos;* and they used strigils to scrape the body, and then oiled or anointed it. They despised the Persians and other Asiatics for their false modesty in keeping the body covered at all times. The Romans took over much of this Greek cult of the body, and carried it farther by building enormous public baths, where people with leisure spent hours daily. This habit, incidentally, reached its peak after Rome had lost its republicanism and had become a despotic empire.

The early Christians felt themselves increasingly in conflict not only with the established pagan religion but with many of its attitudes and trends, its luxuries, art, philosophy. Baths were part of Roman Imperial culture; therefore they soon became construed as instruments not only of paganism but also of vice. Baths cultivated and softened the body instead of saving the soul; and before long overcleanliness, and then what we would consider minimum cleanliness, came to be considered one of the roads to ruin. After Christianity came into control of the government and culture of the Mediterranean, baths and bathing went out with slavery, gladiators, temples and altars, animal sacrifices, mythological and erotic poetry, nature worship and sensitivity to natural beauty, and a lot else both callous and gracious. The ascetic saint neglected his body and was indifferent to filth: keeping oneself scrupulously clean was now perhaps not exactly a sin, but it certainly bred suspicion that one might not be too good a Christian, especially if one were a man. Among the barbarian Christians, feelings smacked of the lumber camp, with piety reinforcing he-manness.

Things went more or less this way through the Dark Ages and the early Middle Ages. The Crusaders must have seemed an unwashed barbarian swarm to the Oriental Saracens from whom they took away the Holy Land. And to the first Crusaders the Mohammedan baths were but another expression of the effeminacy and decadence springing from a false religion.

A change came over Europe after it had passed through the peak of the High Middle Ages in the thirteenth century. By the 1400's, people had begun once more to like to wash, and public baths sprang up. This turn of sentiment after a thousand years was accompanied by many related changes. Established religion was losing its hold. The genuinely pious were fewer, the skeptical and curious-minded more numerous. It was the period of Popes at Avignon instead of Rome, of the great Papal schism, of widespread complaints against the irreligiosity and wealth of the clergy; also of awakening interest in foreign lands, then of exploration; and of new inventions like printing, clocks, iron-casting.

In the 1500's a reaction began. The Protestants aimed to return to primitive Christianity; the Church tried to hold its lines by tightening and purifying them. Moralists and the pious in both camps turned ascetic, once more condemned the baths, and began to demand their suppression. For over two centuries cultivated Europe did not, it is true, exactly glory in dirt, but it washed little and looked on bathing as rarely needed and as likely to be dangerous to health. If we of today had personally met great sovereigns like Elizabeth or Louis XIV, we should probably have been aware of their body odor.

This phase passed away with the slackening of religious intransigeance, with the growth of enlightenment, with the increase and spread of wealth and therewith of comforts, with the rise of the bourgeoisie. But the refinement of social manners on which the late seventeenth and especially the eighteenth century prided themselves definitely preceded the revived manners of bodily cleanliness. It was the countries in which the new wealthy middle class became specially influential that took the lead in the new direction; hence the scrubbing of Dutch doorsteps and the proverbial Englishman with his portable bath. The French Revolution stood for republicanism and increased the power of the bourgeoisie. Before long a mental association grew up, and prosperous democracy became a rough index of frequency of bathing and vice versa. Americans pride themselves almost equally on both, and take for granted that there is an inherent connection: "cleanliness next to godliness."

Other cultures differ equally. Tanks, pools, and bathing evidently figured much more in ancient Egypt than in the coeval and parallel Two Rivers civilization of Mesopotamia; but the Indus Valley civilization again built large baths of brick. India today is full of cow dung and filth, but the higher castes wash their bodies and clothes sedulously. This habit, most accentuated in the priestly Brahmans, is inculcated by religion. Above all, the Brahman must keep himself uncontaminated and pure. Physical cleanliness is the first step toward cleanness of soul, a physical expression of it. This Hindu attitude will prevent any hasty fallacy that religion and cleanliness are in their nature antithetical. Many religions have insisted on clean bodies as symbolic of a clean and holy mind. Japanese Shinto, for instance, uses bathing, washing, and sprinkling as a constant means of purification. Primitive tribes frequently insist on bathing or head-washing as a preliminary to ceremonial. It was especially the great world religions, Buddhism, Christianity, Mohammedanism, with their aim at a deeper theology, that felt physical symbolic acts to be insufficient—too easy, as it were—for spiritual attainments, and emphasized the separation of body and soul rather than their likeness and undifferentiation. From this sprang the frequent ascetic neglect or contempt of the body in order to elevate and free the soul; this in turn was likely to end by making obtrusive cleanliness suspect.

Neatness, daintiness, orderliness are allied to cleanliness. Animals differ so strikingly in these traits according to kind—as the cat from the pig—that we must consider their tendencies genetic by species; that is, inborn. How far impulses toward neatness or slovenliness are congenital in individual human beings is not known. Individuals can at any rate be strongly conditioned in one direction or the other fairly early in life. Human populations presumably average much the same inherently, and the differences between them can be assumed as habitual; that is, determined by their cultures. These differences are great. Witness this traveler's account of the confusion and filth in which one tribe lives, and that one's surprise at the neatness of the homes, belongings. and bodies of another group of "savages."

More orderly cultures as compared to less orderly ones, or better-organized in contrast to little-organized, are shown by the Colorado River Yuman cultures as against the Arizona-plateau Yumans; by the Pueblo as against the Apache; by the Plains Indians as against those of California and the north-western coast of America—though these last probably had a fuller culture, one containing more items, than the tribes of the Plains. Neatness and order are conspicuous around the homes of the supposed Negrito—or dwarf Papuans? —of Dutch New Guinea, as against all other Negritos. Orderliness can be shown in the management of physical living, in systematized organization of ritual or society, in a coherent concept of the world. Even the way a native presents information to an ethnologist can be organized and orderly or hap-hazard and mixed. And tribes seem to differ as much as individuals in this respect.

The cleanliness of the Japanese is proverbial and almost obsessive. Equally compulsive are their neatness and orderliness. There are no incomplete per-formances, no rough edges or loose ends left, in Japan: the poorest object is finished. The contrast is marked with China, where seamy sides are common, but where the great profundities and humanities of East Asia were also worked out. By general consent, the Japanese lost something of these internal qualities in their taking over Chinese civilization; possibly because of their very perfec-tionism toward cultural neatness, finish, order, and efficiency.

250. ANIMISTIC ATTITUDES

Just as one person feels his religion deeply while his neighbor merely goes through the forms, so do cultures differ. One society is genuinely pious, another worldly-minded; or the same society may change from one attitude to another in a few hundred years. Our Western civilization took its religion hard in the seventeenth century, loosened increasingly in the eighteenth and the nineteenth, and in the twentieth has, though unavowedly for the most part, de facto replaced faith in revealed religion to a considerable extent by faith in science. In this period, the Church has been completely divorced from the State in many countries, and religion has largely been segregated off into a special sphere of its own. In Soviet Russia, under extreme conditions of ruthless revolutionary control, religion was in fact virtually outlawed for two decades.

Similar differences occur among nonliterate peoples. These mostly possess little available history of change, but their contemporary differences point to a similar variability. Thus Polynesians in general appear to be less animistic-minded, less driven by religious compulsion, than Melanesians and Australian blackfellows. We have seen (§ 168) with what lightness the Hawaiians voluntarily broke their taboo system and threw away their ancestral cults. Even if this strange revolution was a result of "cultural fatigue," it indicated that religion must have lost much of its hold if the population was tired of it. Similarly, the Samoans are described by Mead as retaining many Polynesian supernatural beliefs and practices, but as adhering to them perfunctorily, with little fervor of feeling. Religion is not an important actuating force: interest is turned toward social mechanisms and relations. The Samoans are pragmatic and realistic. The feeling tone of their life lacks intensity. They are a placid, pleasant people, inclined to be concerned with small, immediate objectives, averse to being stirred deeply.

Another people to whom a partial lack or lapse of animism might be attributed are the Eskimo, especially in contrast with the Indians of their continent. They retain of course a share of the taboos and the supernatural beliefs of all primitive cultures; but their primary and dominant orientation is realistic. They differ from the Samoans in that they have a minimum of social mechanisms and statuses to distract their attention. Their relations are personal, man to man, with little in the way of institutions as a framework. Nor can they be described as emotionally low-toned. While affable and ready to laugh, they are volatile, quick, and passionate, and when they dare, express anger as well as pleasure with little restraint.

The cause for this orientation can perhaps be sought in the extraordinarily trying circumstances of survival in the Arctic. The Eskimo must be mechanical-minded, able-bodied, manually skillful, and practical. Too many taboos or rituals would tie his hands, limit his resourcefulness, take up time that must be given to survival activities to a visibly greater extent than among almost any other people. Supernaturalism thus tends to drop into the background, relatively.

This explanation runs rather counter to a more general theory advanced by Malinowski which holds magic and animism to be man's response to his sense of insecurity in the world (§ 130). Magic appears when there is a hiatus in knowledge or power yet man has to proceed. His emotional state of instability results in substitute action—magical practices or worship—which have at least subjective value: they reintegrate the individual and organize society. In fishing or voyaging on the ocean, according to Malinowski, Melanesians feel insecure, and hence use prayers, charms, and avoidance taboos; but for fishing in sheltered lagoons, they dispense with these.

The contrary Eskimo example cited (also in § 130) shows that as a universal this theory is not watertight. In fact the contradiction is a good example of the difficulty of determining strict laws in the field of human behavior. We may grant a degree of validity to the insecurity theory, but must recognize that it has limits. Magic may be a fantasy response of men in situations of strain, but if the insecurity becomes too immediate and acute, magic may cease to be felt as the primary aid, and there is a return to organic self-reliance, to meeting problems with realistic means. Such a modified interpretation is also supported by the luxuriant development of animism and magic often found among peoples normally not confronted by great difficulties. All along the North Pacific coast of America, for instance, there were no serious rigors of climate, and food was abundant; nevertheless all the tribes here had developed a richer system of magic, rituals, and myth than the Eskimo. The same may be said of the Melanesians: these unquestionably had an easier time making a living than the Eskimo. Yet many of them did not trust themselves to such simple efforts as planting yams without the aid of magic.

For a general explanation in psychological terms, one might thus fall back on this: that marked excess or deficiency of security is prejudicial to the development of belief in the supernatural. The optimum condition for religion and magic would be a middle one, in which the total environmental and social situation gave people some uneasiness but not too much. This rather tame conclusion at least derives support from the undoubted facts that most cultures are religious, and that most of them have recurrent worries but not crushing ones. But the specific causes that make cultures vary in their religious set or orientation are evidently numerous. We cannot predict either the strength or the kind of religion and magic in a given culture from knowing how great the security of life is, nor how advanced the arts are, how much wealth has been accumulated, how militaristic or pacifist the inclinations are.

Some weakening of religious attachments seems generally to occur in the transition from rural to urban life, and is an inherent part of the change from folk to sophisticate cultures (§ 121).

251. SYSTEMATIZING TRENDS

Like individuals, cultures differ in their ability to systematize. Whether the systematization be by reasoning or by feeling and guessing, its essential quality perhaps is a habit of recognizing and dealing in relations, of generalizing. By contrast, the unsystematic-minded tend to take each fact of experience as separate: it remains an event, an item in itself. Like children, they are usually exact in perceiving and remembering the isolated fact, and perhaps its exact absolute place, without awareness of its relation. It is a matter-of-fact attitude of detailed sensory accuracy as compared with the more imaginative and constructive one of seeing significances.

Now certain West African cultures, such as the Ashanti and the Yoruba, have struck all observers as definitely systematizing. Their social structure, law, and beliefs are intricately organized. Other West African groups, like the Nupe, show much less of this tendency: their society is simpler, their religion without a hierarchy of higher and lower gods, their art frankly ornamental; whereas the Yoruba go in for the representative and the symbolic—the meaningful.

It also happens that we have an experimental psychological verification of these trends by Nadel. A short story was told to both Yoruba and Nupe children and they were then asked to retell it; pictures were shown them and they were asked to describe what they saw. The results evinced a tendency of the Nupe children to reproduce rather faithfully the details of what they had heard or seen. Things like the particular time of day were likely to appear in the retelling whether they were significant for the story or only incidental. By contrast, the Yoruba were concerned with the general plot of the story, or the main event or prospective result in the picture. Minor details had a way of being discarded, or misremembered. Motivations, why things happened, whether they ought to have happened, whether an action was good or bad, were accentuated or even invented. Not only was there more reasoning, but also more emotion, in the Yoruba versions. The Nupe remembered in a manner that was more matter-of-fact and externally more orderly in a step-after-step fashion. They catalogued or reproduced: what it was all about did not interest them so much. In the Jung classification, they would be predominantly sensory-minded, the Yoruba more of the rational and feeling type.

A similar difference was found to exist between the reactions of Arizona Hopi and Navaho children to pictures shown them as a stimulus.[5] The Hopi tend to carry the pictured situation through to an outcome, usually a reassuring or happy ending. This may include a moral judgment. The Navaho reactions are less consecutive, and mostly without statement of outcome. Mainly they re-describe the facts of the picture; feelings may be attributed to the people depicted, but ethical judgments are rare. In a general way, the town-dwelling Hopi react like the Yoruba, the Navaho somewhat like the Nupe; and of the two total cultures, the Hopi one is by general agreement somewhat more rationalized, organized, systematized, and sophisticate than the Navaho.

While we have few confirming psychological tests, the cultures of other peoples sometimes obviously differ according to the same criterion. California and Northwest-coast Indians tend to enumerate facts in presenting them to

[5] Technically, the Thematic Apperception Test was used, the pictures having been drawn by a local Indian.

ethnographers, Pueblo and some Plains tribes organize them. The organization may be rudimentary and not seem very significant to us, as when it is by cardinal directions or colors; but it is nevertheless an attempt to see things in relation instead of haphazardly. As these cultures function, the organization of ideas is effected especially in ritual and myth. And it is evident that a ritual of the Zuni Pueblo has much more motivation than one of the California Yurok. Its purpose is explicit, its parts are meaningful, it is full of easily grasped symbolism.

The Eskimo, again, are very sensory, immediate, concrete, and discrete in their ethos.

It would appear that all advanced cultures are relatively systematizing. We might say that if they were not, they would not have been able to advance far. And, complementarily, further organizing capacity is probably a product of higher civilization. Such circular causation is common in human history and affairs. We have already encountered it in the inter-reinforcement of enhancement of subsistence, population growth, specialization of skills, improved technology, and increase of wealth (§ 163).

The great world religions are obviously strong agencies of organization, in that they provide a basic philosophy, with a scheme of causality and motivation. Christianity may at first have been actually narrower, intellectually, than the Hellenism it supplanted; but its scheme was certainly more unified. In the same way Buddhism got rid of thousands of Brahman idols, of sacrifices, of rituals that had become meaningless, of taboos, and of other clutter of detail; with the result that its basic creed, its program of life, stood out much more clearly and coherently. To the sophisticated philosopher who was able to rise above the endless and jumbled items accreted through the centuries, Brahmanism may have provided an equally good base; but the average man could much more easily see a meaningful plan in Buddhism.

It may well be that the degree to which science has of late become for growing numbers a de-facto religion, or equivalent of religion, is due to the fact that with all its intricacy it possesses a coherence, a master plan that organizes innumerable items. This is true also of other successful faiths, notably the world religions. But the plan or system of all of these was devised a long time ago, when the content of culture was considerably simpler. Science on the contrary has largely grown contemporaneously with the growing wealth and complexity of Western civilization in the last few centuries, so that its system may well be more conformable with the total civilization.

252. SADISM

Almost any trend or inclination familiar from individual psychology might be recognized in culture. For instance, for cruelty, or sadism, peoples like the Aztec and the Assyrians immediately come to mind. Both built up conquest empires with imposition of heavy tribute. The Assyrian kings in their inscriptions boast not only of their victories but of their cruelties—whole populations slaughtered, impaled, or otherwise tortured. Their art expresses sternness, and is particularly addicted to scenes of battle or the hunt. Its greatest triumphs were attained in the portrayal of wounded and dying animals. The Aztec are notorious for the bloodiness of their religion. Hundreds of human beings were sacrificed annually by having the chest cut open and the heart torn out. Another device was to flay the victim, and to dress the priest in the victim's fresh skin. Self-penance was by piercing the tongue or other parts of the body. The captor of a war prisoner ate of his flesh at a formal banquet after his sacrifice. Skulls of the victims were kept in huge cribs in the public plaza in front of the temples. Aztec art portrays these scenes over and over again with the utmost unconcern, or rather, with pleased predilection. Death, skulls, flayed skins, rattlesnakes, and jaguars are among its favorite symbols. We think of Roman gladiatorial exhibitions as an example of cruelty; but the Romans, except for some degenerate emperors, were limited in their sadism as compared with Aztecs and Assyrians; they were only callous and brutal.

It would be possible to arrange the cultures of the world roughly according to a scale of the degree of sadistic manifestations. However, any such ranking would of course be wholly one-sided from the angle of the total inherent psychology. If any other trait were chosen, such as imaginativeness, or piety, or sensory predilections, the ranking would come out quite differently. In other words, any classification or ranking from one angle invariably crosscuts classifications made from others, and to that extent is arbitrary.

It is also clear that the extreme cases, as of Assyrians and Aztecs, represent local and temporary exaggerations. Historically related cultures usually show similar but less developed features. The Assyrian cruelties occurred also among neighboring and preceding and subsequent peoples, such as Babylonians and Persians, but without being carried so far. Human sacrifice with flaying and tearing out the heart was a practice common to all southern-Mexican peoples; but it was reserved for the Aztec to riot in the practice. The Maya followed the custom, but much less frequently; and it was only occasionally that they expressed it in their art. The difference accordingly was one of weighting; it was a relative or quantitative one. If consideration is given merely to the presence or absence of features like human sacrifice, without reference to their frequency or integration in the culture, important psychological differences of interests and accentuations are lost. Such relative differences between cultures are socially comparable to those which set off one individual human mind from others within the same society and culture.

253. OTHER PSYCHOLOGICAL BENTS

There is an indefinitely large number of further qualities according to which cultures can be oriented—as many, perhaps, as can be recognized in individuals. It is unnecessary to examine each of these; but a few may be touched on, so as to reinforce the idea of how psychologically plastic and variable the cultures of man are.

Acquisitiveness. Avarice, possessiveness, retentiveness, enter into the goals of societies in quite varying degree. Most primitives look upon Western white men as both greedy and stingy. Of course our highly developed economic system would break down, bringing distress on everyone in the community, as soon as production and maintenance of property ceased. We are therefore compelled to think fairly constantly in terms of acquisition, preservation, and accumulation. Nevertheless, the judgment of primitives that we are obsessed with our possessions probably reflects a fact that is descriptively true. On the contrary, certain primitive cultures also have their interests largely dominated by wealth: property makes for status, rank depends on wealth, and economic exploitation is limited only by opportunity. This is true of nearly all Melanesians, some Indonesians, all the Indians of the northwestern coast of America. In Africa, too, economic considerations are much to the fore. At the opposite pole of this axis are Australians, Negritos, Seri, and other peoples whose customs make them prefer being unencumbered with property and its care (§ 120, 146, 155). This bent cuts down both their responsibilities and their opportunities; but it does leave them untrammeled: Acquisitiveness also enters into the anal character type of the psychoanalysts (§ 255).

Mechanical and Verbal Developments. There are great individual differences in mechanical interest and ability, as well as in verbal fluency and capacity. These differences sometimes begin to be manifest within the first two or three years of life, and between siblings in the same home environment. This suggests that they may be partly congenital. There is ordinarily rather little in the affective relations to which small children are exposed, or in their training within one household, to make one brother more interested and skillful in driving nails or turning nuts on bolts, and another in throwing a ball, or perhaps chattering. So far as there are congenital individual differences, they would normally be heavily reinforced by selective opportunities of practice and training within each culture. As between populations, it is possible that there are true racial differences of significance, but the enormous divergences in cultural emphasis must far outweigh these differences. This conditioning would hold for verbalization as well as for muscular co-ordinations of both the athletic and the mechanical types (§ 88). That this is so is further indicated by the genuine mechanical gifts often suddenly displayed by a large proportion of nonliterate populations when guns or automobiles or motorboats are made available to them. From all precedent in these matters, it is probable that racial averages of congenital faculty vary less than individuals within the same race.

The same may hold for faculty of quantitative apperception and judgment in estimating numbers. Simple cultures may enumerate, but stress on quantitative valuations is largely a specialty of our Western civilization.

Desire for a Closed or an Open World. These affective inclinations are allied to agoraphobia and claustrophobia; and perhaps to bents toward the security of fixity and shelter, and the adventure of restlessness and unattachment, respectively. They probably tend to tie up with attitudes toward possessions. It is clear that strong habits in either direction can be acquired through socialization and experience, and that interference with these habits can cause acute discomfort. Many primitives have a strong urge to die where they were born, so as to close their life cycle by rounding it out. Other groups have become more interested in freedom of movement at will, even though the range be small. The previously cited Yurok and allied tribes of California are at the opposite extreme: they feel most comfortable in a tiny, snug world—one that a man with wings could fly around in a night. In their cosmology they set the ends of the earth, where the sky keeps descending to meet the horizon, only some fifty or sixty miles beyond their own last villages. At times they encounter members of tribes from beyond, and know something of their cultures; but they prefer to ignore this knowledge, and in the fantasies of their mythology and ritual they draw the boundaries of the human world closer in. About where their own highly characterized culture ends is where they like to believe the land of the immortals and everlasting dances begins—the Ultima Thule across the sea. The population adhering to this culture was somewhat under 10,000 at its maximum. The smallness of the society, coupled with the strong specialization of the culture, may have helped build up its restrictive inclination.

Essentially, such tendencies are retractile; and for these there is larger historical precedent. For instance, the Far Eastern cultures, headed by China but also including pre-1868 Japan, have generally been self-sufficient and unexpansive. In the 1500's they began to be reached by ships, traders, missionaries, and adventurers from five western-European nations—Spain, Portugal, Holland, England, France—that had entered an expansionist phase—the "era of discovery and colonization." By the 1600's, the resulting contacts had been sufficiently unpleasant and disturbing to make China, Japan, Korea, Annam, Siam, and Tibet all adopt the well-known policy of exclusion and seclusion. This attitude of nonintercourse and withdrawal some of them supported by refusing to readmit their own nationals who had left home. They all maintained it as well as they were able until forced to yield by threat or force in the nineteenth century.

This seclusion was defense against pressure. But Europe itself underwent a phase of partial cultural self-restriction after its first expansionism was over. This movement was most marked in manners and art in the France of Louis XIV. It represented an endeavor at order, clarity, fixity, centralization; it was a reaction against previous stirrings, tumult, and unsettlement. Regulatory Academies for literature, art, and sciences were established. There were rules for correctness, canons of propriety. Nearly all were negative and restrictive. The alleged aim was polish, refinement. Only elevated subjects were to be dealt with in plays, for instance: noble actions expressed in a limited, purged vocabulary were in the single, most stately meter. The result, whether in drama, poetry, painting, or sculpture, was a classicism that grew more and more elevated and more and more apart from real life. It no longer offended taste, but it had lost vividness and interest. In the early eighteenth century this movement spread to other European countries. In England, for instance, it produced the cold, correct, regular, narrow poetry of Pope, which contrasts so markedly with the earlier Elizabethan and later Romantic exuberance, irregularity, and vitality.

Though this French manifestation is different enough from those of the Chinese and the Yurok, what the three have in common is the impulse to limit or contract activity.

Fixity or Looseness of the Social Structure; Place and Time Mindedness. Here we would have on the one hand a complex of attitudes comprising acceptance of tradition, authority, and status, social docility, class-consciousness, relative permanence of institutions, conscious and desired rooting in the past, perhaps also fixity of residence and generic pessimism. India would be an example: the caste system embodies all these traits and tries to perpetuate them. The opposite pole among nations would be occupied by the United States and modern Australia, with their grudging acceptance of authority, diminution of status, emphasis on individualism, social and geographical mobility, relative lack of interest in the past or in tradition, exaltation of the contemporary moment, and unworried optimism as to the future.

This is an axis of polarity which is only partly psychological, and yet it involves a set of attitudes toward institutions rather than institutions themselves. It is allied to Tarde's distinction between place-minded and time-minded populations; and through this to the familiar rural-urban dichotomy (§ 121). Cultures that are primitive, of peasant or folk type, or definitely slow-changing, tend to be humble about their own moment but proud of the past and attached to their spot. They look down on their neighbors because these are different from them; but they look up to their ancestors. If there is a golden age, it is behind them. On the other side are metropolitan capitals, the later Graeco-Roman society, and increasingly our own modern Western society. Here pride is in up-to-dateness; origins are unimportant. It is the true atmosphere in which fashion and conformity to fashion flourish; but deviations according to locality are looked down upon as provincially backward.

Within a given society, its rural and urban components tend to differ in much the same way, relatively to each other; or again, the provinces and the court. But it would be erroneous to look upon the phenomenon as merely a by-product of country and city life. There have been large cities in India and

China for thousands of years with but little of the metropolitan outlook. On the contrary, pride-in-the-moment outlook is almost as characteristic of rural as of urban United States. Even our small towns participate in the era of streamlining. They drive the same cars, wear clothes of the same cut, see the same films, and read the same features, dispatches, and magazines. Free and rapid communications help bring this about. In fact the twentieth-century American town is likely to be much more exercised over its participation in universal modernity than in its sense of superiority to the neighboring town, which sense is usually pretty negligible except as an occasion for jokes.

One feature is shared by the socially fixed, the proud-of-locality, and the rural and folk cultures: religion remains a genuine influence and sanction, much more than in the cultures of opposite type.

If we try to formulate the most constant general features in this set of contrasts, to get away as much as possible from culture content into attitudes, from eidos to ethos, it would seem that the attitudes under consideration deal with social relation to time, with individual relation to society, and through this to culture. This set of attitudes toward relations comes near to meaning attitude toward tradition; not only in the popular but in the specific socio-anthropological sense of the word "tradition" as denoting social heritage or cultural transmission. In cultures of the folk type, the group or society with which conformity and identification are sought is relatively small, both areally and numerically; but its time dimension aims to be long, its consciousness of conformity with the past is strong. In "civilized" or metropolitan cultures the group is much enlarged—whence the almost frightening degree of areal and numerical conformity—but at the expense of the time dimension. Such a culture and society are like a vast, flat, quivering surface; folk cultures, rather like a long, tough, firmly clasping root.

The theoretical question arises whether there can also be cultures short in both the space and the time dimension, and others large in both. It may be that certain small, lowly, close-to-nature cultures actually approximate the former type; say Andamanese and other Negritos, Tasmanians, possibly Bushmen and Eskimo in some degree. These would have little sense of the past and little attachment to place. Life would tend to be lived in the moment and in the spot. There is no clear example in history of a civilization as extensive as ours but also deeply rooted; such a one just has not happened yet. But there are civilizations, like those of China and of Middle Ages-Renaissance Europe, which approximate such a condition. They have been much larger than most societies in size and area, have been as it were supernational in scope, have also been well integrated and reasonably uniform internally, and at the same time have had vital and conscious relation with their past. With somewhat greater uniformity and more mobility for somewhat more millions, but no other essential change, they would have conformed to the theoretical suggested fourth type, cultures at once vast in their even extent and deeply rooted in time.

The foregoing are descriptions of how cultures actually—and possibly—behave as regards their "social dimensions." The differences are in orientation; but this has psychological involvements.

Sin and Shame. A domesticated animal or a very small child probably does not feel either shame or sin in doing something forbidden. If the child or infant looks guilty, it presumably fears punishment or at least hostile reaction. Shame, of which all normal adult humans are capable, is defensive reaction against social disapproval or expected social disapproval. How far shame is felt spontaneously or is socially determined is a problem for the psychologists. But shame is partly externalized: it is a feeling with reference to others. Sense of sin, however, is internal. One can feel sinful in solitude, over an act involving no hurt to others. Sin implies a disapproving conscience at work within oneself; shame, the knowledge that others disapprove; though shame can also be superadded to sense of sin—perhaps normally is so added. The distinction is not hard and fast; but it is polar.

Of late years, with conscious effort to define the ethos of cultures, a whole array of observers have made a similar finding on culture after culture. They encounter plenty of shame, but little or no sense of sin. Other people's opinions, their remarks, their ridicule or laughter, are what the average man, in most cultures, is sensitive to, are what deters him. This has been remarked equally for nonliterate tribes and for literate nationalities. The Chinese are guided by "face-saving"; the Japanese lack the sense of "contrast of real and ideal" and "do not grapple with the problem of evil."

But the findings about the importance of shame as a social force are a bit too consistent. They leave little explicit sin sense to any culture but our own Occidental one; and within that largely to its Protestant portion (§ 248), in fact outstandingly its Calvinistically influenced sector. It is true that sin and guilt, sin and trespass, sin and evil, were rather imperfectly distinguished in Europe until the Reformation. It seems to have been this religious movement that internalized guilt and shame into sin, and reared conscience on a great pedestal. We took the word "conscience" from French, but then differentiated it from "consciousness"; the French *conscience* still denotes both. It looks therefore as if the reputedly independent and separate verdicts of Anglo-Saxon anthropologists on Asiatic, Oceanic, native American, and African cultures, that shame is a far more influential motivation in them than sense of sin, does not really specifically characterize these cultures nearly so much as its opposite—conscious sinfulness—characterizes Anglo-Saxon and Protestant culture. Shame as a deterrent factor and a social force is probably operative in nearly all cultures. It is perhaps generally expectable except in the special cases—like our own or Manus civilization (§ 248)—where it has been overlaid by some special development such as masochistic preoccupation with evil—preoccupation with other people's sins or our own.

254. SUICIDE

Naïvely, one might assume that suicide was a personal, not a social, matter: that individuals chose death when going on living became too hard for them, and that it was specially tender-minded individuals, or pathologically depressed ones, who reached that limit of endurance sooner than optimistic, tough-minded ones. These differences due to situation and personality make-up unquestionably occur, and largely account for the selection out of any one community of the particular individuals who take their own lives as against those who do not. Suicide can be described as due to the internalizing of hate, shame, or fear, instead of the normal externalizing or projection of these emotions upon others. The internalization takes place either because the possibility of projection is cut off by circumstances, or because inner disturbance or deterioration makes it seem cut off. Except in the case of disease, suicide thus always contains an element of relation to the individual's social environment.

However, there is also such a thing as institutionalized suicide, condoned, approved, or even exacted by a code and therefore by the culture. In that case, the culture not only defines certain situations that call for suicide, but often indicates the correct way to execute it. In large, complex societies, these specified situations and techniques are likely to be restricted to certain situations, classes, or castes, outside of which the attitude toward suicide may be indifferent, regretful, or disapproving.

The Japanese hara-kiri or seppuku immediately rises to mind. This, with its special form of disembowelment, was formerly confined to nobles and warriors. From these it was transferred after 1868 to the new conscript peasant army, to become an obligation, as against the disgrace of surrender, when victory or escape were both impossible. In that case, suicide was mandatory: those who evaded it were ostracized—obliterated by their society; and officers could kill men to prevent evasion. In this way the almost incredibly high suicide rate of from 90 to 99 per cent was built up among cornered Japanese troops in World War II. This of course is not only institutionalization, but enforcement by ultimate sanctions. And the enforcement, in turn, is a carrying of earlier and more widespread attitudes to their extremes.

One of these is the generic East Asiatic idea of suicide as a protest for the right and against the oppressor. By suicide, the oppressor is put in the wrong with public opinion, as having gone too far; a principle must be right, or must at any rate have something in its favor, if people will die for it. Suicide in this situation is well recognized in China, though much less frequent. In the hands of the Japanese, it seems to have led further to the practice of political assassination: the murderer's convictions, it is thought, must be strong, and therefore likely to be right or at least noble, because his presumptive death sentence—he does not try to hide or flee—is equivalent to suicide. Another element that originally went into the making of hara-kiri as an institution has Western parallels: people of rank who had been condemned were formerly allowed to do away with themselves, instead of having low hands violently laid on them. Similarly, more fallen Roman emperors or claimants to the throne killed themselves, probably, than were executed.

Linkage of suicide to aristocracy as a conditional obligation of caste is fairly frequent. Suicide was expected of nineteenth-century European army officers who got into certain disgraces of dishonor: their colleagues would silently leave a loaded revolver for them. Analogous was the attitude of Cato, Brutus, Cassius, Seneca, and other Roman stoics, who considered themselves an aristocracy of the spirit.

Hindu suttee or widow-burning—abolished a century ago—was optional with the widow, and was often chosen because of its halo of extreme merit, social, moral, and religious. Not only was the dead man's memory enhanced by the act, but his family also participated in the prestige; and this tended to build up strong pressures on the widow; not to mention the economic advantage to the family of being rid of her and her dower rights. However, only high castes practiced suttee. It was not expected in low castes, and probably would have been censured as presumptuous.

These are cases of definite institutionalization, verging on the compulsory. At the opposite pole are prohibitory attitudes, as of Christianity, which ever since St. Augustine has branded suicide as a grave sin, and has retaliated with exclusion from hallowed burial. The laws of a few American states still reflect this mediaeval conception in providing punishment for the attempt, though altered public sentiment prevents much rigor of enforcement. Through the sentiment of Mohammed, Islam also took a strongly condemnatory stand against suicide. The same is true of post-Christian Judaism, though the Old Testament seems to have had no particular reaction to suicide one way or another and mentions only four cases. To these three interrelated religions of exclusive monotheism there may be contrasted the basically pessimistic and agnostic one of Buddhism, which views suicide with moral equanimity.

That fewer Catholics than Protestants kill themselves may be attributed to the fact that Catholicism is on the whole the socially stronger institution; that the rate among Jews has risen sharply for some decades appears to be correlated with their withdrawal from both orthodoxy and the close-knit ghetto life.

Between compulsory institutionalization of suicide and its prohibition there lies a range of attitudes: social disapproval, indifference, or sanction in particular situations. Here would fall the Japanese shinju, the joint suicide of hopeless lovers by casting themselves into the water tied together. Later, this old custom was often superseded by the railroad track; and a variant of it, suicide at the Kegon waterfall, reached a temporary peak of fashionable vogue around 1903. Here the stimulus situation is personal instead of class or social, and the government forbade and tried to prevent the practice, although public sentiment tended to condone it.

All sorts of situations are singled out by different cultures as being permissive of suicide; if there is also a standard or favorite technique of carrying it out, we can be sure that there is cultural channeling. Thus in Melanesia, jumping from a coconut palm is a response to a published charge of incest in the Trobriands; but aggrieved, accused, or jealous spouses are likely to vent their self-pity by eating poison, trying thereby to throw the onus on their mates. In near-by Dobu, this latter is the usual motivation and method; but the poison is uncertain, emetics are administered, and many of the suicides fail; which perhaps increases the frequency of trials, especially since the attempt often suffices to bring a readjustment. But the shame of incest is profound and ineradicable, and the Trobriand palm leap is usually fatal.

The Wintu of northern California had a quite special type of self-destruction. Losing gamblers, returning home to be upbraided by their wives, or refused food by them, dived repeatedly into a deep pool and finally failed to come up again. It is hardly conceivable that enough instances of this sort could happen in a small tribe for the cases really to fall into so definite a pattern; but as an imaginary pattern which had worked through to consciousness as a sort of favorite daydream or story theme, this suicide type is perhaps still more interesting.

The Eskimo show a heavy incidence of suicide, especially in the high Arctic, where life is mostly hard and always precarious, and where the old and the incapacitated are so obvious and unwelcome a burden that they often ask to be dispatched. Thus, at Ammassalik in eastern Greenland, an elderly woman whose legs remained swollen from frost "grew tired of life" and drowned herself. This was spontaneous; but another woman threw herself into the sea only after her son-in-law, on whom she was dependent, wondered aloud why anyone so old and useless did not die. A younger woman drowned herself, in this same little community of less than 400 people, from shame, or perhaps jealousy, at her husband's taking her own mother as cowife. A man was so shamed at his sister's going to live with strangers instead of their father that he slept outdoors until it killed him. In addition to starvation, always around the corner, there is no government whatever among these Eskimo, strength prevails, women are taken by force, murders are common and go unrequited, and life in general is in the raw, so that frequent suicide might be thought expectable. Yet if these cases are typical, three suicides follow upon a stimulus of shame,[6] or other feeling trauma, to only one resulting from direct despair of survival. Underneath the emotional hurts, however, there may well exist a habitual sort of trigger balance in a great many Eskimo individuals—due to chronic and widespread

[6] Compare the remarks on sin and shame in § 253.

privations, uncertainties, and shocks to personality. Most such situations are usually more complex than they seem on the surface.

As to racial propensities to suicide, there are differences, but, as usual, these may either be due partly to heredity and partly to culture ("environment"), or wholly to culture. In Oceania, Melanesians, Micronesians, and Polynesians clearly have a high suicide rate, Australian blackfellows a very low one. The Eskimo stand out among the other American Indians. The African rate is definitely low as compared with other continents, for Sudanese and Bantu Negroes as well as Bushmen-Hottentots. This might conceivably be a matter of inborn racial temperament; but, as usual, it is not provably so. Only about two-fifths as many American Negroes commit suicide per million as American whites. But the Negroes are also more largely rural and poorer, two conditions making for a lower suicide rate in most countries. It thus remains uncertain how much if any of Negro lack of inclination toward suicide can be attributed to racial inheritance. The Eskimo are generally accepted as a distinctive subrace of the Mongoloid Americans; this may or may not involve a perceptibly distinctive inherited temperament; but it is obvious that their living conditions keep them uncertain as to outcomes, and their strongly individualistic social code puts few restraints on self-destruction.

In the last analysis, the motivations and methods of suicide seem very largely to be part of cultural patterns. The frequency is less influenced by culture: age, sex, even season, are statistically proved determinants. So undoubtedly are the personality, and what may be called the provocation, the individual circumstances. Race may or may not be a contributory factor to frequency. It may well be; but proof is difficult to bring, because of the inescapable sociocultural overlay.

255. PSYCHOANALYTIC INTERPRETATIONS—AND SUMMARY

Psychoanalysis is a systematic theory of personality development and functioning formulated by Freud, notable for stressing unconscious processes and sexual psychology. Psychoanalysis includes also a therapeutic practice, which operates through the patient's gradually uncovering the portions of his life history of which his memory has become unaware but whose effects are still active and disturbing to him. The therapy is of no further concern to us here; the theory is, and for two reasons. First, psychoanalytic theory has been extended to include interpretations of culture. Second, many of the mental mechanisms with which it operates have come to be accepted by "orthodox" psychology so far as it deals with whole personalities rather than with separate faculties; as also by medical psychology or psychiatry.

The psychoanalytic explanation of culture is intuitive, dogmatic, and wholly unhistorical. It disregards the findings of prehistory and archaeology as irrelevant, or at most as dealing only with details of little significance as compared with its own interpretation of the essence of how culture came to be. In condensation, Freud's own theory is that "the beginnings of religion, ethics, society, and art meet in the Oedipus complex." Primitive man lived in small bands, from which the strongest male drove off the less mature males, normally his sons, in order to have all the women to himself. The expelled sons band together, kill their father, eat him to gratify their revenge, appropriate the women —their mothers and sisters. But then remorse and guilt gain the upper hand in them, they undo their deed, forbid the killing of a totem animal that is set up as a symbolic substitute for their father, and deny themselves the women they have gained, by instituting the incest taboo. All other taboos are secondary displacements or distortions of these two taboos; and later religions are reactions "aiming at this same great event with which culture began." It is not altogether clear whether the "event" was construed by Freud in its ordinary sense of a single actual happening, or as a "typical" recurrent event. But the explanation comes to nearly the same thing in either case: one mechanism is seized upon as cardinal, all evidence of others is disregarded as inconsequential. The theory is obviously as arbitrary as it is fantastically one-sided. It is mentioned only because it is the one *specific* explanation of the origin of culture that has emanated from a psychological source; although Freud was not only far from being orthodox as a psychologist, but treated the findings of psychology almost as highhandedly as he did those of prehistory and culture history.

Most subsequent interpretations of culture or specific cultural situations by converts to the psychoanalytic sect have not been much more open-minded. Thus Roheim concludes a monograph on primitive culture types with the finding that the sexual practices of a people are indeed prototypical and that from their posture their whole psychic attitude may be inferred. In its calm dogmatism, this finding is in a class with Freud's theory on the origin of culture.

On the contrary, in the realm of psychic processes within the personality, there is no doubt that Freud originated, or endowed with new life and meaning, a series of concepts that are exceedingly fruitful and have been largely accepted by nonanalytic psychology and psychiatry and integrated with them. These concepts include repression, infantile persistences and regressions, dream and fantasy symbolism and overdetermination of the symbols, sublimation of frustrations, transference and identification, and perhaps at least the plastic outlines of the Oedipus situation. These ideas and mechanisms may be said to constitute the permanent contribution of psychoanalysis to general science. But there are other parts of the Freudian schema, such as the censor, the castration complex, the primacy of the libido, which have failed as consistently to penetrate into psychology as the culture-origin theory has failed to take root in anthropology.

Among other things, Freud set up oral and anal types of personality, supposed to be the outgrowth of infantile reactions to the functioning of these respective "erogenous zones." The personality of anal character is orderly, economical, and tenacious; or, in its less pleasant aspects, pedantically precise, con-

scientious, and persistent; miserly; and obstinate to vindictiveness. Such a con-
stellation or syndrome of character traits might well occur with a certain frequency and regularity, irrespective of whether Freud's explanation as to its causal
mechanism is true or not. It would in that case have validity as an empirical
clinical finding. Now, just as the anal-type description fits certain individuals
quite strikingly, it seems to agree pretty well with the average or modal personality produced under certain cultures. This holds for instance for the Yurok of
native California and their cotribes of the same culture. It holds also for certain
Melanesians, such as the Manus and Massim. On the contrary, within Oceania,
Polynesians, Indonesians, and Australians are wholly unanal in character—the
Australians in fact standing at a sort of opposite pole of living happily in disorder,
in freedom from possessions, and in the fluctuations of the moment. And the
Siamese are certainly oral (§ 245) if the type has any validity at all.

What has been said above (§ 244) about the limitations of statistical validity
of all types, constitutional and psychological, undoubtedly holds also for the
oral and anal types. Like all physiognomic formulations, they tend to be over-
characterized, but below average in frequency of occurrence. Their value lies
in the felicity with which they can occasionally be applied. And this felicity
may be great in the hands of a great clinical diagnostician like Hippocrates or
Freud.

In recent years, the older psychoanalytic theory construing culture as something universal, derivable directly and spontaneously out of the psychology of
the supposed primitive family situation, has given place to much more moderate
hypotheses attempting to explain the functional relation of particular cultures
and the kinds of personalities dominant in these societies. In psychoanalytic
terminology, this yields a particular "basic personality structure"; in anthropological phrasing, the result is a "modal personality" typical of the culture (§ 135,
245). It is even conceded that the "rules" or ways or forms of the culture help
to determine the relations of parents and children, and the experiences to which
the growing child is subjected; and when he has in this way been molded, that
he then grows up to perpetuate and perhaps reinforce the standards of his
culture.

This is obviously a slightly different way of viewing the process of "socialization" as discussed in § 123. The modern psychoanalysts, or some of them,
admit fully that different kinds (or "structures") of personality are made or conditioned by different cultures. They no longer feel it necessary to derive the
whole personality directly out of a vague, primal substratum. What they are
interested in is showing how people become the kind of people they are in consequence of how their parents and kin treated them in childhood as a result, in
turn, of how their culture had molded these same parents and other adults.
What this amounts to is seeing a culture through the eyes of individuals. This
is a psychological way of viewing cultures through the effects they have on individuals rather than a distinctively anthropological way of viewing cultures

as cultures. This procedure does not supplant cultural interpretation: it is a supplement. It adds a certain depth of apperception; and it seems especially satisfying to certain temperaments that find operating with the undiluted forms and patterns of culture difficult, abstruse, or arid.

In summary of this chapter as a whole, it may be said that the basic relation of psychology and culture is due to the fact that culture ultimately exists, or "resides," only in the behavior, the ideas and feelings, and the products of societies of men. Any and every cultural phenomenon therefore has also a psychological aspect or coloring: it is necessarily imbued with something psychological. It cannot however be satisfactorily reduced to purely psychic terms, which are in their nature individual. There is always a large and definitely significant irreducible communal residue that is specifically cultural.

At the present time we can go farther in discerning the influence of cultural factors on the minds of men than in deriving cultural phenomena from psychological causes. This is because of the enormous plasticity of human minds, the almost limitless degree to which they are conditioned or determined by what they are exposed to. And perhaps the largest set of influences to which they are exposed is the total culture of the society in which they exist as individuals. As against this tremendous and specific cultural influencing, the general nature of man—"human nature"—is a pretty vague and uncharacterized thing out of which to explain culture. Human nature undoubtedly sets some sort of boundaries to the forms that culture can assume. But human nature itself, as such, does not fill this frame, does not create the manifold forms culture takes on within its boundaries.

The heavy overlaying of original or basic human nature by influences proceeding from the individual's life history and from his culture results in a rather remarkable anomaly: Psychologists have become very unwilling to discuss the inherent psychic nature of man. It is definitely unfashionable to do so. When the subject is faced at all, it is usually only to explain human nature away as fast as possible, and to pass on to less uneasy and more specific topics. Human nature is going the way the human "mind" has gone. Instead, psychologists for the last few decades have increasingly dealt with the concept of personality.

"Personality" refers to everything about a human individual that is describable in psychological or psychosomatic terms. Some of the traits or qualities are often explainable as due to such and such an event in the individual's life history, or to this or that influence of his culture or subculture. But there is no assumption made by modern psychologists either as to the original and innate generic human nature—as has just been said—or as to the innate particular individual nature that underlies the personality being dealt with. The whole concept of personality rests on proceeding from the ascertainable outside and going as far inward toward causes as evidence will take us, but assuming nothing general as to original cause or nature.

The concept of personality is in one respect a polar one. The traits or properties it includes range from the idiosyncratic to the common or social. Idiosyncratic features are those which distinguish one individual from all others. Such traits may be congenital, due to heredity. Or they may be the result of specific influences in the individual's sociocultural environment, in his life history. This latter class of influences is sometimes traced back a certain distance into childhood and even infancy, especially by clinical psychologists and psychoanalysts. Hereditary factors in the individual are something that almost all psychologists are once more averse to operating with, because of the difficulty of proving them to be hereditary. At the opposite pole of the axis are such traits as most or perhaps all individuals in a society share. Theoretically, these shared features can also be due either to biological heredity or to sociocultural influences. Again, however, modern psychological explanations are restricted to environmental factors, whether these appear in the form of organic experiences or of sociocultural ones. At this pole, of the socially shared features, we have the modal personality typical of a culture, as contrasted with the idiosyncratic elements that coexist in the same individual alongside his modal personality traits.

Psychological study that goes beyond the study of personality as such and centers its interest in the interrelations of personalities—"interpersonal relations" —is usually called *social psychology*. In the development of this, sociologists had a hand along with psychologists, and the subject is still studied and taught nearly as often by sociologists as by psychologists. Social psychology investigates the mechanisms of interpersonal relations: how people learn from one another, how they influence and control one another, and so on. In this investigation of psychological mechanisms, the *what* of learning, influence, and control—in other words, the specific cultural content involved in an interrelation—this "what" is ordinarily not considered by the social psychologist, except by way of exemplification. For instance, there necessarily are attitudes corresponding to all values, norms, or ideals. The attitudes are frankly psychological: they exist *in* human bodies and "minds." Values however are cultural: they are *products* of personalities, and have a sort of existence of their own in spoken and written words, in religion and art, in definable morals and definable institutions. It is the behavioral attitudes corresponding to the values, not the values themselves, that the social psychologist is concerned with: how the attitudes are acquired, reacted to, changed, and the like. That is why anthropologists as a group have participated less than sociologists in the development of social psychology: they are more directly concerned with the content of culture as such. In fact, they look upon culture as their specific and distinctive field of cultivation, the subject with which they are most immediately concerned when they operate above the organic level of heredity and race.

The psychological qualities of different cultures and their supporting societies can undoubtedly be described with a certain degree of effectiveness even today. These distinctive qualities are evidently due to the influence of the cultures—to something in the organization and weighting in the patterns of each culture concerned. But since the qualities are psychological, they must ultimately reside in the behavior of the people who constitute the society that carries the particular culture. Hence such psychological qualities apply or attach both to societies or populations and to cultures.

To date, such characteristics or qualities have been expressed in three ways. One of these is to begin by setting up a classification or system of psychological types or temperaments, and then fitting to these, as far as may be possible, the several cultures or populations being dealt with. This method is open to the usual drawbacks of working from types to particular cases—especially the drawback that most cases yield only a partial fit. A second method of characterization of cultures is to proceed empirically, without any set plan, merely noting those psychological traits which obtrude themselves in each culture, with special alertness toward such as seem to cohere into a consistent larger orientation. A third procedure begins with psychological traits, or trait groups—such as asceticism, sadism, competitiveness, aggression, neatness, and the like—and then compares the relative strength, variations, and associations that such traits exhibit in a series of cultures. This procedure is analogous, for cultures, to studies made of how impulses toward, say, aggressiveness, or orderliness, vary from individual to individual, and under what circumstances.

None of these three methods has yet been developed with great precision or reliability, and the task is presumably more difficult for populations and their cultures than it is for individual personalities. But there is no reason why it should be an insuperable task. And any dependable, objectifiable conclusions that may be attained in the field of cultural psychology will certainly be of extreme interest and may be of great practical importance.

Whether the findings of a systematically developed cultural psychology will be expressed in the terms and concepts of individual psychology, or whether a new set of concepts will have to be added to these, is something that remains to be seen.

Index

A 3
B 4
C 5
D 6
E 7
F 8
G 9
H 0
I 1
J 2